On the Trail of the

Ice Age Floods
The Northern Reaches

A geological field guide to
northern Idaho and the
Channeled Scabland

Bruce Bjornstad
Eugene Kiver

KEOKEE
BOOKS

Sandpoint, Idaho

Photos by the authors unless otherwise noted

Cover painting "The Inundation of Dry Falls" by Stev H. Ominski
www.stevominski.com

Printed in the United States of America

Keokee Books is an imprint of Keokee Co. Publishing, Inc.

Published by Keokee Co. Publishing, Inc.
P.O. Box 722
Sandpoint, Idaho 83864
208-263-3573
www.keokeebooks.com

Publisher's Cataloging-in-Publication Data

Bjornstad, Bruce, 1951-

On the trail of the ice age floods: the northern reaches: a geological field guide to northern Idaho and the channeled scabland

by Bruce Bjornstad and Eugene Kiver

        p.   cm.

ISBN 978-1-879628-39-7 (pbk.)

1. Geology–Columbia River Basin–Washington (State). 2. Geology–Washington (State). 3. Geology–Idaho. 4. Floods–Washington (State). 5. Floods–Idaho. 6. Hiking–Northern Idaho–Guides. 7. Hiking–Washington (State)–Guides. 8. Trails–Washington (State)–Guides. 9. Trails–Northern Idaho–Guides. 10. Washington (State)–Columbia River Basin–Description and Travel. 11. Idaho–Description and Travel. 12. Glaciation–Washington (State)

1.Kiver, Eugene
551.31 Bjo 2012

Readers who find any errors or have questions or comments for the authors are welcome to contact Bruce Bjornstad at bjorn99352@yahoo.com.

Dedicated to the memory of friend and colleague Dale F. Stradling

Dale Stradling (1930-2008) was born, raised and spent most of his life in the Columbia Plateau, an area that he dearly loved. He taught geography at Eastern Washington University for 33 years and influenced many students during his long career. His dedication to geologic mapping and research has greatly added to our knowledge and appreciation of the complex interaction between Missoula floods and the Pleistocene-age glaciers of northeastern Washington. Many of these discoveries and complications are discussed in the text of this field guide. The authors, as longtime friends, colleagues and fellow researchers, continue his tradition of "following the floods!"

Looking east across Lake Pend Oreille onto former ice dam for Glacial Lake Missoula

Contents

Acknowledgements

First we would like to thank Stev Ominski for the cover art as well as many of our geologic colleagues for valuable discussions and input at various stages in the production of this book, including Vic Baker, Richard Waitt, Roy Breckenridge, Norm Smyers, Brent Cunderla, Pat Spencer, Bob Carson, George Last, Steve Reidel, Frank Spane, Mike McCollum, Nick Zentner, Karl Lillquist, Neil Coleman and James Browne. Other helpful reviews came from Bill Fraser (Washington State Parks), Alex Amonette and Dave Harvey.

We especially appreciate the many exciting aerial flights piloted by John McDonald, David Wyatt, Bob Peterson and Ron Grant. Many thanks go to Gerry Youngblood and Ed Miller who performed field checks for many of the trails. We thank landowners Wade King, Tom Weisharr, John McLean, Mike Trantow, the Belsby family (Nancy, Louise and Gary), and finally Karen and Maury Foisy, who graciously shared unique Ice Age flood features on their properties with us. Special thanks go to Tom Foster who accompanied coauthor Bjornstad on many excursions and field trips through northern Idaho and the Channeled Scabland. Foster shared many of his wonderful photographs included in this volume.

We would like to acknowledge the dedicated assistance provided by several members of the Ice Age Floods Institute, including Gary Kleinknecht, Dale Middleton, Mark Buser, Jim Pritchard, John Moody, Ken and Susan Lacy, and Marv McCamey. The authors also want to thank their partners, Diana Moeller and Barbara Kiver, for their patience and support through the four trying years that went into this writing project. Finally we appreciate the insight and vision provided by Chris Bessler and Billie Jean Gerke at Keokee Co. Publishing, Inc. and Laura Wahl who patiently worked through the sea of graphics presented herein that we hope brings into focus the exciting and remarkable story of the Ice Age floods.

Introduction

"Unparalleled in the whole wide world, scarcely even approached by any landscape of similar origin, are the Channeled Scablands on the Columbia Plateau in eastern Washington."

– J Harlen Bretz (1959)

Clues to repeated decimations by colossal Ice Age floods are written all over the landscape of the Pacific Northwest. The paths of the Ice Age floods in northern Idaho and the Channeled Scabland, the features they left behind, and how to recognize them are the subjects of this book. The Scabland is of special significance because it inarguably contains the most dramatic and impressive evidence for flood erosion anywhere in the world. Part I of the book introduces readers to the floods and provides a primer on how to identify specific flood features. Sixty-five of the most significant features in the Scabland (see page 23), including those found in Grand Coulee, Moses Coulee, the Cheney-Palouse and the Telford-Crab Creek scabland tracts are described.

Also included are several spectacular overlooks at Riddle Hill, Steamboat Rock and Dry Falls where one can see multiple features while taking in a broad view of the floods' path of destruction. For ease of understanding, features are segregated into seven specific geographic regions of eastern Washington and northern Idaho. The discussion of features starts with the area of ice-dam breakout within the Rathdrum Prairie-Spokane Valley. From here we follow the floods downstream through the Spokane and Pend Oreille river valleys before they spilled over into the Cheney-Palouse Scabland Tract, Telford-Crab Creek Tract and Grand Coulee. Finally we present two other areas impacted less frequently by Ice Age floods – Moses Coulee and the Columbia River valley along the western margin of the Columbia Plateau.

Because the best way to understand and appreciate the Ice Age floods is to get out and immerse oneself in the landscape, Part II provides trail and tour descriptions along with more detailed maps. Readers can discover the aftermath of the floods firsthand in a variety of ways, depending on time, physical ability and budget either by: non-motorized trails on foot, mountain bike or horseback; public roadways via automobile or bike; watercraft through innumerable lakes and waterways; or aircraft.

Although individual flood features rarely provide conclusive evidence for large-scale floods, when examined collectively, they tell an amazing tale of repeated cataclysms. Join us in discovering, firsthand, the wild landforms left behind by the Ice Age floods, much as they existed when legendary geologist J Harlen Bretz unraveled this amazing geologic tale early in the 20th century. Our geologic heritage, no less important than our valuable cultural heritage, belongs to all of us. And, like artifacts, many flood features are threatened by development. It is the authors' wish that, by drawing special attention to these awesome and often unique features, they may be preserved for future generations to enjoy and appreciate. An important step in that direction was taken in 2009 by the U.S. Congress when it approved legislation to establish an Ice Age Floods National Geologic Trail (see sidebar, page 21).

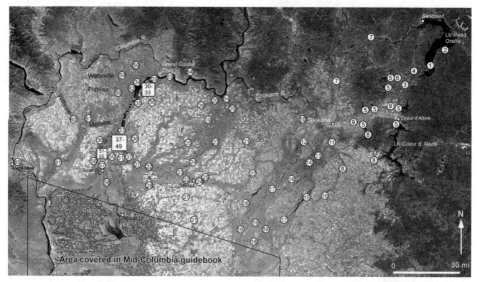

Locations of 65 major flood features within the Channeled Scabland and adjacent areas. The braided paths of the floods are apparent from outer space where the floods completely removed the loose, light-colored Palouse topsoil, eroding down into the underlying dark basalt bedrock. Each numbered feature is identified in the table of contents and further described in chapter 3. Flood features downstream of the Channeled Scabland, within the Mid-Columbia Basin, are covered in volume 1 of On the Trail of the Ice Age Floods, published in 2006.

"No one with an eye for landforms can cross eastern Washington in daylight without encountering and being impressed by the 'scabland.' ... The region is unique: let the observer take the wings of the morning to the uttermost parts of earth: he will nowhere find its likeness."

– J Harlen Bretz (1928)

Located following page 338 in this guidebook are 32 pages of color plates that illustrate with pictures, aerial photographs and maps some of the most visually striking features and landforms of the Ice Age floods. In general, the plates are arranged geographically starting with the outburst area for the Missoula floods and progressing westward through the Channeled Scabland.

Chapter 1 provides introductory and background information on floods responsible for the Channeled Scabland, beginning with hundreds of hot, burning flows of molten basalt lava that flooded the region 17.5 million to 6 million years ago, long before the first Ice Age floods. The volcanic lava flows form the canvas on which the floods painted an intricate tapestry of landforms. A primer of Ice Age flood features follows in chapter 2 where each of the 18 major types of flood landforms is explained and illustrated in more detail. Chapter 3 provides more detailed descriptions for 65 selected flood features within the flood-breakout zone of northern Idaho and the Channeled Scabland of eastern Washington. While many more floods features exist, we have chosen a subset that we believe best represents the range and diversity of flood-borne features. These include landmarks directly created by outburst floods (e.g., Rock Lake, Steamboat Rock, Pangborn Bar) as well as some features that did not come in direct contact with floodwaters, but played an instrumental role in determining the relative timing and paths for hundreds of separate flood events (e.g., Hoodoo Channel, Withrow Moraine). Undoubtedly, covering such a large area, the authors have missed some important flood-related sites. Readers are encouraged to suggest areas to include in future editions or supplements to this publication.

Part II presents trails and tours within the floods' terrain, designed to lead readers into the field to discover the story of the Ice Age floods and its matchless features for themselves. Directions and the geologic highlights of more than 40 non-motorized trails on publically accessible lands are presented in chapter 4. The five road tours in chapter 5 are designed to cover the greatest number of interesting flood features in the least amount of distance and time. Readers who want to create their own auto-tour routes can do so by linking any of the roads and features herein. Because of the floods' huge scale, aerial tours in chapter 6 are ideal for those who want to take advantage of two customized routes that provide a vantage point to more fully envision the "big picture" of the floods.

The conclusions and interpretations presented herein build upon almost 100 years of research performed by dozens of other scientists. At the end of the book is an exhaustive list of references, both technical and non-technical, that are the scientific foundation for this book. Finally, located at the very back, is a glossary of geologic and other terms that may not be familiar to the general public for whom this book is designed.

"The physiographic expression of the region is without parallel; it is unique, this channeled scabland of the Columbia Plateau."

– J Harlen Bretz (1928)

In this age of rapid change, it's good to know there are places on Earth that have not changed much since the West was settled many decades ago. This is true of much of eastern Washington. Traveling through the Channeled Scabland is like going back in time where you can explore places such as Krupp, Bluestem, Ewan and Stoner. These communities have not changed appreciably since the 1920s when Bretz first combed the countryside piecing together his "outrageous" hypothesis for a Spokane Flood. Come enter this unique landscape and discover for yourself the wild and peaceful solitude of the Channeled Scabland.

Part I: The Floods

Facing page: View across Steamboat Rock, Upper Grand Coulee

Looking across flood-scoured Scabland toward Deep Lake

1

Relentless Monster Floods

Like nowhere else on Earth, eastern Washington is a dynamic land of contrasts shaped by colossal, cataclysmic floods, first of hot, searing basaltic lava, followed millions of years later by frigid, massive glacial outbursts. The Channeled Scabland was the end product of both of these earth-changing processes; one without the other would have produced a landscape far less unique and dramatic than that observed today.

Burning Lava Floods

For more than 10 million years, one flow after another of volcanic lava, known as the Columbia River Basalt Group (Figure 1-1), inundated the region, creating the broad, rolling plain of the Columbia Plateau (Plate 2). Altogether this included about 175 separate lava flows in Washington alone, which caused the Earth's crust to sag under the massive weight of the dense, basalt lava. Individual basalt flows range from 50 feet to 300 feet thick. The Columbia River basalt covers about one-third of Washington state as well as large parts of Oregon and Idaho. The basalt reached its maximum thickness (almost three miles!) in the Tri-Cities area of south-central Washington. The basalt flowed out of thousands of long, straight vents 30 feet to 300 feet wide, called feeder dikes (general locations shown in Plate 2). After shooting out of fountains from the long, linear fissures, the molten lava flowed under the influence of gravity toward lowlands to the west and north. Based on distinctive chemical and physical characteristics, some of the same flows that originated in the higher, eastern part of the plateau can be traced clear across to the opposite end, all the way to the Pacific Ocean. The basalt flows must have erupted rapidly and were extremely fluid based on: 1) the lack of any significant buildup by volcanic debris along the vents, and 2) distance traveled by many of the flows (i.e., hundreds of miles) before cooling and solidification. Apparently an insulating, hardened crust developed at the top and bottom of each flow, which allowed the molten interior to continue flowing and expanding outward. The total amount of time – somewhere between weeks to decades – required to emplace each basalt flow remains controversial.

The hundreds of lava flows making up the Columbia River Basalt Group are divided into three geologic formations for the Channeled Scabland portion of the Columbia Plateau: the Grande Ronde Basalt (oldest), Wanapum Basalt and Saddle Mountains Basalt (Figure 1-1). Basalt-eruption events occurred much more rapidly at first (averaged about 4,000 years apart).

COLUMBIA RIVER BASALT GROUP FLOWS FOR THE NORTHERN COLUMBIA PLATEAU INCLUDING THE CHANNELED SCABLAND

Age (mya)	Formation	Member	Number of Flows	Area in Square Miles	Volume in Cubic Miles
6.0	Saddle Mountains	Lower Monumental	1	170	4
8.5		Ice Harbor	4	830	18
		Buford	1	220	5
10.5		Elephant Mountain	2	5,190	105
12.0		Pomona	1	8,710	180
		Esquatzel	1	1,050	17
		Weissenfels Ridge	4	470	5
13.0		Asotin	1	2,490	53
		Wilbur Creek	2	1,190	17
		Umatilla	2	5,830	170
	Total Saddle Mtns		19	11,800	574
14.5	Wanapum	Priest Rapids	3	22,120	670
		Roza	4	15,580	310
15.3		Frenchman Springs	21	26,930	1,540
		Eckler Mountain	8	2,350	41
	Total Wanapum		36	37,050	2,561
15.7-15.6	Grande Ronde	7 members (N2)	33	44,190	6,690
15.9-15.7		4 members (R2)	45	45,450	12,740
16.0-15.9		2 members (N1)	15	39,510	7,530
16.5-16.0		4 members (R1)	27	37,320	8,680
	Total Grande Ronde		120	57,530	35,640
	GRAND TOTAL		*175*	*106,380*	*38,775*

Figure 1-1. Stratigraphy of the Columbia River Basalt Group for the northern Columbia Plateau including the Channeled Scabland (modified after Mueller and Mueller 1997). This table excludes the older Imnaha and Picture Gorge basalts that lie south of the Channeled Scabland.

Over time, however, the span between eruptions lengthened – eventually each was separated by a million years or more. Each of the basalt units may contain dozens or more individual basalt flows, often separated by a glassy weathered zone (Figure 1-2) and/or thin layer of sediment between flows, which accumulated at the land's surface between volcanic eruptions. Most of the basalt flows within the Channeled Scabland belong to the Grande Ronde Basalt, also the most extensive formation, followed by the Wanapum Basalt; the bulk of the Saddle Mountains Basalt pooled in the central Columbia Plateau mostly to the south of the Channeled Scabland.

The internal vagaries of basalt flows had a profound effect and played a significant role in how they were eroded by the Ice Age floods and the types of features and landforms left behind. A universal characteristic of basalt flows are fractures, or joints, that represent shrinkage cracks that developed as the molten lava cooled, contracted and solidified (Figure 1-2). Some of the thicker basalt flows may have taken as long as 50 years to cool and solidify. Towards the top of the flow, where cooling occurred more rapidly, a higher density of cracks developed in a random pattern called the "entablature" zone. Deeper within the same lava flow, where the lava was insulated beneath the hardening entablature zone, the lava remained molten for a longer period of time, and thus the basalt cooled more slowly. This allowed the growth of larger, more regular fractures that created a honeycomb-like network of five- to six-sided columns referred to as the "colonnade" (Figure 1-2). These shrinkage cracks started at the base of the molten flow interior and slowly propagated upward towards the interior of the cooling lava flow. The end results are almost-continuous vertical columns spanning the entire breadth of the colonnade. Rubbly zones of broken-up rock may be present both at the very tops and bottoms of flows. Another common feature of basalt flows are what geologists call "vesicles." Essentially these are gas bubbles, normally preserved in the entablature at the tops of flows that froze in place as the less-dense gases rose through the solidifying lava, although vesicles may also be found at the base of the flow.

When attacked by erosive floodwaters, large columns of basalt from the colonnade were more easily plucked out and removed than the more cohesive, entablature above. This may seem odd, since the entablature contains many more smaller fractures that might be expected to erode more easily, but in fact the fractures around the smaller basalt blocks behaved like the interlocking pieces of a picture puzzle. Thus it appears basalt flows, especially along recessional cataracts, were eroded from the bottom up during megafloods. That is, as columns were preferentially plucked from coulee walls and cataracts, the entablature would be left overhanging (e.g., see Figure 2-13). As more colonnade was removed from the bases of flows, the overhanging entablatures became more and more unstable. At some point the overhang would collapse, upon which the entablature would break up into smaller constituent blocks, to be quickly transported away in the flood torrent. In this way coulee walls and recessional cataracts were able to maintain their near-vertical walls, and continually recede upvalley for miles.

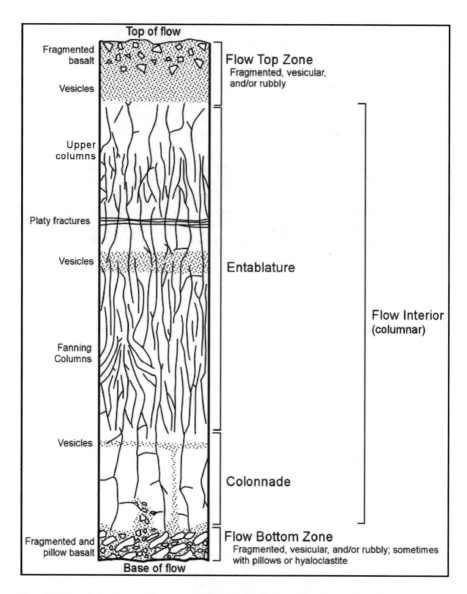

Figure 1-2. Internal structures and fracture patterns within basalt flows. When Ice Age floods later eroded into basalt flows, they preferentially plucked out larger basalt columns within the colonnade, often producing overhanging cliffs and rock shelters. Some rock shelters, such as those at Lake Lenore Caves (see Figure 3-93), were used by indigenous peoples since the last megafloods.

Pillow basalt (Figure 1-4) is another type of diagnostic structure that is observed along the bottoms of some basalt flows. Pillow basalt is especially common along the margins of the Columbia Plateau where the lava flows blocked rivers and streams draining into the Columbia Plateau. These dams of basalt lava created lakes into which the next basalt flow would enter. As hot lava flowed into these lakes, the molten rock collapsed into rounded pillows of suddenly chilled basalt. This produced a lot of steam and volcanic glass that filled the spaces between pillows with a yellow-orange glassy material called palagonite. The end result is what geologists call a "pillow-palagonite complex" consisting of dark basalt pillows floating in a matrix of brightly colored, rubbly palagonite.

Figure 1-3. Basalt flow features. Above: Rusty, weathered soil horizon formed on the top of lava flow No. 1, prior to burial by flow No. 2. This outcrop was exposed by flood erosion along Crab Creek coulee. Left: Well-developed, five- to six-sided, polygonal columns within the colonnade of a Priest Rapids Member (upper Wanapum Basalt) flow. The missing columns at Drumheller Channels were plucked away, column by column, and whisked away by Ice Age floods. TOM FOSTER PHOTO

Two other types of larger fractures, very different from the fractures that develop within individual basalt flows, can occur in the Columbia River basalt: curvilinear and tectonic. Curvilinear fractures consist of long, gently curving fractures seen on flood-scoured upland plateaus in the Channeled Scabland that may be several tens of feet apart and can be traced for many hundreds of feet. One of the best examples is in the Whitney Canyon area of the Upper Grand Coulee (Figure 1-6) and atop nearby Steamboat Rock (Plate 24). At first one might be tempted to attribute these curving features solely to grooves created during erosion by Ice Age floods. However, on closer inspection, many of the grooves at Whitney Canyon and elsewhere are oriented in a completely different direction than the flood flow. Therefore, it appears the grooved undulations formed as the lava was advancing and cooling and later accentuated during erosion by Ice Age floods.

Figure 1-4. Pillow-palagonite zone in basalt along Pine Creek Coulee (No. 16). Dark, rounded "pillows" of basalt lava float in a disorganized palagonite matrix, formed when the molten lava of a Priest Rapids Member basalt flow encountered a pre-existing lake. Note how pillows dip to the left due to "stretching," which developed as lava lobes advanced into the boiling and steaming water body. In contrast, note how the basalt in the upper half of this roadcut is without pillows suggesting the upper part of the flow lay above the ancient lake level.

Figure 1-5. Lifting a column of super-dense basalt is no small feat! Roger Christianson and John Moody of the Ice Age Floods Institute are no match for a colossal flood.

Labels on image: groove trace; Flood-accentuated grooves; grooves open into cracks along cliff edge; Chock stone; Canyon; Whitney; SR 155

Figure 1-6. Curvilinear grooves (one set shown by white dashed lines) atop east side of the Upper Grand Coulee. Above: Note how grooves (flood-etched fractures) are oriented transverse to direction of flood flow (big arrow), indicating the grooves weren't purely the result of scouring by megafloods. The grooves appear to have been etched out along weaker rock within fractures in the basalt that were created before the floods. Looking southeast. Left: A basalt chock stone (arrow) lodged in vertical, flood-etched fracture atop edge of coulee wall (shown in above image). Note slight roundness of chock stone, suggesting it was transported by floodwaters some distance before becoming lodged inside the crack.

Lastly, long and straight tectonic fractures also occur in a few places within the Channeled Scabland, especially along the Cheney-Palouse Scabland Tract. Subparallel sets of tectonic fractures can be many miles long and perhaps only a few feet wide. One well-developed fracture zone in the Channeled Scabland is the Cheney Fracture Zone, an area 15 miles long and 10 miles wide that extends from near Cheney to Rock Lake (Figure 1-7). Tectonic fractures formed from strong, regional forces applied to the basalt by stresses generated deep in the Earth's crust. Tectonic fractures are best differentiated from other types of fractures based on their extremely long and straight character. This suggests they formed from much larger, regional and deep crustal forces, in contrast to other types of fractures that occur at a much smaller scale.

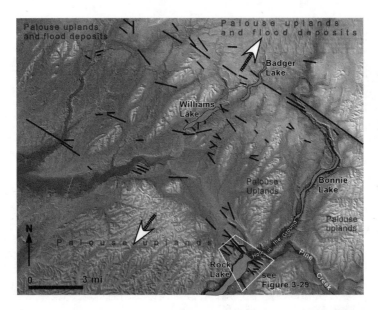

Figure 1-7. Long and straight tectonic fractures in basalt bedrock within the Cheney Fracture Zone. These fractures strongly influenced floodwater flow into Rock and Bonnie lakes. Weaker rock within the fractures was preferentially plucked out during powerful megafloods. The predominantly southeast trending fractures were originally the result of tectonic forces that extended deep into the Earth, pulling the crust in opposite directions (arrows) to the northeast and southwest. The end result was a series of vertical, mostly parallel fractures shown by heavy dark lines. Notice the fractures do not project up into the overlying windblown loess of the Palouse Uplands or the flood deposits. This indicates the fractures developed prior to the deposition of the Palouse loess and flood deposits (more than 2 million years ago), but sometime after the eruption of the Columbia River basalt (less than or equal to 15 million years ago). See Figure 3-29 for a close-up, aerial view of tectonic fractures at the head of Rock Lake.

Frigid Glacial-Outburst Floods

"Great rivers were born suddenly, operated for a very brief time, and then abruptly ran dry."

— J Harlen Bretz (1930)

With the close of basalt volcanism, about 6 million years ago, only a few more million years elapsed before the region succumbed to a new era of flooding, this time of icy, cold, glacial meltwater. The Ice Age began with a period of distinct climatic cooling at the beginning of the Pleistocene Epoch, about 2.6 million years ago, and continued off and on until about 14,000 years ago. During this period climatic cycles with extended periods of glacial advance and retreat occurred about every 100,000 years for at least the last million years (Figure 1-8). The last glacial cycle, sometimes called the Wisconsinan or Fraser glaciation, lasted from about 14,000 to 28,000 years ago.*

* In this guidebook, ages younger than 40,000 years are reported in actual calendar years before present, based on corrected variations of carbon-14 production through time (Stuiver and Reimer 1993). An age of 13,000 years, commonly reported for the last Ice Age floods, is based on uncorrected radiocarbon ages. An age of 15,000 calendar years before present for the last Missoula flood is based on corrected radiocarbon dates associated with the Mount St. Helens "set S" volcanic-ash layer, which lies near the top of the last sediment sequence laid down by these floods.

During glacial periods, with so much of the Earth's water tied up in glaciers, sea level was up to 460 feet lower than today, which pushed the coastline several tens of miles farther west than the coastline of today (Plate 1).

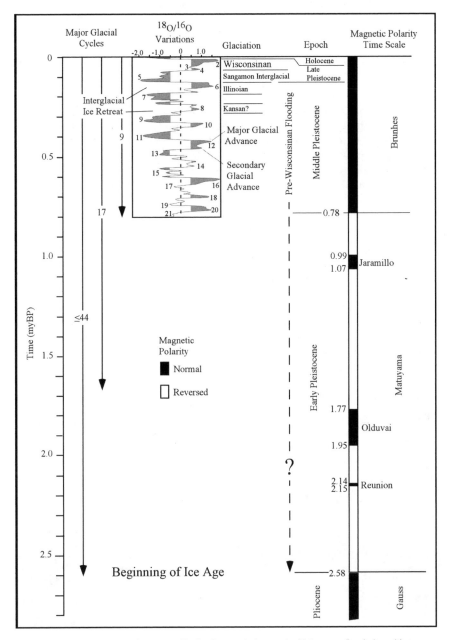

Figure 1-8. Ice Age floods in geologic time. The Ice Age, equivalent to the Pleistocene Epoch, lasted between about 2.6 million to 14,000 years before present.

Outburst floods are associated with periods of glaciation when fingers of the Cordilleran Ice Sheet crept south across the northern border of the United States into Washington, Idaho and Montana (Plate 1). The glacial ice blocked river drainages, including the Clark Fork near the Idaho-Montana border. These blockages created huge, ice-dammed lakes. The largest of these was Glacial Lake Missoula, which extended 200 miles east, creating an inland sea of fresh, glacial meltwater equal to about half the volume of Lake Michigan. This gargantuan lake was up to 2,500 feet deep and spread out over 3,000 square miles of western Montana.

So what's so important about this glacial lake? A popular theory among geologists is that about every several dozen years glacial meltwater that deepened behind the ice dam began to tunnel through the 20- to 30-mile-long ice dam (Plate 3). Once the highly pressurized water slowly worked through cracks and tunnels within the ice dam the impoundment disintegrated and the entire dam suddenly let loose, releasing an earth-shaking glacial-outburst flood, also referred to as a jökulhlaup (Icelandic term). The largest floods consisted of up to 530 cubic miles of bashing, grinding, roaring water that raced through Idaho, across eastern Washington and down the Columbia River valley all the way to the Pacific Ocean. The maximum speed of the floodwaters locally was in excess of 65 mph.

A recent, sophisticated computer model constructed by U.S. Geological Survey scientists Roger Denlinger and Daniel O'Connell show that Lake Missoula completely drained within three days or less of ice-dam breakup but took up to 25 days for all the water to find its way to the Pacific Ocean. (The delay in drainage was the result of temporary pooling behind several hydraulic constrictions lower in the flood route.) After each flood the Cordilleran Ice Sheet continued to advance, and apparently within a few years the ice dam reformed, creating a new Lake Missoula. Some geologists believe that during the last glacial cycle (about 14,000 to 28,000 years before present) alone, there were as many as 100 separate outburst floods from Glacial Lake Missoula.

Figure 1-9. Prior to the Ice Age floods, most of the Channeled Scabland was covered with a thick mantle of gently rolling hills consisting of fertile, windblown, Palouse loess. Today hills like these in the Palouse region of southeastern Washington make up one of the world's most productive dryland, wheat-growing regions.

Palouse Hills Under Attack

Prior to the Ice Age floods, most of the Channeled Scabland was covered by a continuous, thick (up to 250 feet) blanket of windblown sediment called loess, referred to by geologists as the Palouse Formation (Figure 1-9).

The loess deposit began forming as predominantly southwest winds blew sediment up onto the Palouse Slope at the beginning of the Ice Age perhaps as early as 2.6 million years ago (Figure 1-8). The earliest floods eroded into and carried some of this sediment back downstream where it was redeposited in the backflooded Pasco and Quincy basins. Periodic dust storms, like the one shown in Figure 1-10, blew some of the sediment back to the northeast, starting the cycle all over again. The dust storms were especially intense and effective at transporting sediment after each outburst flood, which wiped out and/or covered over the anchoring vegetation. Thus, the fresh blanket of flood sediment was easily picked up by the wind and carried back toward the Palouse region. The Palouse hills, then, are the end result of back-and-forth winnowing of flood sediment by desert winds over the eons.

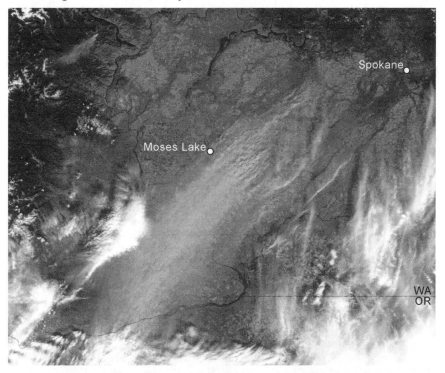

Figure 1-10. A thick plume of dust kicked up by strong winds settles over eastern Washington on October 4, 2009. Darker lines of flood-scoured basalt of the Channeled Scabland are visible through the dust cloud west and south of Spokane (from earthobservatory.nasa.gov).

The paths of the floods are easily discernable from space where the fine Palouse soil was stripped away down to the dark underlying basalt bedrock along scabland coulees producing the "Channeled Scabland" (Plate 10). The name "scabland" came into use by farmers and others who first settled the region; they quickly learned that rocky areas swept clean of soil were not as productive as other, often immediately adjacent areas covered with a thick blanket of fertile Palouse soil. One of the earliest published references to the "scabland" was from Lieutenant Thomas Symons who in 1882 wrote: "Considerable scab land exists in the western and northwestern parts of this section (Palouse Country). The land so designated by the people of the country is that where the original volcanic rock is exposed and uncovered by any soil."

The Long and Winding Flood Paths

"The volume of the invading water much exceeds the capacity of the existing streamways. The valleys entered become river channels, they brim over into neighboring ones, and minor divides within the system are crossed in hundreds of places."

– J Harlen Bretz (1928)

Flowing water naturally follows the path of least resistance, and the Ice Age floods were no exception. After their escape from Lake Missoula, floodwaters overwhelmed the existing drainage systems, thereby allowing water to spill across intervening divides, all the way to the Pacific Ocean. The floods first raged through northern Idaho's Rathdrum Prairie, a mountain valley between present-day Sandpoint and Coeur d'Alene. Floodwaters slammed into Mica Peak near present-day Post Falls, Idaho, diverting the water westward into the Spokane Valley. Earlier floods appear to have raced down the Columbia Valley via Wenatchee when no other ice dams existed downvalley. Later floods, on the other hand, encountered an ice dam at either Grand Coulee (forming Glacial Lake Columbia) or the Columbia Lobe (forming Glacial Lake Spokane) farther east (Plate 11). These other ice dams and associated lakes downstream of Lake Missoula effectively diverted all the floodwaters out across the Channeled Scabland.

Unlike Lake Missoula, Glacial Lake Columbia did not repeatedly fail on its own. Perhaps it was because Lake Columbia was a shallower lake (maximum 1,500 feet deep) in contrast to Lake Missoula (more than 2,000 feet deep). Reduced buoyancy and pressure behind a shallower Lake Columbia might have kept pressurized water from completely permeating the ice dam. Because Glacial Lake Columbia was already in place for most of the Missoula floods, the outbursts quickly finished the job of filling the Spokane and Columbia river valleys. Upon reaching the brim of the valley, the floodwaters rapidly spilled over several low points across the divide and onto the Channeled Scabland (Plates 10 and 11).

The Okanogan Lobe blocked most Missoula floods from continuing down the Columbia Valley west of Grand Coulee. Spillover occurred in at least three places – the head of the Cheney-Palouse Scabland Tract, Telford-Crab Creek Tract and Grand Coulee. At times all three of these spillover areas were simultaneously occupied by outburst floods. At other times the Columbia Lobe blocked the Columbia Valley at the Spokane River confluence, which diverted all floodwaters down the Cheney-Palouse Tract alone. During the Ice Age, when full to the brim, Glacial Lake Spokane (and Columbia) backflooded into the Spokane Valley and Rathdrum Prairie, almost all the way to the Lake Pend Oreille sublobe and outburst area for the Missoula floods (Plate 3).

Farther west, early in the evolution of the Grand Coulee when the Okanogan Lobe was not fully advanced, the ancestral Horse Lake and Foster Creek sometimes transmitted floodwaters as far west as Moses Coulee when glacial ice was in the B and C positions illustrated in Figure 1-11. Evidence suggests that one or more Missoula floods early in the last glacial cycle continued west all the way down the Columbia Valley, instead of across the Channeled Scabland at a time when the Okanogan Lobe had not yet fully extended across the Waterville Plateau (Figure 1-11, position A). Evidence also exists for a flood along the Columbia Valley that post-dates the last Missoula flood. This flood probably resulted from the final breakup of the Okanogan Lobe and cataclysmic release of Glacial Lake Columbia (Plate 11) at the very end of the Ice Age. So Ice Age floods took many different paths and at different times, depending on the existence and locations of ice blockages that lay in their path.

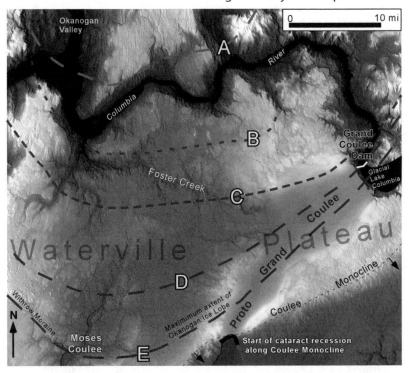

Figure 1-11. Various positions of the Okanogan Lobe had a profound influence on the paths of outburst floods. The largest flood(s) occurred early in the last glacial cycle when the ice was near position A, which allowed floodwaters to race unobstructed down the Columbia River Valley. By the time the ice sheet advanced into positions B and C, however, the Columbia River became blocked, causing Glacial Lake Columbia to back up for more than a hundred miles to the east. About this time several or more megafloods were diverted across the Waterville Plateau into Moses Coulee, but only before the proto-Grand Coulee was deepened by cataract recession. Floods also spilled over into the Telford-Crab Creek and Cheney-Palouse scablands to the east (Plates 10 and 11) until such a time that the cataract receded the full length of Grand Coulee before finally breaching with the Columbia Valley. When the ice sheet reached its maximum extent at position E (defined by the Withrow Moraine) even the deepened Grand Coulee was filled with ice. However, this didn't stop some of the floodwater from flowing across the upland plateau above the east side of Grand Coulee in the gap between the ice sheet margin and the Coulee Monocline ridge.

Floods Came, and in a Geologic Blink of an Eye – Were Gone!

"The rainfall of the plateau today is inadequate to maintain a single permanent and continuous stream from its own run-off. Yet the region is strongly marked almost everywhere by running water."

– J Harlen Bretz (1928)

Each flood from Glacial Lake Missoula is estimated to have taken only a few days to drain the lake and perhaps several weeks for all the water to drain into the Pacific Ocean because of several hydraulic constrictions downstream (e.g., Wallula Gap, Rowena Gap). Within the Channeled Scabland the flow from Lake Missoula peaked after only one day in the Cheney-Palouse and Telford scabland tracts before starting to wane. Grand Coulee (Figure 1-12) persisted a few days longer. The largest floods from Lake Missoula are believed to have flowed at a rate that approached one billion cubic feet per second – many times more than the flow of all the rivers in the world combined! The speed of the floodwater varied along the route, going faster (60 to 70 mph) in places where the land surface was tilted more steeply or where the water squeezed through narrow chasms, such as Grand, Lake Creek, or Rock Creek coulees. Elsewhere, the floodwaters slowed temporarily to perhaps only 10 to 20 mph where the land surface flattened or where the water spread out or backed up behind flow constrictions.

Combined, the floods' path across the Channeled Scabland, from edge to edge, spreads out for 100 miles! (Plate 1). Depending on the size of the flood, and various positions of the ice lobes downstream, it may have occupied one or many of the scabland routes at the same time. Once the flood-channel network was established early in the Ice Age, later floods naturally followed the same routes, sometimes perhaps with only minor changes.

Floodwaters that followed the path through Grand Coulee picked up speed when it squeezed between the coulee's narrow 900-foot-tall rock walls. From there, the deluge drained into what is called the Quincy Basin, a broad, open area that includes the towns of Moses Lake, Ephrata and Quincy, Washington. Floodwaters that spilled over into the Cheney-Palouse and Telford-Crab Creek scabland tracts, west of Spokane, spread out fast and free across the Channeled Scabland because of the tilted rock surface (Palouse Slope) that slopes gently to the southwest. The waters slowed temporarily and the flood surface flattened in the Quincy Basin. Here they merged with waters from Grand Coulee and continued south into the Mid-Columbia region. Detailed descriptions of flood features in this area were described previously in the first volume of *On the Trail of the Ice Age Floods: A geological field guide to the Mid-Columbia Basin*, by author Bruce Bjornstad, Keokee Books, 2006.

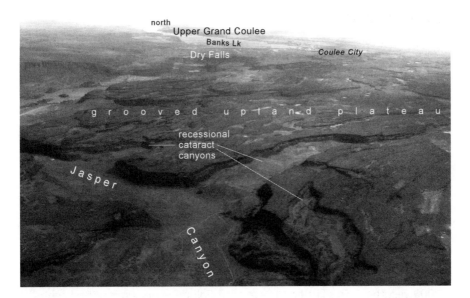

north
Upper Grand Coulee
Banks Lk
Dry Falls
Coulee City

g r o o v e d u p l a n d p l a t e a u

recessional
cataract
canyons

Jasper

Canyon

Figure 1-12. Scabland topography of the Lower Grand Coulee. Scabland is characterized by barren basalt bedrock (lacking soil cover) that is eroded into a complex maze of now-dry channels, grooves, potholes, rock benches, mesas, buttes and recessional cataract canyons. Flood deposits locally accumulated along canyon bottoms. During the largest Ice Age floods, this entire landscape (except upper left corner) was submerged under hundreds of feet of turbulent floodwater raging at 60 mph or more.

Figure 1-13. J Harlen Bretz around 1930.

The original theory of Ice Age floods was the brainchild of one man – J Harlen Bretz (Figure 1-13), who first proposed the idea in 1923, and then spent the next several decades attempting to convince a skeptical geologic community of their existence. It wasn't until the 1970s, when geologists began observing the Channeled Scabland from the air (e.g., Plate 10), that Bretz's theory gained general acceptance.

Ice Age Floods' Sources

The exact timing and sources for Bretz's Spokane flood(s) are still being unraveled. It appears that most floods during the last glacial cycle occurred from repeated outbursts from Glacial Lake Missoula. However, floods from other sources in the Pacific Northwest are also known to have occurred during this time. Other sources of floodwater geologists have identified include a single flood from Lake Bonneville, a giant, mountain-rimmed lake in the Salt Lake basin of Utah; other ice-dammed lakes in the Columbia River drainage, including Glacial Lake Columbia; or, possibly even from outbursts from beneath the Cordilleran Ice Sheet itself (Plate 1).

From what geologists have pieced together, Lake Bonneville flooded the Columbia Basin from the east via the Snake River only once about 17,500 calendar years ago. The Lake Bonneville flood, however, entered south of the Channeled Scabland and therefore didn't affect the scablands directly. Furthermore, because the flood devastation happened over a six-week period, instead of a few days like Lake Missoula, it was, by geologic accounts, less devastating. Also, it appears that at least one flood occurred, from the final breakup of Glacial Lake Columbia, at the end of the last glacial cycle, about 14,000 years ago. This last flood from Lake Columbia occurred several centuries after the last outburst from Glacial Lake Missoula.

One thing we do know is that evidence exists for much older floods throughout the Ice Age, long before those generated during the last glacial cycle that lasted from about 14,000 to 28,000 years ago. The trend among geologists lately has been to refer to Ice Age floods synonymously as Missoula floods. But as one can see, floods from multiple sources throughout the Ice Age shaped the region. So far, geologists have not developed the ability to positively identify floods from different sources in the geologic record. Therefore, the generic term "Ice Age floods" more inclusively describes these floods and will be used throughout this book, except when the source is known for certain.

They're How Old?

The Pacific Northwest has a long history of Ice Age flooding (Figure 1-8). The oldest floods could be as old as 2.6 million years (beginning of the Pleistocene Epoch and global cooling associated with the Ice Age). By 15,000 years ago the Pleistocene was coming to an end and the Cordilleran Ice Sheet that had extended south into northern Washington, Idaho and Montana was rapidly thinning and receding northward. The last floods probably occurred between 14,000 to 15,000 calendar years ago.* At least one of these last floods may have come from the final break up of an ice dam (Okanogan Lobe) that formed Glacial Lake Columbia. Unlike most (or all) floods from Glacial Lake Missoula, this flood did not flow out across the Channeled Scabland, but was restricted to the main valley of the Columbia River, which drains the perimeter of the Columbia Plateau.

*The last Ice Age flood occurred sometime between about 13,500 years and 15,400 calendar years ago. This age is based on two dated volcanic ash layers. The older age is associated with an eruption from Mount St. Helens, whose ash lies between layers from the last floods. The younger age is from volcanic ash from Glacier Peak that always lies above flood deposits and therefore is younger than the last flood.

During the Ice Age, glaciers may have advanced and retreated dozens of times. In the last cycle of glaciation (referred to by geologists as the Wisconsinan glaciation), which lasted from about 80,000 years to 14,000 years ago, there were at least two periods when glaciers pushed far enough south into the Pacific Northwest to generate Ice Age floods. The earlier period (early Wisconsinan) lasted from about 80,000 years to 65,000 years ago, and the later from about 28,000 years to 14,000 years ago (late Wisconsinan or Fraser glaciation). Between these advances the ice temporarily retreated back into Arctic Canada.

The geologic record of flooding is best preserved in the last glacial cycle. Much less evidence exists for floods from previous glacial cycles because the last flood(s) tended to erode or cover up the evidence for older floods. However, there is also evidence in places such as Moses Coulee (e.g., Withrow Moraine) to suggest that floods occurred not only as the glaciers retreated, but also as the glaciers advanced, so that floods could have occurred at any time during a glacial cycle – not just during waning stages.

The timing and frequency of climate change and glacial periods are well-preserved in sediment cores collected at depth in the Pacific Ocean. Here sediments have been laid down uninterrupted for millions of years and there is a continuous record of at least nine major glacial-interglacial cycles over the last 800,000 years (see Figure 1-8). As many as several dozen of these glacial-climatic cycles may exist going back to the start of the Ice Age, which began about 2.6 million years ago. Some geologists believe as many as 40 to 100 floods occurred during the waning stage of the last glacial cycle alone. If that's the case and if as many floods occurred during previous glacial cycles as the last, then the total number of floods for the entire Ice Age could easily add up to hundreds or even a thousand or more!

How do we know how old the floods are? One way geologists can identify the land record of old floods is by looking at the magnetic polarity of fine-grained deposits that was imprinted onto the sediment as it was laid down. The Earth's magnetic field has periodically "flipped" back and forth over geologic time. The last significant reversal occurred about 780,000 years ago, when the magnetic field changed from a "reversed" direction to the "normal" direction we observe today. (The change also defines the boundary between the early and middle Pleistocene Epochs, see Figure 1-8.) These changes often are preserved in sediments since some sediment grains are magnetic and, like tiny magnets, tend to align themselves with the Earth's magnetic field at the time they are deposited. So, early Pleistocene flood deposits retain a reversed magnetic polarity while middle Pleistocene and younger deposits record a normal magnetic polarity.

Evidence for the oldest floods on land can also be found by examining how flood deposits have weathered at the surface over time. Deposits from the last floods (late Wisconsinan), which are relatively young (14,000 to 15,000 years), show little or no weathering. In contrast, old flood deposits exposed to the elements for a much longer time display extensive weathering. In a semi-arid climate, like that of the Channeled Scabland, soils that developed on old flood deposits are rich in a calcium-carbonate precipitate – called caliche – that takes many thousands of years to accumulate into a hardpan (Figure 1-14).

- -

Figure 1-14. Extremely old Ice Age flood gravels at the base of this exposure near Revere are covered with a thick calcic paleosol (light-colored zone in middle). Seven samples were collected within the paleosol for paleomagnetic analysis. All seven samples have a reversed magnetic polarity obtained at the time of deposition greater than 780,000 years ago, the age of the last major magnetic reversal. Thus, the flood gravels must be from a flood at least this age or could be from a much older flood going all the way back to the beginning of the Ice Age about 2.6 million years ago. N47.0910, W117.9395

Unfortunately, evidence of the earliest floods is limited to a few, isolated, widely distributed places in the region. Within the Channeled Scabland almost all the evidence for the much older floods is preserved in the Cheney-Palouse Scabland Tract. Perhaps, as more roads and excavations expose fresh outcrops of flood deposits, new evidence for old floods will be uncovered to help work out the chronology for the earlier Ice Age floods. But the Rosetta stone for the timing and frequency of Ice Age megafloods lies off the Pacific coastline where a continuous record of flooding is likely preserved. Perhaps someday a carfeully placed borehole will reveal the complete picture of 2 million years or more of flood history.

Ice Age Floods National Geologic Trail

In 2009, the U.S. Congress recognized the importance of the Ice Age floods to the Pacific Northwest and the nation by authorizing a first-of-its-kind, Ice Age Floods National Geologic Trail (NGT). The NGT will be a network of marked touring routes extending across parts of Montana, Idaho, Washington and Oregon, with several special interpretive centers located along the 700-mile-long route of the floods. The proposed trail will be managed by the National Park Service (NPS), which will use only existing public lands and facilities to tell the story of the megafloods, beginning with the pioneering work of legendary geologists J Harlen Bretz and Joseph T. Pardee. This "park without boundaries" will include kiosks and signs placed on the existing network of public lands and roadways that pass through the floods' region.

The road to national designation of the NGT was long and difficult. A move to expand public awareness of the floods began in 1994 as a grassroots organization of Pacific Northwest geologists and engaged citizens joined forces to organize the Ice Age Floods Institute (IAFI), a nonprofit educational organization dedicated to bringing the unique story of repeated megafloods to the public. In 1999, the NPS commissioned an environmental assessment and study of alternatives to tell the story of the floods. Two years later the recommendation to Congress for a NGT came as a result of the NPS and IAFI study.

As managing organization, the NPS will coordinate with the IAFI as well as other federal, state and local agencies, along with public, tribal and private interpretive efforts to tell a cohesive and impactful story. Interpretive signage along the NGT generated by the NPS and other agencies is forthcoming. Some agencies, such as the Idaho and Washington state park systems and Turnbull National Wildlife Refuge have gotten a head start and already have interpretive displays in place within their domains. Signage at kiosks and other public areas along the trail should not only increase public awareness and appreciation of our geologic heritage, but also inspire young minds – perhaps providing a catalyst for a new generation of devoted earth scientists.

Figure 1-15. U.S. Representative Doc Hastings (R-Wash.) and U.S. Senator Maria Cantwell (D-Wash.) cosponsored the Ice Age Floods bill, passed by Congress in 2009. The two admire ice-rafted erratics gifted to them in a Tri-Cities ceremony to celebrate the bill's passage.

Looking south across Dry Falls Lake and Umatilla Rock, Lower Grand Coulee

2

Features: What the Floods Left Behind

The Ice Age floods created a unique collection of landforms that were produced either by erosion, the wearing away of the land, or deposition, the building up of the land (Table 2-1). These landforms are called features. In this chapter we define the Ice Age flood features and provide the best places to see examples and the characteristics of each type of feature found in the Channeled Scabland. Specific features described in further detail in chapter 3 are numbered and identified throughout the book with parentheses (e.g., No. XX).

Table 2-1. Ice Age flood features of the Channeled Scabland

Erosional Features	Depositional Features
Interconnected networks of abandoned channels and coulees	Giant flood bars and fosses
Divide crossings and spillover channels	Giant current ripples
Longitudinal grooves	Slackwater rhythmites
Rock basins and potholes	Ice-rafted erratics
Cliff overhangs and rock shelters	
Natural bridges	
Rock benches, mesas and buttes	
Rock blades	
Pinnacles and pillars	
Cataract cliffs and plunge pools	
Trenched spurs	
Hogbacks	
Residual, streamlined Palouse hills	
Faceted escarpments	
Ringed craters	

In general, the floods created mostly erosional features in the Channeled Scabland where floodwaters moved fast and furiously. The Channeled Scabland is the best example of a place where the speed of the floodwaters accelerated across a tilted land surface, called the Palouse Slope, resulting in extreme erosion from powerful currents. A sloping land surface wasn't the only cause for high flood velocity, however. High speeds can also be generated, even in areas of relatively flat terrain, where floodwaters were forced to squeeze through narrower openings such as Steptoe Ridge Spillover Complex (No. 12), Upper Grand Coulee, Spring Coulee (No. 40), or Dry Coulee (No. 50). It's a natural law, called the venturi effect, which makes the flow of fluids automatically speed up when forced through a bottleneck. (As an example, think of the difference in the speed of the water flowing through a bathtub drain versus the rest of the bathtub.)

Throughout the Channeled Scabland, fast-moving floodwaters scoured down through the blanket of loose soil (Plate 10) into the basalt bedrock below, carrying away massive amounts of sediment of the Palouse Formation, as well as loosened fragments of eroded basalt rock. The Palouse Formation is a deposit of fine-textured, windblown sediment, in some places up to 250 feet thick, that slowly accumulated over the basalt (see Figure 1-9), beginning near the start of the Ice Age (more than 2 million years ago). After being eroded by the floods, some of the sediment collected along the downstream ends of obstructions or up into backflooded valleys along flood paths or in the broad, open valleys of the Quincy, Othello and Pasco basins (see companion volume, *On the Trail of the Ice Age Floods: A geological field guide to the Mid-Columbia Basin*). Not all the eroded sediment came to rest in these basins, however. Most remained mixed with the turbid floodwater and were quickly flushed out to sea with each of the hundreds or more, short-lived, outburst-flood events.

Erosional Features

"The loess-mantled basalt plateau of eastern Washington possesses a system of linear anastamosing denuded tracts, the channeled scabland."

– J Harlen Bretz (1930)

On the Channeled Scabland the Ice Age floods carved erosional landforms out of ancient lava flows of Columbia River basalt and the Palouse Formation (fine windblown dust called loess) that lay above the basalt bedrock. The first Ice Age floods could have occurred with the beginning of the Ice Age as early as 2.6 million years ago. The earliest floods began to erode into Palouse loess, leaving behind teardrop-shaped islands known as "streamlined Palouse hills," especially within the Cheney-Palouse Scabland Tract in the eastern scablands. As the floods cut deeper and with each successive flood, they eventually breached the loess cover, cutting down into the underlying layers of basalt (Figure 2-1).

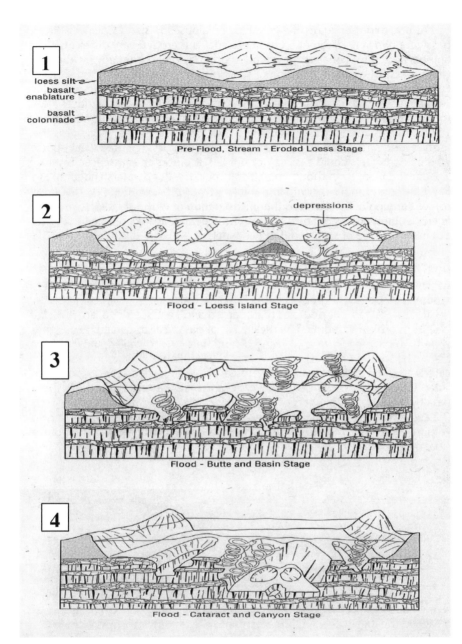

Figure 2-1. Evolution of a scabland tract. Stage 1: Before Ice Age floods a thick blanket of windblown Palouse loess covered a stacked sequence of layered basalt lava flows. Stage 2: Early floods begin to remove the Palouse cover leaving behind eroded, streamlined hills of loess. Stage 3: More erosion during subsequent floods carve channels and rock basins deeper into the basalt bedrock. Stage 4: Late-stage recessional cataracts and deep inner canyons incise farther into the basalt.

As one might imagine, the windblown Palouse loess and Columbia River basalt are two very different types of material and eroded very differently. The fine-grained, semi-cohesive loess eroded grain by grain, primarily by abrasion (the process of wearing, grinding or scraping away of the Earth's surface). Furthermore, surfaces of Palouse loess are relatively smooth and do not induce strong erosive turbulence in the floodwaters. In contrast, basalt surfaces are rough, a situation that promotes turbulence when engulfed in racing flood-waters. And even though it is hardened rock, basalt is riddled with cracks that formed long ago as the lava cooled. Cracks, or fractures, created weak spots where floodwaters could easily pluck out basalt blocks en masse (see Figures 1-2 and 1-5). So, even though basalt was rock, the floodwaters ended up erod-ing it faster and more easily than the relatively "soft" loess deposits that lay on top of the basalt. This explains the phenomenon of why "islands" of stream-lined Palouse loess were able to withstand repeated attacks by the floods, even out in the middle of scabland flood channels.

Where the floods were especially powerful and eroded into basalt, they left behind a topography referred to by J Harlen Bretz as "butte and basin," which characterizes much of the Channeled Scabland. In places, the floods scoured long, straight grooves in the basalt bedrock. As grooves expanded, the floods gouged out potholes that merged and coalesced into larger rock basins. As erosion continued, vertical walls of basalt called cataracts (now dry waterfalls) receded upvalley, leaving behind deep, steep-walled, inner canyons below the cataract cliffs (Figure 2-1, stage 3). Scalloped, horseshoe-shaped cataracts, often dividing into two or three alcoves, receded upvalley for miles. Later floods might continue to widen the channels, cutting deeper into the basalt, creating multiple tiers of recessional cataracts and inner canyons. Figure 2-2 shows examples of many different types of erosional landforms preserved within Lower Grand Coulee, one of the most dramatically eroded areas of the Channeled Scabland.

Scabland Homonyms

A number of widely dispersed features on the Channeled Scabland have identical names. Steamboat Rock, for example, is a prominent feature of the Upper Grand Coulee and even has a state park named after it. Few probably know of the other Steamboat Rock in the Three Devils scabland complex of Moses Coulee (see Figure 5-42). At least three Castle Rocks exist, one along the Upper Grand Coulee, a second in the Castle Lake basin and a third along the east side of Rock Lake, 90 miles to the east on the opposite side of the Channeled Scabland. A very long Dry Coulee splits off from the Lower Grand Coulee, but a much shorter (1.5 miles) Dry Coulee lies along Moses Coulee, too (see Figure 2-19). There are two Long Lakes, 75 miles apart; one lies within Turnbull National Wildlife Refuge and the other lies between Northrup and Spring Canyons (see Figure 3-61). And don't get us started on the number of different Rock Creeks and Rattlesnake Creeks out there.

Why so many different landmarks with the same name within the scablands? Apparently, since the entire Channeled Scabland shares a common geologic and erosional history (colossal Ice Age floods eating away at layered basalt flows), many similar-appearing features were duplicated. Most local farmers and ranchers, who originally named the features, probably didn't get around to see other parts of the scablands enough to know the name given to their special feature was perhaps already in use elsewhere.

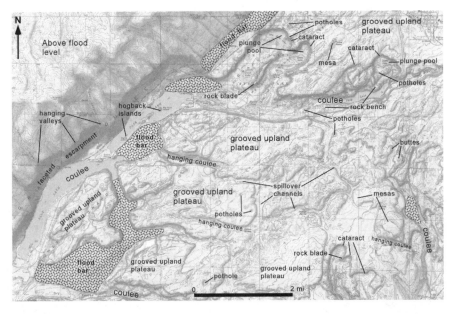

Figure 2-2. Major flood features in a portion of the Lower Grand Coulee. Dry Falls dual cataract canyon is at top center. All features on this map, except for flood bars, are the result of erosional megaflood scouring. See Figure 1-12 for an oblique aerial perspective in the vicinity of this map.

After removal of the cover of Palouse soil, the many unique erosional landforms of the Channeled Scabland are as much the result of the Columbia River basalt bedrock as they are about the floods themselves. Multiple layered basalt flows with regular, alternating fracture patterns between entablature and colonnade were conducive to the preferential plucking and rapid disintegration of the basalt flows, especially along columnar zones (see Figure 1-2). This promoted the rapid deepening and undercutting of basalt flows during flooding, leading to the formation of potholes, recessional cataracts, rock benches, blades, mesas and buttes. In contrast, none of these types of landforms developed in granitic or other rocks along the flood route. Therefore, it was the combination of the floods and the unique erosional behavior of the basalt that created the characteristic landforms of the Channeled Scabland.

Anastomosing Channels and Coulees

"Canyons in the scablands are multiple and anastomosing, amazingly so in some tracts; deep canyons and shallow ones uniting and dividing in a labyrinthine fashion about bare rock knobs and buttes unlike any other land surfaces on the earth."

– J Harlen Bretz (1927)

Flood channels are long, continuous, straight to broadly curving features eroded by short-lived outburst floods (Figure 2-3). A coulee is a type of channel that has been more deeply eroded into a distinct, steep-walled, flat-bottomed valley (Plate 49), which today is likely to be completely dry, or in a few cases, occupied by what geologists call an "underfit" stream. An underfit stream is one that is greatly out of proportion with the size of the coulee it occupies (see Plates 16 and 20, left, for examples). The bottoms of coulees are generally flat, except where they suddenly drop off over cascades or cataracts sometimes hundreds of feet tall. The Channeled Scabland is characterized by a network of channels and coulees that repeatedly divide and rejoin, forming an interconnected, braided-stream pattern (Plate 10). This anastomosis, as it is sometimes called, expanded over an area almost 100 miles wide (Plate 1).

Figure 2-3. Flood channels and coulees. Left: Sinuous flood channel eroded into upland plateau leading to Dry Coulee (No. 50) in the background. Looking southwest. Right: A side coulee hangs high above the floor of lower Moses Coulee. Most scabland coulees have been completely void of natural stream flows since the end of the last Ice Age about 14,000 years ago. Looking northeast.

Deep coulees with steep walls are characteristic of the Channeled Scabland where floodwaters incised into the basalt bedrock, especially below recessional cataracts. As floods receded, water levels would be confined to lower and lower channels. Continued flood erosion along a lower channel would often cut off higher channels, thus leaving them hanging, as in Figure 2-3 (right). Later Ice Age floods were also smaller and therefore may have not occupied the older and higher flood channels but would truncate and cut them off at their lower ends. Deep, dry coulees similar to those in the Channeled Scabland are also present on the planet Mars (Figure 2-4), suggesting great floods once occurred there as well. Besides Grand Coulee and Moses Coulee, other impressive flood coulees include Monument Coulee (No. 42; Plate 35), Deep Lake Coulee (No. 46; see Plate 34, left), Rock Creek Coulee (No. 17, see Figure 6-3) and Lake Creek Coulee (No. 23; Plate 18b).

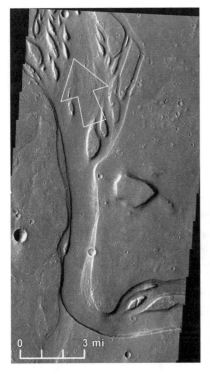

0   3 mi

Figure 2-4. Many of the erosional channel features on Mars are similar to those in the Channeled Scabland. Here is an interconnected flood-channel network on Hebrus Valles, Mars for comparison. Flow direction is indicated by block arrow. Note how excess flow overtopped divides, spilling over into adjacent channels, as in the Channeled Scabland. Streamlined and scarped rock islands lie within the main channel, showing a steep "prow" on the upstream end and tapering tail at the downstream end similar to Steamboat Rock (Plates 24 and 26). THEMIS VISIBLE LIGHT IMAGE V20080523A

Divide Crossings and Spillover Channels

"Only extraordinary flooding could have crossed the violated preglacial divides, and only extraordinary velocity (born of huge volume) could scarify the bedrocks so tremendously."

– J Harlen Bretz (1969)

A special type of channel associated with the Ice Age floods is the "spill-over channel." These elevated, now-dry, flat-bottomed channels developed where floodwater spilled across and trenched into drainage divides when megafloods overflowed into adjacent valleys. If enough floodwater moved through the divide crossings, a flat-bottomed channel with planed-off, scarped sides often developed, giving the channel a trapezoid-shaped profile (see Figure 3-15). Geologists use these spillover channels to identify the maximum heights of floods; these are useful for reconstructing the slope of the highest water surface during flooding (see Figure 3-52). With this information, scientists using computer models have been able to make estimates on the depth, speed and duration of the floods.

Good examples of spillover channels are shown in Figure 2-5, where the largest floods from Glacial Lake Missoula spilled out of Hangman Creek into the head of Pine Creek Coulee. Here the floodwaters rose to at least 2,530 feet in elevation; an adjacent divide at 2,560 feet was not crossed by the floods. This suggests the highest elevation for megafloodwaters at this location was about 2,550 feet.

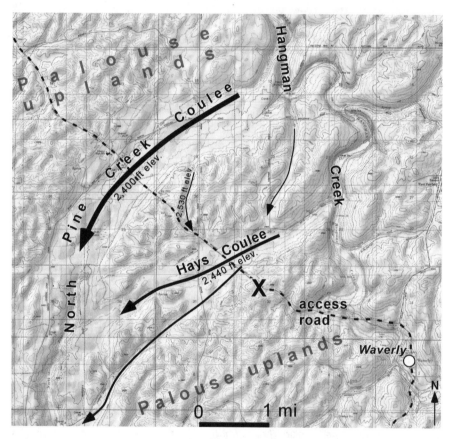

Figure 2-5. Spillover channels. Above: Spillways (arrows) eroded by Ice Age floods that flowed over into North Pine Creek Coulee and Hays Coulee from Hangman Creek. Elevations shown are for the maximum height of coulee floor. Photo on following page: The Spangle-Waverly Road descends across Hays Coulee that carried spillover from Hangman Creek. Photo taken from location "X" in above image.

northwest

Palouse uplands

Hays Coulee (2,440 ft elevation)

Besides Pine Creek Coulee, high divide crossings and spillover channels lie at the head of Grand Coulee (No. 29), along the U.S. 2 Spillover Complex (No. 20) and Northrup Canyon (No. 32).

Longitudinal Grooves

Once the floods eroded away all the topsoil, oftentimes the first stage in the erosion of the underlying basalt was formation of mostly straight, parallel, longitudinal grooves separated by low, flood-molded, bedrock ridges of basalt (Figure 2-6). Floodwaters eroded longitudinal grooves into the upper surface of flows, mainly in the entablature (see Figure 1-2) portion. Grooves generally range from 100 to 200 feet apart, and about 10 feet high. The grooves are often partially filled with fine-grained, windblown soil that collects in these lower areas. Most (but not all) grooves are aligned with the direction of floodwater flow. They may have formed from kolk-like, elongated vortices oriented in a horizontal direction, parallel to the grooves, rather than in vertically directed kolks (circulating vortices within floodwaters) that form potholes. Sometimes they can be curved and oriented in directions dissimilar to flood flow (see Figure 1-6). Some grooves, especially those that curve, may follow relict flow structures that formed as the basalt lava advanced and cooled soon after extrusion.

Grooves

Figure 2-6. Longitudinal grooves. Left: On upland plateau above Jasper Canyon, Lower Grand Coulee. Looking northeast. DALE STRADLING PHOTO. Right: At ground level, grooves are less obvious. Grooves are composed of slightly higher ridges of basalt separated by parallel, sediment-filled hollows. Looking southwest down the floor of East Lenore Coulee (No. 55).

With continued erosional scour, potholes and rock basins may develop out of expanding grooves. In the Channeled Scabland, straight longitudinal grooves are best preserved in upland plateaus in the vicinity of Dry Falls (No. 41, see Plate 29), Blue Lake, Castle Rock Cataracts (No. 33, see Plate 26) and East Lenore Coulee (No. 55). Curving grooves are common near the head of the Telford Tract, the Summit Plateau Scabland (No. 35, see Figure 1-6) as well as atop Steamboat Rock (No. 31, Plate 24).

Rock Basins and Potholes

"Closed basins as deep as 135 feet were bitten out of the underlying basalt."

– J Harlen Bretz (1969)

Fast-moving floodwaters passing through scabland channels gouged farther into the basalt, scouring out rock basins and augering deep holes into basalt (Figures 2-7 to 2-10, see Plates 34, 40 and 42). Like a powerful vacuum cleaner, floodwaters actually sucked up all the loose material off the land surface, including huge columns of basalt, taking advantage of any weaknesses in the rock, such as fractures or rubbly basalt-flow bottoms. Deeper basins are often filled with water, where floods eroded holes below the present water table. Coffeepot Lake (see Figure 6-9) and Rock Lake (Figure 2-8), are two good examples of deep, water-filled rock basins. Rock basins are often elongated and oriented in the direction of floodwater flow. Other scoured-out depressions in scablands include circular potholes, which were literally drilled out by violent, swirling vortices within the floodwater called kolks. Figures 2-7 and 2-9 show examples of circular potholes. Occasionally, pothole lips are beveled and smoothed on the downstream side (see Figure 2-9); this attests to the powerful, abrasive nature of the floodwaters as the potholes formed. Potholes sometimes align in a row (Plate 34, right), but most often are randomly distributed on rock benches (No. 46) or upland plateaus (No. 45). As potholes expanded during flooding, they may merge together to form channels (Figure 2-10), elongated rock basins or, rarely, natural bridges (Plate 19).

Figure 2-7. A saucer-shaped pothole atop the Summit Plateau Scabland (No. 35), Upper Grand Coulee. Shallow potholes such as this one dry out during summer evaporation. Looking northeast.

Places in the Channeled Scabland with impressive, lake-filled, flood-scoured rock basins include Sprague Lake (see Figure 3-32), Sylvan Lake within Crab Creek Coulee (No. 22, see Figure 2-34) and Coffeepot Lake. Some of the best places to view potholes are near Deep Lake (No. 46, Plate 34), East Lenore Coulee (No. 55, Figure 2-9) and Spring Coulee (No. 40, see Figure 4-103).

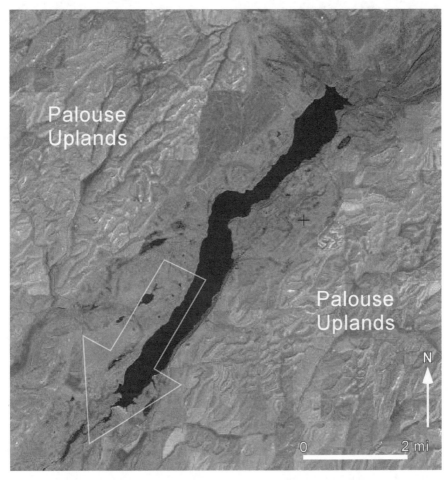

Figure 2-8. Rock Lake, along Rock Creek Coulee (No. 17) occupies a rock basin eight miles long and one mile wide. Up to 400 feet deep, Rock Lake is the deepest of all the scabland lakes. Floodwaters eroded out the darker areas along either side of Rock Lake but little of the adjacent Palouse uplands. Note the numerous dark potholes on rock bench above Rock Lake.

Figure 2-9. East Lenore Coulee (No. 55) potholes eroded into Grande Ronde Basalt. Above: a narrow and deep pothole. Right: Arrow points to the beveled lip on the downstream side of this pothole that suggests the floodwaters must have been highly abrasive to create this planar, smoothed surface. Floodwater flow was in the direction of the arrow. Both images looking west.

Figure 2-10. A channel incised into this potholed rock bench of Grande Ronde Basalt at East Lenore Coulee. The channel developed from a series of adjacent potholes that coalesced during flood erosion.

Cliff Overhangs and Rock Shelters

Overhanging cliffs of basalt, some of which have served as rock shelters for American Indians for thousands of years, are common in the steep walls of coulees, rock basins and potholes. Good examples are the Giant Cave Arch rock shelter (Figure 2-11) near Barker Canyon (No. 34) and Lake Lenore Caves (No. 52, see Figure 3-93). The cliff overhangs formed as a result of differential erosion by Ice Age floodwaters, which locally eroded away the more easily plucked, large columns of basalt in the colonnade and rubbly basalt toward the base of some lava flows. Thick layers of more cohesive overhanging entablature resisted these plucking forces to a greater degree.

Figure 2-11. Giant Cave Arch (arrow) is a huge rock shelter at the south end of the Barker Canyon Scabland Complex (No. 34). The overhang formed when the floods preferentially plucked out weaker rock from several thin basalt flows beneath a stronger and more massive entablature zone. Looking southwest.

Figure 2-12. A pair of rock shelters in a single basalt flow along the east wall of the Lower Grand Coulee. The small amount of talus beneath the shelters does not appear to be any greater than that away from the overhangs, suggesting they have not grown appreciably since the last megaflood about 15,000 years ago. Looking northeast.

Some overhangs leading to the formation of rock shelters may have been enlarged by rock fall due to the effects of gravity and weathering (i.e., freeze-thaw activity) since the end of the Ice Age. However, some rock shelters, such as those in Figure 2-12, do not appear to have expanded much since the last Ice Age floods.

Natural Bridges

Natural bridges are defined here as freestanding rock spans with an open passageway produced by the action of running water erosion. A natural bridge, such as the one shown in Plate 19, formed where two overhanging potholes expanded and merged into one another during flooding. Natural bridges are extremely rare since the combination of closely spaced potholes that simultaneously become undercut during flooding were only preserved in a few places. Figure 2-13 is a good example showing basalt flows that were undercut by preferential plucking of columns along a flow bottom. This produces an overhang of the stronger entablature above (see Figure 1-2). Generally, most potholes are undercut and overhang more on the downstream side of potholes. One can easily envision that if another overhanging pothole formed immediately adjacent to the one in Figure 2-13 that a natural bridge might form.

Figure 2-13. Undercut pothole in the Roza Member of Wanapum Basalt in the vicinity of the natural bridge shown in Plate 19. The upper entablature portion of a basalt flow hangs over the colonnade of the same flow, where swirling floodwaters preferentially plucked out the more easily eroded basalt columns. Maximum undercutting occurs on the downstream end of potholes. Above: Looking southeast. Left: Same pothole looking northeast from beneath the wide overhang.

Figure 2-14. Natural bridge along Hole-in-the-Ground Canyon between Rock Lake and Bonnie Lake (No. 15). View of bridge from above where Ice Age floods preferentially plucked out the colonnade into an adjacent pothole along Rock Creek Coulee. Looking southeast.

Similar to architectural arches, once formed, bridges and rock shelters may remain structurally strong and stable and resist further collapse and disintegration. Both the Marlin Hollow and Hole-in-the-Ground Canyon natural bridges in the Channeled Scabland are on private lands and, therefore, not accessible to the general public.

Rock Benches, Mesas and Buttes

After carving channels into the basalt, the floods peeled away the once-continuous basalt layers, one-by-one, away from the walls of coulees and rock basins (Figures 2-15 and 4-57, Plate 14). Since the uppermost basalt layers were attacked first, they are typically eroded farther away from the center of the coulee. The end result was a stair-stepped, tiered landscape of rock benches, as well as isolated mesas and buttes (Figure 2-15). Rock benches are flat areas, usually eroded out along the base of a flow, bordered by basalt cliffs of the next younger flow. They developed where a relatively weak colonnade, or occasional sediment layer, lay between more resistant layers of basalt entablature. Floodwaters preferentially eroded away the weak layers, undercutting the rock. Unstable, the cliff collapsed above the undercut, maintaining the vertical wall of basalt above the stronger cap rock on the bench below. Continued undercutting resulted in continued collapse and recession of the wall down to the underlying rock bench.

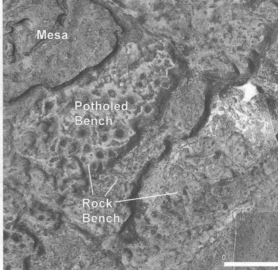

Figure 2-15. Rock benches. Like layers of an onion, the floods peeled away once-continuous basalt flows exposed along the edges of flood channels and coulees. Left: Benches formed atop a half dozen or more flows of Wanapum and Grande Ronde basalt eroded along lower Moses Coulee (No. 61). Looking northwest. Right: Vertical air photo along Black Rock Coulee (No. 28). Potholes occur atop some, but not all the rock benches, suggesting some basalt flows are more prone to the formation of potholes than others. Four separate basalt flows are represented by the three rock benches and one mesa.

Mesas represent isolated, flood-eroded remnants of once-continuous volcanic-basalt flows. They are similar to rock benches except their upper surface is surrounded by cliffs on all sides. Mesas are wider than they are tall, and their flat top is normally composed of more resistant basalt entablature. Buttes are like mesas except they are taller than they are wide. Over time, after repeated attack by floodwaters, rock benches may evolve into mesas, which may eventually be reduced to isolated buttes. In Figure 2-16 are examples of rock benches, mesas and buttes located along lower Lake Creek Coulee (No. 23).

Good examples of rock benches, mesas and buttes lie along Lower Grand Coulee, Rock Creek Coulee (No. 17), Lake Creek Coulee (Figure 2-16), Deep Lake Coulee (No. 46), and East Lenore Coulee (No. 55).

Figure 2-16. Rock benches, mesas and buttes along lower Lake Creek Coulee (No. 23). The buttes here are also known as the Odessa Towers (see also Plate 18a). Looking west.

Rock Blades

Rock blades appear as elongated rocky buttes or mesas. They typically form where dual amphitheaters, or alcoves, form below recessional cataract canyons. Here a narrow rib of basalt bedrock may be left behind between two or more of the alcoves as the cataracts recede headward. The best example of a rock blade is The Great Blade (No. 54, Figure 2-17), which dramatically separates two recessional cataract canyons – East Lenore Coulee on the east and Lower Grand Coulee on the west. During further flood erosion a rock blade may segregate into one or more isolated, elongated rocky buttes or mesas. Rock blades that are detached from the receding cataract that formed them are also called "goat islands." Bretz named them after the Goat Island at Niagara Falls, which he used as his model for Dry Falls and related features.

Figure 2-17. The Great Blade Lower Grand Coulee. Looking northwest. See Plate 39 for a different perspective on this terrain.

Figure 2-18. The basalt pinnacle on the left was once attached to the cliff on the right. Ice Age floods attacked and eroded away the rock in between, isolating the pinnacle. Looking west toward Park Lake within the Lower Grand Coulee.

Another example of an eroded rock blade includes Umatilla Rock (No. 43), which straddles the two alcoves immediately below Dry Falls (No. 41, Plate 32). Steamboat Rock (Plates 24 and 26) is also a rock-blade remnant left after a dual cataract completely receded and consumed itself during the last Ice Age floods at the head of Upper Grand Coulee (No. 29). Other good examples of rock blades, or goat islands, occur at the Castle Rock Cataracts (No. 33, see Figure 3-62) and Hudson Coulee (No. 49).

Pinnacles and Pillars

Occasionally, Ice Age floods scoured the fractured basalt flows into tall, isolated pinnacles, also called pillars (Figure 2-18). Pinnacles and pillars are much taller than they are wide and have uneven tops, unlike mesas and buttes that usually have flat tops. Some of these pointed features may represent the eroded remnants of past mesas and buttes from which they evolved after repeated episodes of flooding. Pinnacles and pillars, like mesas and buttes, usually have a protective cap of more resistant entablature, leading to their preservation.

Cataract Cliffs and Plunge Pools

"Hundreds of extinct waterfalls, many of which during recession became wider, several two to three miles wide."

– J Harlen Bretz (1927)

As floods raced across the Columbia Plateau, single to multi-alcoved recessional cataract canyons formed (e.g., Plates 31 and 32). Cataracts are characterized by tall, now-dry cliffs with horseshoe-shaped alcoves – some hundreds of feet high. At the bottoms of many cataracts lie deep, round plunge pools. Plunge pools are a special type of rock basin gouged out as floodwaters dropped vertically off the tall cataract cliffs. Today, plunge pools are often naturally filled with groundwater-seepage lakes. Below a cataract is an inner canyon that follows the path of the cataract recession (Figure 2-19).

Cataracts, like rock benches, formed by more rapid erosion and undercutting of weaker basalt layers (colonnade) or interlayered sediments at the base of the cataract. In some places, such as the Upper Grand Coulee, up to 30 miles of cataract recession occurred from undercutting at the base of the cataract as it steadily retreated up the valley with each subsequent flood. Similarly, a second recessional cataract is responsible for the Lower Grand Coulee canyon that retreated 15 miles from Soap Lake to present-day Dry Falls (Plate 30). Deep, steep-walled inner canyons lie downvalley while multiple, horseshoe-shaped alcoves form at the heads of the recessional cataracts (Figure 2-19). Cataract canyons may occur in pairs separated by a long, tall "blade" or rib of basalt that runs down the middle. Umatilla Rock (No. 43), beyond Dry Falls, is one of the best examples (Plate 32); The Great Blade (No. 54, Figure 2-17) is another.

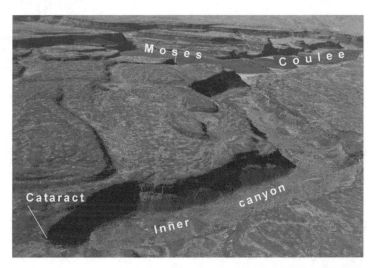

Figure 2-19. A short, 1.5-mile-long recessional cataract canyon, one of two so-called Dry Coulees (see "Scabland Homonyms" sidebar on page 27), feeds into lower Moses Coulee (No. 61). Looking southwest.

Sometimes multiple cataracts are found along the length of a coulee. Initially, erosion scoured down to a weak layer in one of the upper basalt flows. Over time, erosion steps down to deeper weak layers in the basalt sequence, beginning a new recessional cataract while the original cataract has receded farther upvalley. Perhaps the most famous and accessible cataract is Dry Falls (No. 41, Plates 29, 31 and 32), which separates the upper and lower Grand Coulee cataract canyons (Plate 30). Other coulees with multiple, tiered cataracts are Lake Creek Coulee (No. 23), East Lenore Coulee (No. 55, Plate 39) and Amber-Williams-Badger Lakes Rock Basins (No. 14).

Trenched Spurs

Because of the tremendous force and momentum behind the floodwaters, they tended to flow like a fire hose, in straight lines or broad arcs. This is unlike normal rivers, which lazily flow along in sinuously curving meanders that often do not cover their valley bottoms, even during normal flood stages. In contrast, Ice Age floods were not constrained to valley bottoms and instantly overwhelmed the valleys they occupied, quickly overtopping the sides of the valleys and spilling into adjacent valleys. In some of these valleys, rapidly moving floodwaters overtopped spurs of basalt bedrock along the valley, which regular streams normally flowed around. An amazing feature called trenched spurs formed where floodwaters flowed straight up and over the rocky spurs, scouring one or more channels across the top. Good examples of trenched spurs lie along Rock Creek Coulee (No. 15, Figure 2-20) and Crab Creek Coulee west of Wilson Creek (No. 22, see Figure 3-47).

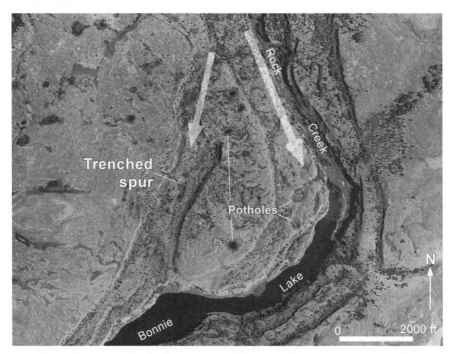

Figure 2-20. Trenched-spur channel at north end of Bonnie Lake, within the Cheney-Palouse Scabland Tract. Flood deluges temporarily rose over the top of the rock spur, carving a new, straighter channel across the spur.

Hogbacks

In the Channeled Scabland hogbacks consist of triangular-shaped knobs that formed where megafloods eroded into tilted layers of basalt (Figure 2-21, Plates 37 and 38). They are especially prevalent in the Lower Grand Coulee, which parallels tilted basalt flows along the Coulee Monocline. As Ice Age floods ate away at the weakened basalt rock within the core of the monocline, an erosion-resistant layer of Grand Ronde Basalt was encountered, which protected the underlying rocks and prevented total obliteration of the hogback. The hogback landform is not restricted to Ice Age floods terrain, however, they may be found most anywhere rock layers are tilted and eroded due to other processes.

Figure 2-21. Two hogback islands within Lake Lenore of Lower Grand Coulee. The hogbacks are remnants of the flood-scoured core of the Coulee Monocline (No. 36). The flood-resistant layer of Grande Ronde Basalt capping these hogbacks is tilted to the right (east) due to folding of the basalt along the monocline that parallels the west side of Lower Grand Coulee (Plate 30). Looking northeast.

Residual Streamlined and Scarped Palouse Hills

"The 'islands' of loess which make striking features on many broad scabland tracts are almost invariably elongated with the gradient of that tract and are almost invariably scarped on the sides and upgradient end."

– J Harlen Bretz (1928)

Streamlined and scarped Palouse hills (Plates 14 and 15) developed where floods eroded and sculpted the blanket of windblown sediment, called loess, that overlay basalt along flood paths. Unlike the underlying basalt, loess is unconsolidated sediment – not rock. Fractures do not occur in these younger sedimentary deposits and therefore, no erosion occurred by plucking, the principal form of erosion in basalt. Instead, these landforms were molded via the much-slower, grain-by-grain abrasion by the floodwaters.

Figure 2-22 shows some examples of streamlined Palouse hills. These hills consist of "islands" of loess that appear to float in a sea of "scrubbed" basalt scabland. Their teardrop shape, similar to an airfoil, consists of a prominent, steep prow on the upstream end and long, tapered tail on the downstream end. This shape, which was repeated over and over again in the formation of streamlined Palouse hills, is not a coincidence. During Ice Age flooding, the hills were streamlined so their length was usually about three times longer than their width; this hydrodynamic shape provided the least amount of drag to the floodwaters that formed them.

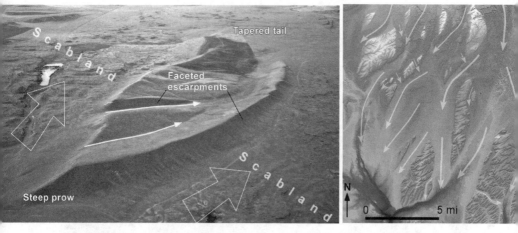

Figure 2-22. Streamlined and scarped Palouse hills of the Cheney-Palouse Tract. Left: Anatomy of a solitary island of Palouse loess eroded by floodwaters (block arrows) that created oversteepened escarpments on either side. Notice how some of the floodwater crested over the top of the loess island, carving a couple of cross channels (smaller arrows). Looking south. Right: Shaded-relief image shows rough, uneven areas of Palouse loess surrounded by smoother surfaces that are flood channels eroded down to basalt bedrock. Arrows show flow direction and interconnected, anastomosing nature of the flood channels between loess islands. Notice again how floodwaters overtopped some of the hills, spilling over into adjacent channels.

Palouse hills that lie along flood channelways were frequently planed off by the fast-moving, abrasive floodwaters. This resulted in the formation of faceted, planar surfaces called scarps that mark the upper level of flood erosion on these islands (Figure 2-22, Plates 14 and 15). Scarps are usually steeper and are aligned along margins of flood channels. They are distinctly steeper than the naturally rolling slopes of the hills themselves (see Figure 1-9).

The best places to observe streamlined and scarped Palouse hills are within the Cheney-Palouse Tract especially within the Rock Creek-Cow Creek Scabland Complex (No. 17). Streamlined Palouse hills are featured in the Cheney-Palouse Road Tour (chapter 5) as well as Cheney-Palouse/Telford-Crab Creek Aerial Tour (chapter 6).

Faceted Escarpments

Along the walls of high-energy flood channels, the immense power and speed of the floodwaters was enough to plane off and bevel the sides of coulees. Aligned scarps of loess facing the scablands are common along flood channels carved in Palouse loess (Plate 15) but may also develop in basalt (Figure 2-23). Faceted escarpments are useful tools for determining the widths and depths of the floodwater, as well as determining changes in flood depth that occurred downstream. The best examples of faceted basalt escarpments occur in Grand Coulee, the Castle Lake basin (No. 44, see Figure 3-83) and Moses Coulee (Figure 2-23, left).

Figure 2-23. Faceted-basalt coulee walls. Left: Truncated basalt butte sheared off along the side of lower Moses Coulee. Looking west. Right: Faceted escarpment along Lower Grand Coulee above Lake Lenore. Note how hanging valleys (No. 56) lie above the near-vertical escarpment planed off by the floods. Looking southwest.

Ringed Craters

In the area around Odessa, and a few other locations in the Channeled Scabland, are swarms of quasi-circular, ringed structures in basalt bedrock, eroded out by the Ice Age floods (Figures 2-24, 3-42 and Plate 21). These are variously named ring-dikes, basaltic ring structures or Odessa Craters. Most of these unusual structures, up to 1,600 feet in diameter, have one or more concentric, raised rings with hollowed-out centers. Other ringed structures have central peaks surrounded by one or more ringed moats composed of near-vertical dikes of basalt. The Odessa ringed craters formed in a flow (or flows) of the Roza basalt (see Figure 1-1) as the lava cooled about 15 million years ago. After that the Odessa Craters were blanketed in a cover of Palouse loess for eons. The ringed craters didn't appear until much later when the basalt was exhumed by floodwaters that etched and preferentially plucked out the looser basalt rock within the ring structures.

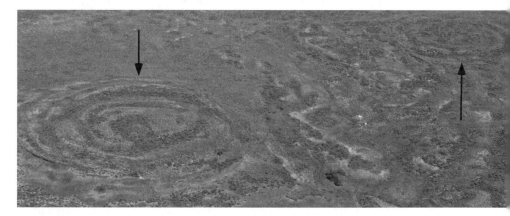

Figure 2-24. Aerial view of two flood-scoured, ringed craters (arrows), each hundreds of feet in diameter, near Odessa.

The dikes themselves are composed of basalt columns, which tilt outward away from the center of the feature (Figure 2-25, see Figure 4-55). The columns were more resistant to erosion by the floodwaters, while the intervening dike contact zones were more easily removed, causing the dikes to stand out in relief. This is opposite of how basalt flows normally eroded during Ice Age flooding. Basalt columns are more prone to plucking in horizontal lava flows, and overlying entablature zones are more resistant to this erosion. The columns in the dikes of ringed craters, however, are tilted, which perhaps made them better at resisting flood erosion.

Figure 2-25. Two inclined dikes (brackets) stand out in relief along the east end of the Lakeview Ranch Crater (N47.4124, W118.7508). Note how the dikes themselves dip outward while the columns within the dikes dip inward toward the center of the ringed crater (located out of view on the left). Looking northeast.

While we know ring structures had to have formed as the basalt lava was being emplaced and started cooling, their exact origin is still under debate. Some ideas for their formation include: a sag-flowout model (Figure 2-26), in which the collapse of the hardened crust of lava into the molten interior squeezed up along concentric, dike-forming cracks, filling the sagged surface; earthquake tremors that shook the ground as the lava cooled; or even a meteorite that broke up before impact, coincidentally peppering the cooling lava flow with dozens of smaller impact features.

The most popular, recent explanation, however, is that the ring dikes are principally the result of violent steam explosions as the lava flowed over a wet surface. In this scenario pressurized steam is produced as the hot lava comes in contact and flashes with the water. The pressurized steam forces its way upward through the cooling lava flow along concentric vents, forming a pathway for still-molten lava in the flow interior to escape to the surface. Lava coming to the surface fills a depression created by the sagging flow interior as illustrated in panel No. 2 of Figure 2-26. After solidification, ring dikes form where the lava once moved through concentric conduits to the surface. Millions of years later Ice Age floods moving over basalt removed the basalt between the dikes more than the dikes themselves, leaving them to stand out in relief.

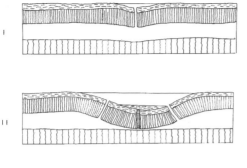

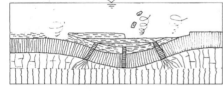

Figure 2-26. Sag-flowout model for development of ringed craters (after McKee and Stradling 1970). I. flowout of lava from the molten interior of a crusted lava flow. II. sagging of lava flow crust induced by loading, forming circular cracks allowing additional lava to flood the sagging surface. III. plucking and erosion by Ice Age floods long after formation of the ringed structures. IV. present topography.

The highest concentration of ringed craters lies within the Odessa area (Figure 3-43). However, they are also present along the Upper Grand Coulee (Plate 27) and about 10 miles northeast of Ritzville (Figure 2-27), where they share striking similarity to Martian ringed structures in basalt.

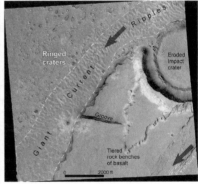

Figure 2-27. Flood features on Mars, including ringed craters, are similar to those of the Channeled Scabland. Left: Tight cluster of circular, ringed craters along flood channel between Tokio Station and Crab Creek. Nearby, the craters lie buried beneath flood bars blanketed with giant current ripples (dashed outline). Center of crater grouping is located at N47.240, W118.235. Right: Similar-appearing ringed craters in basalt and megaripples atop flood bar in Athabasca Valles, Mars. Note similarity in scale of flood features on both planets. Arrows show inferred paleo-flood flow direction.

Ringed craters are best viewed and appreciated from the air. However, one especially good and accessible location to view eroded ringed craters is along the Odessa Craters Trail (chapter 4, Trail U2).

Depositional Features

"The depositional land forms associated with the channeled scabland are chiefly mounded masses of little worn basaltic gravel. They occur on the down-gradient side of eminences and other protected places in the scablands."

– J Harlen Bretz (1927)

The Ice Age floods locally scoured away hundreds of feet of Palouse soil and underlying basalt rock across the Channeled Scabland. Because of all the suspended sediment, the ice-laden floodwaters may have resembled the color and consistency of a rich, frothy milkshake. And because of the high velocity of the floodwaters, which was maintained over much of the scablands, most sediment carried by the floods was quickly transported beyond the area, either into one of the many basins downstream or out to the Pacific Ocean. Locally within the Channeled Scabland, eroded gravel and sand did pile up into flood bars on the downstream sides of basalt obstructions or Palouse hills. Where the floods moved fastest, everything up to large boulders was suspended with the floodwater. As floodwaters slowed the largest sediment grains settled out first, followed by smaller grains as the power and energy of floods continued to slacken. Coarse sediment also floated in icebergs, some of it ending up dropping out or rafting into quieter waters along the floods' route. Because of turbulence during flooding, much of the finer sediment, such as sand, silt and clay, remained stirred up and suspended in the floodwater. The ultimate resting place for most of the fine-grained sediment, though, was on the continental shelf, many miles from where the Columbia River emptied into the Pacific Ocean.

The floods naturally sorted the sediment moving along with the water, especially in areas where the floods expanded and slowed. At the base of the floodwaters' flow, gigantic boulders bounced and rolled along while a slurry of finer-grained clay, silt and sand remained suspended in the turbulent flow. In contrast, the top of the water column probably carried only fine sand-, silt- and clay-sized particles, along with any floating vegetation, animal carcasses and icebergs. As a result, coarse cobbles and boulders, except for those transported in floating icebergs, are generally absent at higher elevations.

Because of the high velocity and turbulence of floodwaters, often only coarse-grained sediments, such as those in Figure 2-28, were deposited within the Channeled Scabland. Finer gravel and sand remained in suspension and were carried away from the site. Flood gravels are mostly composed of angular basalt clasts, which show a wide range of clast sizes. Gravel clasts are often coated with a thin layer of silt, as they settled through the turbid column of floodwater. These characteristics indicate the sediment did not travel very far before being quickly deposited and buried. In other places on the scablands, where the flood currents were less vigorous or at places higher along flood channels, only sand-sized sediment was transported and deposited (Figure 2-29). Sometimes coarse sand grades up into finer sand or silt-sized sediment grains forming sedimentary beds called "rhythmites." Some geologists believe each rhythmite represents a deposit from a separate Ice Age flood event.

Figure 2-28. Coarse, high-energy flood deposits. Above: Gravel and sand deposited within the Coulee City Expansion Bar (No. 37) along U.S. Highway 2, one mile north of Dry Falls. Several gradations between sand and gravel may represent separate floods. Left: Giant "mudballs," or rip-up clasts, consist of oversized boulders of cohesive Palouse loess picked up by Ice Age floods and dumped in a flood bar on the West Plains (No. 10).

Figure 2-29. About a dozen rhythmite beds of mostly loose, basalt-rich sand, perhaps representing separate floods, deposited in a flood bar along upper Crab Creek Coulee (No. 22). These sediments are exposed in the borrow pit along the downstream end of the flood bar shown in Plate 21. Looking south.

A different type of rhythmite occurs along the northern margin of the Columbia Plateau, in places such as the Sanpoil Valley, Hawk Bay (No. 64) and Hangman Creek (No. 11), where floods, most likely from Glacial Lake Missoula, debouched into Glacial Lake Columbia downstream (Plate 11). In these places a sequence of up to several dozen varves (multiple, thin, annual lake layers of fine silt and clay) are separated by a bed of flood sand, deposited in a matter of hours or days during an Ice Age flood (Figure 2-30).

- -

Figure 2-30. Varves of Glacial Lake Columbia (No. 64). Left: At the Hangman Creek Rhythmites (No. 11) site, light-colored varves (thin annual layers of silt and clay) are sandwiched between flood beds. Dark, sandy flood beds were laid down when a Missoula flood invaded Lake Columbia. After floods passed, the glacial lake remained and continued to deposit lake varves for up to several dozen years before the next Missoula outburst flood laid down another bed of high-energy sand and gravel. Right: Close up of a succession of Lake Columbia varves. Each varve consists of a lighter layer of fine sand introduced into the lake during more vigorous spring-to-early-summer runoff, separated by a darker layer of silt and clay laid down in the still, ice-covered lake in late fall and winter.

Still another type of feature observed in flood deposits are "flame" structures resulting from what geologists call "soft-sediment deformation." These features form when sediments are rapidly deposited in a saturated setting such as that existing at the bottom of Glacial Lake Columbia during Missoula flood pulses. After the sudden influx of flood sediment, the underlying waterlogged sediments became unstable and unable to support the weight of all the added sediment during a flood event. As a result the different sediment layers became fluidized, deforming and mixing together into wavy beds such as those in Figure 2-31.

Figure 2-31. Interstratified Ice Age flood and glacial lake deposits at Hangman Creek (No. 11). Wavy, convoluted bedding and giant "flame" structures such as these suggest that sediment layers remained saturated with water from Glacial Lake Columbia between Missoula flood events at this locality.

Giant Flood Bars and Fosses

Giant, Ice Age flood bars can be divided into five types as shown in Figure 2-32. These are: crescent bars (C), forming where flood currents slowed temporarily, along the inside of bends in flood coulees; pendant bars (P), forming on the downstream ends of Palouse hills or other obstructions; eddy bars (E), forming by eddying currents at the mouths of dead-end tributaries near where they enter a coulee; expansion bars (X), forming where flood flow expanded suddenly after being constrained; and longitudinal (L) bars, forming along the margins of coulees. Flood bars may exist as one or any combination of these five types.

Flood bars occur along most coulees of the Channeled Scabland, especially along inside bends and downstream of basalt buttes, mesas or upland plateaus, or below streamlined Palouse hills within, or along, flood channel ways.

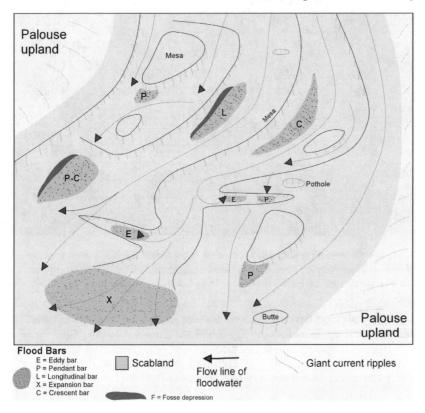

Figure 2-32. Schematic showing possible locations and distribution of Ice Age flood bars along a flood channel.

Commonly, the tops of flood bars, especially longitudinal bars, do not extend all the way to the edge of the channel. Instead, a trough or depression called a fosse separates the top of the bar from the valley wall. Fosses are related to changes in floodwater flow and localized increase in the speed of the floodwaters along steep canyon walls. They may occur along longitudinal and pendant bars; other types of bars usually don't display fosses.

Perhaps no more variety of flood bars exist in one place than Jasper Canyon (No. 48), within the Lower Grand Coulee (Figure 2-33, Plate 37). Jasper Canyon is oriented crosswise to the main flood current, which flowed south from the direction of Dry Falls. Crosswise flow across Jasper Canyon created lots of turbulence and eddying of currents that favored flood bar development. Here, up to several hundred feet of flood sediment accumulated. Several pendant-longitudinal crescent bars formed downstream of upland plateaus; some of the bars rise almost to the lip of the plateau. Elsewhere eddy bars formed where floodwaters swirled around the mouths of the side canyons.

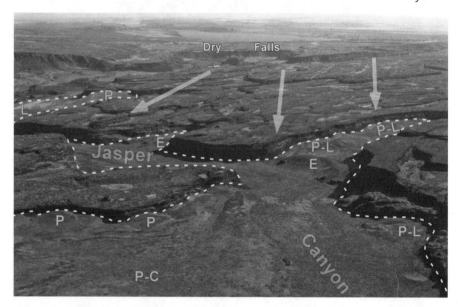

Figure 2-33. Many different types of flood bars occur along Jasper Canyon (No. 48). All areas within the dashed lines are underlain by flood bars. Bar types include: L = longitudinal, P = pendant, E = eddy and C = crescent. View looking northeast towards Dry Falls and Upper Grand Coulee. Bold arrows indicate direction of flood flow.

A variety of flood bars are dispersed along most other coulees as well, including Northrup Canyon (No. 32), Trail Lake Coulee (No. 47), Spring Coulee (No. 40), upper Crab Creek Coulee (No. 22), Lake Creek Coulee (No. 23), Wilson Creek Coulee (No. 27), Ephrata Fan (No. 58) and Pangborn Bar (No. 65) along the west margin of the Columbia Plateau.

Giant Current Ripples

"Giant current ripples on gravel bars, difficult to identify at ground level under a cover of sage brush."

– J Harlen Bretz (1969)

Bretz never had the luxury of aerial photographs until late in his career. This is unfortunate, for if he and his critics would have seen the many fine examples of giant current ripples on flood bars across the Channeled Scabland (Figure 2-34, Plate 21), Bretz's flood theory would have been accepted far sooner and likely saved the "heretic" geologist many years of professional isolation. As early as 1925, Bretz recognized that many flood bars displayed "a horizontal fluting and minor mounding on their side." By 1930 he had theorized they were giant current ripples, but it wasn't until years later, after the introduction of aerial photography, that geologists began seeing these features everywhere along the floods' path, confirming Bretz's outrageous flood hypothesis for the Channeled Scabland.

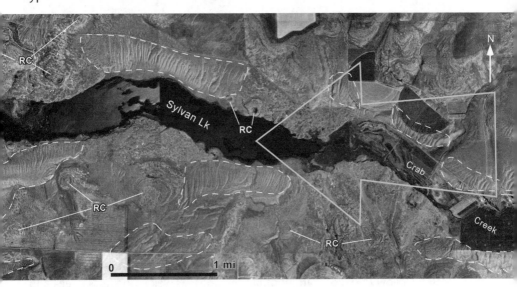

Figure 2-34. Flood bars with giant current ripples (outlined) along Sylvan Lake. Asymmetry of the giant ripples indicates flood flow here was to the west (block arrow) down upper Crab Creek Coulee. A number of ringed craters (RC) in the basalt bedrock are visible but only where they are not covered by flood bars and giant current ripples. See also Figure 3-40 for a topographic map showing ripples and ringed craters represented in this aerial image.

Several types of bars, especially longitudinal, pendant and crescent bars, may be blanketed with giant current ripples. Ripples are less common on eddy and expansion bars, probably because of the uneven flow and turbulence associated with these bar types. Geologists were originally clueless to their origin because of their huge scale and low relief, which made them difficult or impossible to detect at ground level. Just like ripples on a stream, giant current ripples are usually steeper on the downstream side than the upstream side and provide an indication of flood-flow direction.

Giant current ripples are among the features geologists have used to estimate the speed and depth of the Ice Age floods. Based on the height and spacing of ripples, as well as the sizes of boulders transported, geologist Vic Baker estimated floodwaters were traveling up to 50 miles per hour when the ripples were created and the water was up to 500 feet deep. More recent estimates have placed a maximum speed of the floods in excess of 70 miles per hour. The sizes of giant current ripples generally increase with depth and velocity of the floodwaters that produced them.

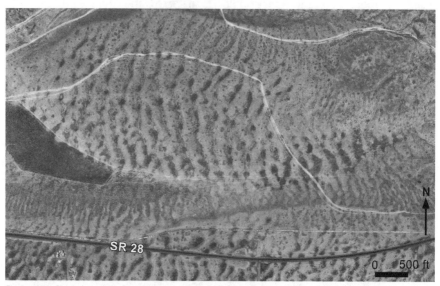

Figure 2-35. Giant current ripples along upper Crab Creek Coulee 3.5 miles southwest of Odessa. Ripples, created by floodwaters flowing hundreds of feet deep from right to left, are spaced an incredible 200 to 300 feet apart! Note two-lane, paved highway (SR 28) for scale. N47.313, W118.767

Some of the best examples of giant current ripples within the Channeled Scabland described in this book are found along upper Crab Creek Coulee (No. 22, Figure 2-35), Spring Coulee (No. 40), West Plains (No. 10, see Figures 5-18 and 6-10), Cross-Connect Coulees (No. 21), Lake Creek Coulee (No. 23), Marlin Hollow (No. 25), Pangborn Bar (No. 65), as well as the Rock Creek and Cow Creek Scabland Complex (No. 17). An impressive drive across an undulating field of giant current ripples is located along Rambo Road off U.S. Highway 2, just north of Airway Heights (see Figure 5-19).

Slackwater Rhythmites

Rhythmites (Figure 2-36) are composed of graded, sandy sedimentary beds, and each rhythmite is believed to represent the deposit from a single flood. In a few places such as Hangman Creek (No. 11), Hawk Bay and the Sanpoil Valley, flood rhythmites are interrupted with silt-to-clay varved deposits where the floods debouched into the former Glacial Lake Columbia (Plate 11). In the Columbia Valley north of the Channeled Scabland sand beds at the bottoms of rhythmites represent rapid (few hours or days) deposition associated with a Missoula flood invading Glacial Lake Columbia that persisted between many of the Missoula floods. The sand bed transitions upward into up to dozens of annual fine layers of silt and clay, called varves. Varves were laid down very slowly, over a span of dozens of years or more between flood events, each varve couplet representing a single year of deposition within Lake Columbia (Figure 2-30). Rhythmites may also occur in the Channeled Scabland but without the intervening varved lake beds; varves are absent since no permanent lakes existed there – all the flood flow was overland across a surface not covered by water between flood events. An example of flood rhythmites in an overland setting is along upper Crab Creek Coulee (see Figure 2-29).

Figure 2-36. Ice Age flood rhythmites exposed along the Sanpoil Arm of Lake Roosevelt, looking east. Each dark, sandy rhythmite was deposited in minutes or hours as a flood rushed into pre-existing Glacial Lake Columbia. Capping each rhythmite is up to several dozen, lighter-colored, thin silt-clay varves. Each varve represents a single year of deposition within the stillness of Glacial Lake Columbia (see Figure 2-30) that existed for decades between outburst floods.

Ice-Rafted Erratics

Icebergs, from the sudden breakup of the ice dams, were carried along with the floodwaters. Boulders encased within ice (similar to the one in Figure 2-37), hitchhiked their way to the Channeled Scabland and beyond via floating icebergs. Most of the boulders are composed of angular, exotic granitic and metasedimentary rocks, identical to the types of rocks observed today in the vicinity of the ice dam for Glacial Lake Missoula. Ice-rafted erratics are relatively scarce within the Channeled Scabland itself, however, since the rushing water kept the icebergs constantly moving. This changed downstream of the Channeled Scabland, however, where the water slowed in several backflooded basins (e.g., Pasco Basin and Willamette Valley). This is where most icebergs became grounded and many more erratics were deposited. Occasionally, however, icebergs did become grounded, or hung up in eddies, or other traps along route through the scablands.

- -

In the Pasco Basin, almost all erratics consist of rocks very different from the dark-colored Columbia River basalt, the only local rock type. More than 75 percent of erratics are light-colored granitic rocks. The remainder are mostly metasedimentary rocks of the Belt Supergroup composed of mostly quartzite and argillite. Belt rocks are extremely old (1.4 billion to 1.6 billion years old!) that, not coincidentally, came from the vicinity of the ice dam for Glacial Lake Missoula.

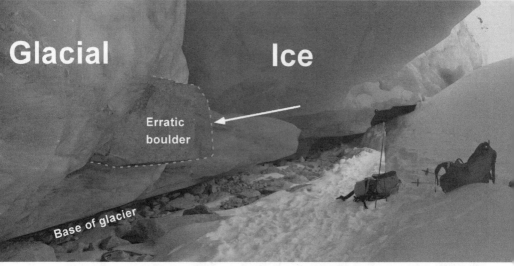

Figure 2-37. Granitic boulder embedded in ice at the base of modern-day Omoo Glacier, British Columbia. Notice angularity of the boulder, unlike water-transported boulders, which are generally rounded (Figure 2-38).

In geology, a true erratic is strictly defined as a boulder transported by ice to a place where it rests on a different type of bedrock. According to this definition, then, any non-basalt boulder transported onto the Channeled Scabland via floating icebergs is a true erratic. Furthermore, since these boulders were encased in a protective covering of ice, most are angular. Rounded, non-basalt boulders on the scablands, on the other hand, were more likely transported via tumbling and rolling along the bottom of the flood. In this case, boulders not transported in icebergs do not fit the strict definition for erratics. It's possible, however, that some erratic boulders could have been rounded and smoothed in streams prior to being picked up and enveloped in glacial ice. Some grinding and rounding of stones is also known to occur at the base of glaciers as well.

Figure 2-38. Which of these two granite boulders is a true erratic? Two very different exotic boulders of granite are shown near Park Lake within Lower Grand Coulee. The darker, lichen-encrusted granitic boulder (lower right) is rounded — an indication that it rolled and tumbled along as bedload at the base of an older flood. The lighter-colored, unweathered boulder in the upper left, on the other hand, is angular — an indication it was rafted into place within a floating iceberg. Furthermore, the lack of weathering on the boulder's surface suggests it was probably deposited during the last Ice Age flood (a debris-dam flood from Glacial Lake Columbia, see Plate 45) around 14,000 years ago. Only the angular boulder in the upper left is a true erratic. If the rounded boulder was not ice transported, then it is not, in a strict sense, an erratic. Even though the rounded boulder may have started out floating in an iceberg, it appears to have ended up as bedload, and therefore not a true erratic. The angular boulder, on the other hand, was clearly ice rafted to its final resting place and thus considered an authentic erratic.

Another type of erratic in the Channeled Scabland exists (i.e., glacial erratics). These were transported solely by glacial ice, in contrast to ice-rafted erratics that floated in icebergs during Ice Age flooding. Glacial erratics occur in the Channeled Scabland where the former ice sheets encroached, as they did on the top of Steamboat Rock within the Upper Grand Coulee (see Figure 4-77). Any floodwaters that overtopped Steamboat Rock were moving too fast for icebergs to become grounded, although it is easy to imagine these boulders deposited by a slowly creeping ice sheet.

Ice-rafted erratics are visible in the Lower Grand Coulee east of Park Lake (Figure 2-38), East Lenore Coulee (No. 55) and Lake Creek Coulee (No. 23).

Lake Pend Oreille occupies the valley once filled with glacial ice that held back Lake Missou

3

Flood Feature Highlights by Region

This chapter describes in greater detail the unique characteristics of 65 of
the most distinctive and striking flood features within northern Idaho and the
Channeled Scabland. In general, the features are described in order of their
approximate distance from Glacial Lake Missoula.

Ice-Dam Breakout Area

After the sudden breakup of the ice dam holding back giant Lake
Missoula, most of the floodwaters burst out of the intermontane valley that
today holds Lake Pend Oreille (Plate 3), which, of course, didn't exist in its
present form during the Ice Age. The valley was filled with up to thousands
of feet of glacial ice that at times extended all the way to Bayview and
beyond (Plate 9). At other times the ice dam may have only advanced as far
as Green Monarch Ridge before a flood breakout occurred. In either case we
know the ice dam must have failed instantaneously, releasing up to 530 cubic
miles of ice-laden floodwaters into the upper reaches of Rathdrum Prairie.
Even though the flow of water from Lake Missoula lasted up to three days,
the flow at the head of the Rathdrum valley probably peaked after only a
few hours. This is because the flow was increasingly being influenced by the
backup of the floodwaters downstream.

The generally rounded, lush, green, forested mountainsides and clear blue
waters make it difficult to fathom that this idyllic setting for the ice dam and
breakout area has anything in common with the barren, scarred landscape
wrought by the same Ice Age floods downstream in the Channeled Scabland.
The striking contrast is for two reasons – one climatic and the other geologic.
The breakout area for the Missoula floods lies at a higher elevation and receives
significantly more precipitation, and therefore is much more vegetated than
the semiarid Columbia Plateau. The breakout area also lies beyond the extent
of a thick pile of volcanic lava flows of Columbia River basalt. Instead, the rocks
underlying the Missoula floods breakout area consist mostly of older granitic
as well as metasedimentary rocks known to geologists as the Belt Supergroup.
These rocks were more resistant to erosional forces created by the ice and
escaping floodwaters and thus were smoothed and rounded by these forces,
unlike its basalt counterparts in the Scabland that responded to the erosional
forces much more differently.

Areas affected by the breakout of the Missoula floods include Lake Pend
Oreille southward through Rathdrum Prairie on to the Spokane Valley (Plates 3
and 9). Some megaflood outbursts also escaped north and west via the Pend
Oreille and Little Spokane river valleys past Newport (see Figure 3-11).

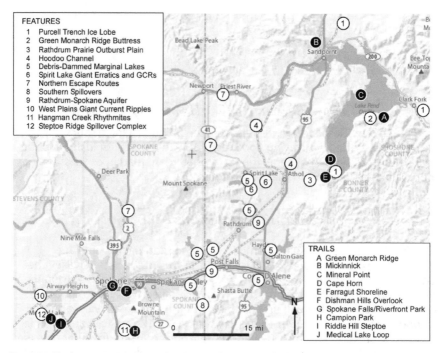

Figure 3-1. Key features in the vicinity of the ice-dam breakout and Spokane urban areas. Non-motorized trails are presented in chapter 4.

1. Purcell Trench Ice Lobe

Features: Ice-sculpted and polished bedrock, beveled slopes, glacial till and erratics

Best Observation Points:

Automobile: Cape Horn Road northeast of Bayview and Idaho State Highway 200 along the north side of Lake Pend Oreille

Non-motorized trails: Green Monarch Ridge (Trail A), Mickinnick (Trail B), Mineral Point (Trail C), Cape Horn (Trail D) and Farragut Shoreline (Trail E)

Watercraft: Anywhere on Lake Pend Oreille

Elevation of Feature: The Purcell Trench Lobe rose to an elevation of at least 3,150 feet (over 1,000 feet above valley floor at Cape Horn, see Plate 5) increasing to the north.

- During the Ice Age a huge tongue of ice thousands of feet thick flowed south from Canada along the Purcell Trench.
- In northern Idaho the Purcell Trench Lobe was bounded by the Selkirk Mountains on the west and the Cabinet Mountains to the east (Figure 3-2, top).
- The massive tongue of ice plowed into the Green Monarch Ridge (Figure 3-2, bottom and 3-4) splitting into the Clark Fork and Lake Pend Oreille sublobes, creating the ice dam for Glacial Lake Missoula (Plate 3).

Figure 3-2. Intermontane valleys once filled with glacial ice. Top: The Purcell Trench looking north over Lake Pend Oreille. Above: The Purcell Trench Lobe pushed hard against the Green Monarch Ridge Buttress (lower right). From here a sublobe of ice slowly flowed east *up* the Clark Fork Valley 10 to 15 miles, completely sealing off the Clark Fork River and creating the temporarily solid ice dam for Glacial Lake Missoula.

- The ice dam was 30 to 35 miles long and backed water up in Glacial Lake Missoula as much as 200 miles.
- Cataclysmic failure of the ice dam released as much as 530 cubic miles of water over three days or less.
- The bedrock basin beneath today's Lake Pend Oreille lies 600 feet below sea level (Figure 3-3) as a result of Ice Age erosion.
- 1,500 feet of glacial sediments separate the lake bottom from the underlying bedrock.

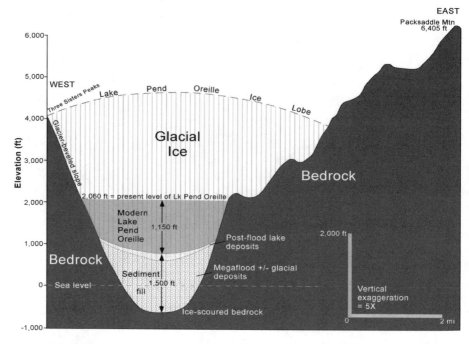

Figure 3-3. Geologic profile across lower Lake Pend Oreille (based on data provided by the U.S. Navy, reported in Breckenridge and Sprenke 1997). During the Ice Age, Lake Pend Oreille was replaced with up to 5,000 feet of glacial ice from the Lake Pend Oreille sublobe. Note the U-shape of the valley bottom, typical for a deep glacial valley.

- Today evidence of the former ice lobe is apparent from the glacier-beveled slopes above Lake Pend Oreille (Plates 5 and 6, Figure 3-5).
- At 1,150 feet deep, Lake Pend Oreille is the 13th deepest lake in the world!

2. Green Monarch Ridge Buttress

Feature: Rocky ridge that deflected the south-flowing Purcell Trench Lobe of glacial ice

Best Observation Points:

Automobile: Interpretive display along Idaho State Highway 200

Non-motorized trails (chapter 4): Green Monarch Ridge (Trail A) and Mineral Point Trail (Trail C)

Watercraft: Via Lake Pend Oreille, a few miles southeast of public boat ramps at Garfield Bay, and at Sam Owen Campground off Highway 200

Elevation of Feature: The ridge of Belt rocks rises 3,000 feet above present-day Lake Pend Oreille to a height of 5,200 feet elevation.

- Flow of ice diverged with one tongue that went east up the Clark Fork

River Valley (Plates 3 and 4, Figure 3-2, bottom); a second tongue headed south into the Lake Pend Oreille trench.

- The tall north face of the ridge was oversteepened and beveled by the grinding action of the ice (Figure 3-4).

- Thousands of feet of ice pressing hard against Green Monarch Ridge created a temporarily tight seal for Glacial Lake Missoula.

Figure 3-4. Green Monarch Ridge, a 3,000-foot tall ridge, is seen in this aerial view over Lake Pend Oreille, looking southwest. Another view of this buttress can be seen beyond interpretive displays for Glacial Lake Missoula and Ice Age floods along Idaho State Highway 200 (N48.2570, W116.3250).

3. Rathdrum Prairie Outburst Plain

Feature: A broad, mostly featureless sediment apron in the area of ice-dam breakout for Glacial Lake Missoula

Best Observation Points:

Automobile: Cape Horn Road northeast of Bayview (viewpoint from Figure 3-5). Featured in Road Tour No. 1 (chapter 5)

Non-motorized trail: Cape Horn Trail (chapter 4, Trail D)

Elevation of Feature: The head of the plain at the mouth of Lake Pend Oreille lies at about 2,400 feet. The lower end of the plain is about 2,100 feet where it merges with the Spokane Valley. An old, eroded part of the plain is preserved about 10 miles to the west in the vicinity of Spirit Lake (Figure 3-6, Plate 9). Overall, the plain dips gently to the south where it merges with Rathdrum Prairie (Plates 6 and 7) and the Spokane Valley.

Maximum Flood Depth (Elevation): 700 feet (2,800 feet)

- Outburst plain is composed of bouldery flood deposits, hundreds of feet thick.

- The plain is slightly elevated, lying 300 feet above the south shore of Lake Pend Oreille (Figure 3-5).

Figure 3-5. View across the breakout area for Missoula floods at the south end of Lake Pend Oreille. Beveled slope on Bernard Peak was planed off by glacial ice perhaps in combination with Missoula floodwaters.

- The surface of the plain is covered with a network of low-relief braided channels (Figure 3-6), giant current ripples and oversized ice-rafted erratics.

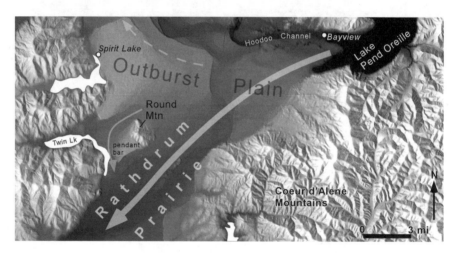

Figure 3-6. Megaflood bars and channels in the vicinity of the Rathdrum Prairie Outburst Plain. Note the well-developed pendant flood bar that formed on the more protected downstream side of Round Mountain. The flow of water from Glacial Lake Missoula continued for up to three days into the Rathdrum Prairie, depositing its load of flood sediment onto the outburst plain where the megafloods expanded into the basin.

- Although some of the floods contributing to the outburst plain may have escaped northward, most went south through Rathdrum Prairie.

- A string of kettle holes lies at the upper end of the outburst plain (Figure 3-7), left behind from the melting of sediment-covered ice blocks.

- Today there is no surface drainage across the outburst plain because of the extremely coarse nature of the flood deposits. These allow for rapid infiltration of surface waters through the underlying sediments, which percolate downward to replenish the Rathdrum-Spokane Aquifer (No. 9) below.

- The outburst plain is higher to the west near Spirit Lake, deposited during one or more of the larger, earlier floods. The eastern part of the outburst plain appears to be dissected by more recent, smaller outburst floods and/or glacial-meltwater channels.

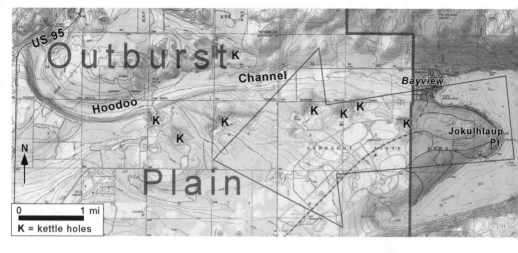

Figure 3-7. Topographic map at the head of Rathdrum Prairie Outburst Plain, showing a string of aligned glacial-kettle holes. Block arrow indicates outburst direction for the Missoula floods. At right is the extreme south end of Lake Pend Oreille.

4. Hoodoo Channel

Feature: Sinuous channel incised into the Rathdrum Prairie Outburst Plain

Best Observation Point:

Automobile: Along U.S. Highway 95, three miles north of Athol, Idaho. Featured in Road Tour No. 1 (chapter 5)

Elevation of Feature: The base of the channel at its head near Bayview lies at about 2,180 feet, and its junction with the Pend Oreille River is about 2,060 feet.

- Hoodoo Channel formed from the melting ice from the Lake Pend Oreille sublobe (Figure 3-8) or possibly from much smaller Missoula flood(s) at the very end of the Ice Age.

- The head of the channel hangs about 100 feet above the present level of Lake Pend Oreille at Bayview (Figure 3-7).

- The Rathdrum Prairie Outburst Plain proved too high for the Hoodoo Channel, which forced all its drainage northward toward Priest River, Idaho, and into the present-day Pend Oreille River Valley.

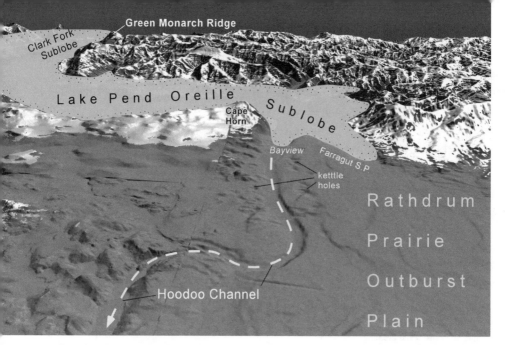

Green Monarch Ridge

Clark Fork Sublobe

Lake Pend Oreille

Sublobe

Cape Horn

Bayview

Farragut S.P.

kettle holes

Rathdrum

Prairie

Outburst

Plain

Hoodoo Channel

Figure 3-8. The sinuous Hoodoo Channel carried glacial meltwater from the Lake Pend Oreille sublobe at the very end of the Ice Age, or perhaps from a much smaller, late Missoula flood burst through this area. Looking east.

5. Debris-Dammed Marginal Lakes

Feature: Pristine mountain lakes at mouths of sidestream valleys blocked by the buildup of outburst flood deposits along Idaho's Rathdrum Prairie and Washington's Spokane Valley (Plates 8 and 9)

Best Observation Points:

Automobile: Spirit Lake just west of Idaho State Highway 41 and Hauser Lake just north of Idaho State Highway 53. Featured in Road Tour No. 1 (chapter 5)

Watercraft: Via any of the subject lakes (Spirit, Twin, Hauser, Newman, Liberty, Coeur d'Alene, Fernan or Hayden lakes)

Elevation of Feature: Spirit Lake is the highest (2,444 feet) of the lakes, which steadily decrease in elevation downvalley to 2,050 feet at Liberty Lake.

Maximum Flood Depth (Elevation): 500 feet (2,800 feet)

- During ice-dam breakout, Missoula floods peaked after about 16 hours but continued to flow for up to three days.

- Huge quantities of sediment were transported with the floodwater that piled up within Rathdrum Prairie and the Spokane Valley. As floodwaters expanded into the Rathdrum Prairie and Spokane Valley, a lot of sediment was deposited onto flood bars, ultimately raising the valley floor hundreds of feet.

- The aggrading sediment debris backfilled the mouths of nine tributary valleys draining into Rathdrum Prairie and the Spokane Valley (Plate 9). Sediment debris in flood bars blocked the flow of normal stream water coming down the tributaries (Figure 3-9).

- Today debris-dammed lakes (Spirit, Twin, Hauser, Newman, Liberty, Coeur d'Alene, Fernan and Hayden) occupy the mouths of eight stream tributaries. A ninth lake (Saltese) was artificially drained by human activity in the early 1900s.

- Less deposition occurred along the south side of the Spokane Valley since the floods moved faster and eroded more around the outside bend in the valley. This explains why Newman Lake, along the inside of the bend, lies at a higher elevation than Liberty Lake (Figure 3-9).

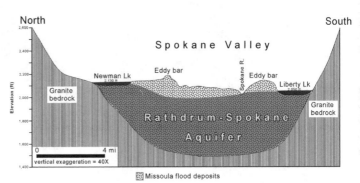

Figure 3-9. The Rathdrum-Spokane Valley along the Washington-Idaho border. Left: Shaded-relief map shows three of the debris-dammed lakes at mouths of three tributary valleys. The buildup of flood deposits in eddy bars at the mouths of side tributaries blocked these drainages, creating the flood-debris-dammed lakes. Right: Profile across the Spokane Valley, based on groundwater wells available between Newman and Liberty lakes (cross-section location is shown with dashed line in left image). Illustrated is the extremely thick accumulation (up to 600 feet here) of coarse, permeable flood deposits that make up the bountiful Rathdrum-Spokane Aquifer (No. 9). The elevation of the lakes decreases downvalley, consistent with the decrease in the surface elevation of Rathdrum Prairie and the Spokane Valley in that direction.

6. Spirit Lake Giant Erratics and Current Ripples

Features: Elevated flood bar of the western Rathdrum Prairie Outburst Plain with giant current ripples and huge erratics

Best Observation Point:

Automobile: Coarse gravel and sand composing a series of rolling, giant current ripples is exposed in roadcuts along Idaho State Highway 54, a few miles east of Spirit Lake. Several giant erratics (including the one in Figure 3-10, bottom) lie on either side of Idaho State Highway 41, two to three miles south of Spirit Lake. Featured in Road Tour No. 1 (chapter 5).

Elevation of Features: about 2,600 feet

Maximum Flood Depth (Elevation): 200 feet (2,800 feet)

Figure 3-10. Flood features of the western Rathdrum Prairie Outburst Plain. Above: Field of giant current ripples near Spirit Lake. Arrows indicates a northwesterly flow direction toward the Blanchard Channel. Left: A giant, ice-rafted erratic of granodiorite rests atop giant current ripples just south of Spirit Lake. This erratic measures 49 feet by 40 feet and weighs more than 1,600 tons. N47.9312, W116.8520, elevation 2,610 feet.

- A huge field of giant current ripples covers the Rathdrum Prairie Outburst Plain (No. 3) northeast of Spirit Lake (Figure 3-10, top).

- The orientation of the flood ripples in Figure 3-10 reveal that they were deposited by an outburst flood moving northwest, although other ripples farther south are oriented to the southwest. This suggests that a northern escape route (No. 7) for the Ice Age floods via the Blanchard Channel (Figure 3-11, right) was temporarily open when this bar was flooded.

- Giant, angular, ice-rafted erratics (Figure 3-10, bottom) locally lie atop the ripples, an indication of the immense power of the floods here. The giant boulders, composed of granodiorite, are true erratics since they are different than the gneiss bedrock that underlies this area.

7. Northern Escape Routes

Features: Northern, alternate routes for Missoula floodwaters at times when the ice sheet was not fully advanced; flood channels, divide crossings, flood bars, erratics

Best Observation Point:

Automobile: U.S. Highway 2 between Sandpoint and Spokane. Featured in Road Tour No. 1 (chapter 5)

Elevation of Features: 2,000 feet to nearly 2,700 feet

Maximum Flood Depth (Elevation): 800 feet (2,800 feet)

- When glaciers were at their maximum extent, Missoula outburst floods were almost exclusively routed through Rathdrum Prairie (Figure 3-11, left). At other times, when glacial ice did not block the Pend Oreille River Valley, some of the floodwaters also detoured to the north (Figure 3-11, right).

- After deflecting off the northern ice lobes, floodwaters would become redirected south through the network of channels south and west of Newport, including Scotia Gap (Figure 3-12), before racing down the Little Spokane River Valley.

- The maximum height of the floodwaters within the northern escape routes was about the same as those within the upper part of the Rathdrum Prairie (about 2,800 feet). The method for determining the maximum height of the floods is illustrated in Figure 3-13 by examining elevations of the ridge divides in the area.

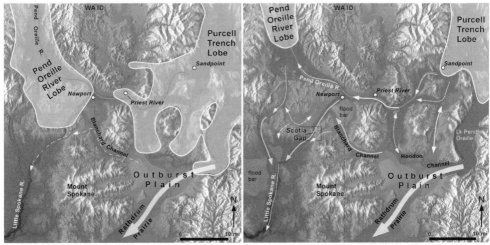

Full ice advance   Partial ice advance

Figure 3-11. Pathways of Missoula floods during full advance versus partial advance of glacial ice. During full advance (left) two lobes of ice merged near Priest River, blocking much of the area from the Missoula floods. Right: During partial ice advance, on the other hand, a larger area was inundated by floodwaters that bypassed Rathdrum Prairie by going west via the Pend Oreille River Valley through Priest River and Newport and then south to Spokane via the Little Spokane River.

Figure 3-12. Ice Age floods reamed out the channel at Scotia Gap (arrow) where the Little Spokane River flows today; N48.0939, W117.1743, elevation 2,060 feet. See relative location of Scotia Gap in Figure 3-11 (right).

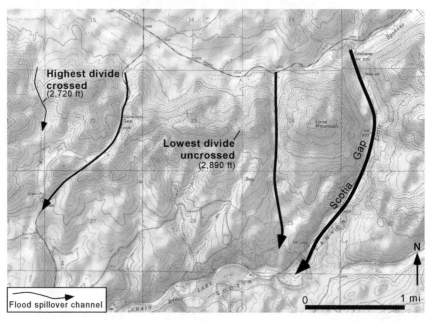

Figure 3-13. The highest level of the floods can be determined by identifying the highest divide crossing with a spillover channel (2,720 feet) versus the lowest potential divide crossing without evidence for spillover (2,890 feet). The maximum flood height must lie in between these two levels, here estimated at about 2,800 feet elevation. These elevated channels may have also carried glacial meltwater from the Pend Oreille River Lobe that at one time butted up against the north side of this ridge. See Figure 3-11 (right) for location of this map in relation to the bigger flood picture.

- Several longitudinal and pendant flood bars built up along these flood channels or on the downstream sides of obstructions along the northern escape routes (Figure 3-11, right).

8. Southern Spillovers

Features: Subtle, elevated, low-relief spillover channels across divide crossings south of the breakout area for the Ice Age floods, which overfilled the Coeur d'Alene Lake Valley, the Spokane Valley and Hangman Creek

Best Observation Point:

Automobile: U.S. Highway 95 a mile south of Setters Road; Washington State Route 27 near Mica; Spangle-Waverly Road at head of Pine Creek Coulee

Elevation of Features: Base of highest spillover channel near Setters is 2,600 feet; near Mica, 2,510 feet; and at the head of Pine Creek Coulee, 2,530 feet; relief across these channels is generally low (less than 100 feet)

Maximum Flood Depth (Elevation): 200 feet (2,700 feet)

- After racing south across Rathdrum Prairie, some floodwaters continued south via the Coeur d'Alene Lake and Spokane valleys. At Coeur d'Alene Lake, Missoula floods caused the backwaters of Glacial Lake Columbia to rise another 200 to 300 feet and spill over a low divide (elevation 2,600 feet) at the head of Lake Creek near Setters (Figure 3-14).

- Another spillover area drained directly from the Spokane Valley via a group of channels cut at the head of Chester Creek near Mica, just west of Mica Peak (Figures 3-14 and 3-15).

- After rushing through the Spokane Valley, some of the floodwaters took a hard left turn, rushing up into the Hangman Creek arm of Glacial Lake Columbia. Rising floodwaters in Hangman Creek, in turn, spilled over another low divide at the head of North Pine Creek (No. 16).

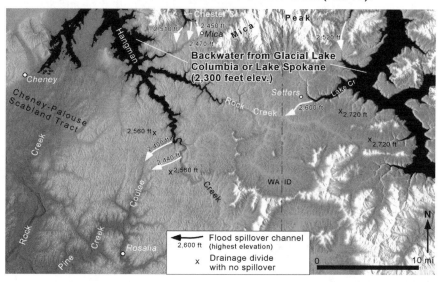

Figure 3-14. Floodwater spilled over drainage divides near Setters, Mica and Hangman Creek, carving spillover channels. The heights of the spillover channels generally decrease toward the west, affirming that the surface of the floodwaters descended downstream. The Spokane Valley lies just out of view parallel to the north edge of this map.

spillover channel

Figure 3-15. Western spillover channel that flowed southwest out of the Spokane Valley near Mica. The trapezoid-shaped channel lies at about elevation 2,510 feet. Floodwaters probably crested several tens of feet higher than the channel bottom in order to overtop and carve the channel. N47.5550, W117.2595.

- The height of the Pine Creek spillway was about 200 feet lower than that at Setters, more proof that the surface of the floodwaters was decreasing downstream.

Spokane Area

Within minutes of ice-dam disintegration and run out across the Rathdrum Prairie, floodwaters from Glacial Lake Missoula invaded the Spokane Valley. During most of the earlier Ice Age floods, this valley was already underwater beneath the backwaters of Glacial Lake Columbia that backed up behind another ice dam downstream, near Grand Coulee Dam (Plate 11). At other (earlier) times the ice dam lay about 40 river miles upstream, where the Columbia River joins the Spokane River, forming what is called Glacial Lake Spokane. The upper end of Glacial Lake Columbia (or Spokane) extended almost all the way to the ice dam for Glacial Lake Missoula and far up the Coeur d'Alene and St. Joe river valleys – far beyond the present boundaries of modern-day Coeur d'Alene Lake (Plate 3). With the Spokane Valley already partially full of water, it didn't take much more additional water from Lake Missoula to spill over low divides at Setters and Mica and farther west into the Cheney-Palouse Scabland Tract.

It was only during the last Missoula floods, after the head of Grand Coulee was breached and suddenly lowered by 900 feet, that ancient lakes didn't flood the environs of the Spokane Valley. The old lakes buffered somewhat the erosion wrought by the Missoula floods, except for the last Missoula floods that ran overland across the Spokane Valley. But the last Missoula floods were also smaller, so that many may not have spilled over into adjacent valleys, except for Grand Coulee far downstream.

9. Prolific Rathdrum-Spokane Aquifer

Feature: Slowly moving underground river flowing beneath the Rathdrum Prairie and the Spokane Valley

Best Observation Point:

The aquifer is deep underground and therefore not visible; it is known from scores of groundwater wells in the area and is exposed in a few deep borrow pits (Figure 3-16) generally not accessible to the public.

Elevation of Feature: The surface of the aquifer rises to about 2,000 feet elevation (generally 100-150 feet underground).

- The water source for the Rathdrum-Spokane Aquifer is Lake Pend Oreille and tributaries that feed into the valley.
- The aquifer discharges into the Spokane River several miles west of Spokane, Washington.
- The aquifer lies about 100 to 150 feet below the surface and is up to 800 feet thick. (Figure 3-9)
- Groundwater within the aquifer moves very slowly (about 30 feet per day) toward the west.
- The tortuous path of the groundwater through the coarse flood deposits acts to purify the water along its path.
- Increasing population in the area, however, continues to slowly degrade the quality and quantity of the groundwater.

Figure 3-16. A borrow pit exposes gravelly flood deposits within the Spokane Valley. The top of the Rathdrum-Spokane Aquifer (i.e., water table) is visible at lower left about 100 feet below land surface. Looking north. Notice the slightly tilted, foreset bedding (arrow), indicating floodwaters flowed to the left (west) when they deposited the sediment layers.

10. West Plains Giant Current Ripples

Features: Flood bars blanketed with giant current ripples on flood-swept basalt plateau west of Spokane

Best Observation Point:

Automobile: In roadway 1.5 miles west of Airway Heights on Rambo Road one mile north of U.S. Highway 2 (see Figure 5-19). Featured in Road Tour No. 2 (chapter 5)

Elevation of Feature: 2,400 to 2,450 feet

Maximum Flood Depth (Elevation): 300 feet (2,700 feet)

- Between most Missoula floods, the Spokane Valley was already partially filled with backwater from Glacial Lake Columbia (Plate 3).

- Within an hour of ice-dam failure, Missoula floodwaters had overfilled the Spokane Valley and spread out across the West Plains on their way to the Cheney-Palouse scablands (Plate 10).

- The floods stripped away all the topsoil and locally blanketed the basalt plain with coarse, gravelly flood deposits (Figure 3-17).

Figure 3-17. Partially rounded, huge basalt boulders uncovered from West Plains megaflood bar near Airway Heights.

- The orientation of giant current ripples on flood bars indicate a south-westerly flow direction for the torrential floodwaters (Figure 3-18).

- Flood gravels exposed in some local borrow pits contain a layer of Mount St. Helens "S" ash (15,400 calendar years old) beneath several layers of flood sediment. This indicates some floods must have coursed down the Cheney-Palouse Scabland Tract after 15,400 years ago.

Figure 3-18. Giant current ripples atop the West Plains near Deep Creek. Arrow indicates flow direction (southwest). See also Figure 6-10 for a different perspective on these ripples.

11. Hangman Creek Rhythmites

Features: Slackwater flood rhythmites, some separated with varves, indicating multiple flood events only dozens of years apart; ancient landslides

Best Observation Points:

Automobile: Visible from U.S. Highway 195

Non-motorized trail: Campion Park (chapter 4, Trail H)

Elevation of Feature: The rhythmites form a terrace, about 150 feet tall. Top of terrace is about elevation 2,000 feet.

Maximum Flood Depth (Elevation): 700 feet (2,550 feet)

- Missoula floods backflooded into Hangman (Latah) Creek near Spokane.
- An arm of Glacial Lake Columbia already occupied Hangman Creek earlier in the last glacial cycle when Missoula floods backflooded into this tributary valley (Plates 3 and 11).
- Today, eroded streambanks along Hangman Creek expose up to 20 slackwater flood rhythmites from as many Missoula floods (Figures 3-19 and 3-20).

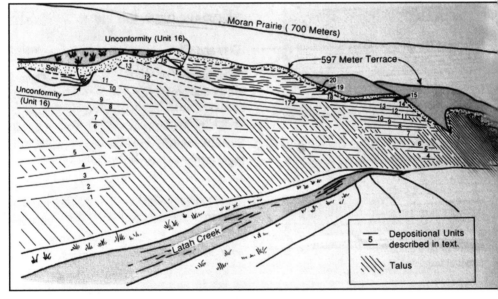

Figure 3-19. Hand-drawn sketch of 20 slackwater flood rhythmites exposed in natural cross section along Hangman Creek riverbank (after Rigby 1982). Looking southeast. Most rhythmites below No. 16 are capped with varves from Glacial Lake Columbia, which record the sudden influx of Missoula flood sediment into the backwaters of Glacial Lake Columbia. The last four rhythmites, without any capping varves, indicate the last Missoula floods did not encounter a pre-existing Glacial Lake Columbia in Hangman Creek.

- The lowermost 16 rhythmites in the flood sequence are capped with up to dozens of annual varves quietly laid down in Glacial Lake Columbia between Missoula floods.

- Another four rhythmites, uncapped by any varves, overlie a high-relief, erosional unconformity. These beds record Missoula floods that invaded Hangman Creek after Glacial Lake Columbia had disappeared here.

- Lake Columbia disappeared from Hangman Creek after the glacial lake drained through the Grand Coulee Spillover Breach (No. 29) during an Ice Age flood that eroded a 900-foot-deep channel at the head of Grand Coulee. This event suddenly lowered the lake an equivalent amount.

- Subsequent Missoula floods invaded a lake-free Hangman Creek late in the last glacial cycle.

- Some slumping occurred during or between Missoula floods, indicated by exposures of displaced rhythmites along Hangman Creek (Figure 3-20).

Figure 3-20. Slackwater flood rhythmites exposed in cut bank of Hangman Creek. Looking east. Evidence for slumping of the waterlogged sediments during flooding is revealed at lower right. N47.5920, W117.4002

12. Steptoe Ridge Spillover Complex

"Four heads northwest of Cheney contain nine named lakes in rock basins and multitude of rock-basined swamps and smaller lakes. Five of these lakes lie essentially on the plateau divide."

– J Harlen Bretz et al (1956)

Features: Ridge of older (pre-basalt) rock partially blocking the floods' path into the Cheney-Palouse scablands; spillover channels, rock basins, streamlined hills

Best Observation Points:

Automobile: Interstate 90 near Four Lakes. Featured in Road Tour No. 2 (chapter 5)

Non-motorized trails (chapter 4): Riddle Hill Steptoe (Trail I) and Medical Lake Loop (Trail J)

Elevation of Feature: Scabland lakes are 2,340 to 2,420 feet; the highest step-toe hill (Fancher Butte) is 2,940 feet.

Maximum Flood Depth (Elevation): 400 feet (2,700 feet)

- After crossing the West Plains, Missoula floods encountered a ridge of older rock protruding above the basalt plain, referred to here as Steptoe Ridge (Figure 3-21).

- The Steptoe Ridge is related to the ancient Coeur d'Alene and Selkirk mountains that stood above the Columbia Plateau during volcanic extrusion of the basalt.

- The steptoes are a string of low hills (Fancher Butte as well as Riddle, Wrights, Needam and Prosser hills) belonging to a basement complex composed of mostly Precambrian-age rock of the Belt Supergroup that is 1.4 billion to 1.6 billion years old (Figure 3-22).

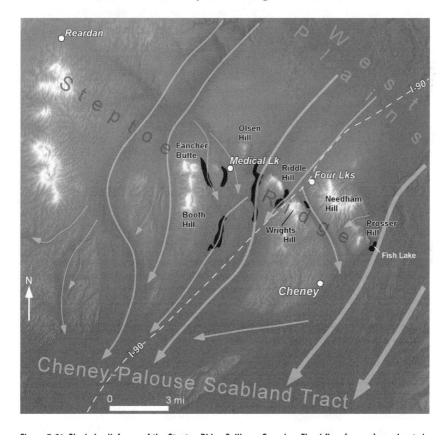

Figure 3-21. Shaded-relief map of the Steptoe Ridge Spillover Complex. Flood flow (arrows) accelerated through the gaps between steptoes, scouring out a number of rock basins now occupied by groundwater-seepage lakes (shown in black).

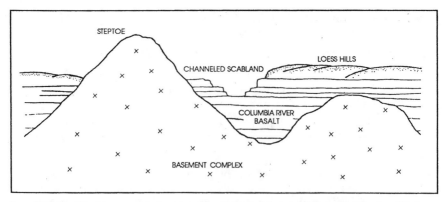

Figure 3-22. Like islands in a sea, steptoes rise above the level of the volcanic Columbia River basalt that flowed around the protruding steptoes. Later, rolling hills of windblown Palouse loess blanketed the basalt. Lastly, Ice Age floods locally eroded through the Palouse loess and channeled into the underlying basalt flows (after Stradling and Kiver 1989).

- Lava flows of Columbia River basalt that cover and lap up onto the Belt rocks along Steptoe Ridge, are a mere 14 million to 15 million years old. That's only one-thousandth the age of the Belt rocks!

- Slightly constricted, floodwaters rose to an elevation of 2,700 feet in front of the Steptoe Ridge.

- Floodwaters, up to 400 feet deep, were funneled through saddles along the flood-resistant Steptoe Ridge; the speed of the floodwater increased through these gaps due to the venturi effect.

- Hills along Steptoe Ridge were streamlined into an airfoil shape (blunt upstream and tapered downstream end) by the floods (see Figure 4-19).

- In the gaps between the steptoe hills, Missoula floods preferentially eroded through the thin basalt cover and down into the weathered basement rock underneath.

- Today, multiple lakes occupy the rock basins that were scoured out by the floods between steptoe hills (Figure 3-21).

- The very tops of the steptoe hills were above flood level and thus retained their caps of windblown loess; the loess was stripped off the lower slopes of steptoes by Missoula floods.

Cheney-Palouse Scabland Tract

"The scablands of the Palouse drainage, with channeled basalt, deposits of stratified gravel, and isolated linear groups of Palouse Hills, their marginal slopes steepened notably, bear abundant evidence of a great flood of glacial waters from the north."

– J Harlen Bretz (1923)

Within an hour or two after ice-dam collapse, Missoula floodwaters first spilled overland to the south out of the Spokane Valley into the head of the Cheney-Palouse Scabland Tract. Peak flow through the Cheney-Palouse occurred after only a single day before beginning to subside about four days later. At its upper end the 30-mile-wide Cheney-Palouse Tract consists of a network of shallow, marshy channels and often forested land. This is in sharp contrast to its lower reaches that display deeper channels and coulees covered in drier, shrub-steppe vegetation. The vegetation difference is due to higher elevations and more moisture along the northeastern Channeled Scabland. Dark, ragged channels across the entire tract stand in stark contrast to the smoothed and streamlined hills of light-colored, windblown Palouse loess dividing the channels (see Figure 2-22, Plates 14 and 15).

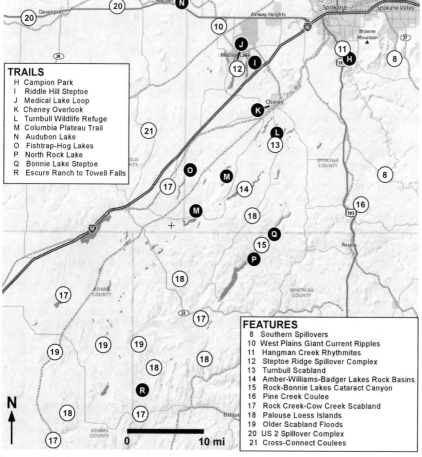

TRAILS
H Campion Park
I   Riddle Hill Steptoe
J   Medical Lake Loop
K Cheney Overlook
L   Turnbull Wildlife Refuge
M Columbia Plateau Trail
N Audubon Lake
O Fishtrap-Hog Lakes
P North Rock Lake
Q Bonnie Lake Steptoe
R Escure Ranch to Towell Falls

FEATURES
8   Southern Spillovers
10 West Plains Giant Current Ripples
11 Hangman Creek Rhythmites
12 Steptoe Ridge Spillover Complex
13 Turnbull Scabland
14 Amber-Williams-Badger Lakes Rock Basins
15 Rock-Bonnie Lakes Cataract Canyon
16 Pine Creek Coulee
17 Rock Creek-Cow Creek Scabland
18 Palouse Loess Islands
19 Older Scabland Floods
20 US 2 Spillover Complex
21 Cross-Connect Coulees

Figure 3-23. Key features and trails in the vicinity of the Cheney-Palouse Scabland Tract. Non-motorized trails are described in chapter 4.

13. Turnbull Scabland

Features: Flood-scoured, shallow, rock-basin wetlands and ponds, flood bars, Mima mounds, streamlined and scarped Palouse hills

Best Observation Points:

Automobile: Pine Lakes Auto Tour Road, Turnbull National Wildlife Refuge. Featured along Road Tour No. 2 (chapter 5)

Non-motorized trails (chapter 4): Turnbull Wildlife Refuge Trails (Trail L) and Columbia Plateau Trail (Trail M)

Elevation of Feature: 2,230 to 2,350 feet

Maximum Flood Depth (Elevation): 200 to 300 feet (about 2,500 feet)

- Scabland within the Turnbull National Wildlife Refuge, a few miles south of Cheney, lies near the center of the 30-mile-wide Cheney-Palouse Tract (Plate 10).

- Floods raced through with exceptional force, completely removing a once-thick cover of Palouse loess before attacking the basalt bedrock below.

- A complex network of elongated, low-relief basins and rocky ridges are aligned northeast to southwest, parallel to the flood-flow direction.

- In a few places flood currents slackened enough to allow the accumulation of basaltic, bouldery flood debris (Figure 3-24).

- The water table lies close to surface here creating extensive wetlands that support a rich abundance and variety of flora and fauna.

Figure 3-24. Coauthor Kiver examines boulders excavated from the Blackhorse pendant flood bar (see Figure 4-25) within the refuge.

14. Amber-Williams-Badger Lakes Rock Basins

Features: Groundwater-filled rock basins; recessional cataract canyons with well-developed, marshy plunge pools, streamlined and scarped Palouse hills, Mima mounds

Best Observation Points:

Automobile: From Cheney take Mullinix Road 11 miles to Williams Lake Road. Turn left and continue 2.2 miles to Badger Lake Road, turn left and park at head of Williams Lake canyon after 0.3 mile. Currently a short walk to the edge of cataract affords a great view down the throat of the recessional cataract canyon (Figure 3-26). However, the land along the edge of the cataract is for sale, so this area may be closed to public access in the future.

Watercraft: Via launch sites at both Williams and Badger lakes

Elevation of Feature: A precipitous, 100-foot tall recessional cataract separates Badger Lake (2,175 feet) from Williams Lake (2,050 feet). Plunge-pool fen below cataract is filled to an altitude of 2,080 feet.

Maximum Flood Depth: Williams Lake (1,730 feet elevation) is 115 feet deep – floodwater rose up to 2,450 feet in the adjacent Palouse hills, an indication floodwaters here were as much as 800 feet deep!

- Amber, Williams and Badger lakes lie near the heads of a group of recessional cataract canyons eroded into the Cheney-Palouse Tract (Figure 3-25).

- The recessional canyons are flanked by remnant, streamlined and scarped Palouse Loess Islands (No. 18), many of which were also overtopped by Ice Age floods.

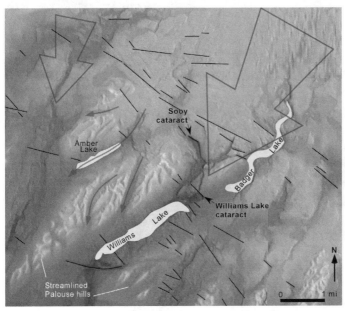

Figure 3-25. Northwest trending, dark, straight lines are flood-etched fractures in the basalt bedrock of the Cheney Fracture Zone (see Figure 1-7). Block arrows indicate primary flood flow direction; smaller arrows show secondary flow around and through the streamlined and scarped Palouse hills.

- Large-scale tectonic fractures within the basalt bedrock, which lay transverse to flood flow, were etched out by the powerful flood currents.

- Heads of some cataracts terminate at the weakened rock along fracture lines (e.g., Williams Lake and Sooy cataracts, Figure 3-25).

- The area upstream of Amber, Williams and Badger Lakes is characterized by a gentle regional slope covered with subdued butte and basin topography all the way to the Steptoe Ridge Spillover Complex (No. 12). The lakes mark the northern extent (knickpoint) for cataract recession after the last Ice Age flood. Below this area lie inner canyons created during cataract recession (see Figure 2-1, stage 4). During future outburst floods the knickpoint and cataract will continue their headward recession to the northeast.

Figure 3-26. Williams and Badger lakes. Above: Sinuous, flood-scoured Badger Lake with straighter, Williams Lake in background. Left: Cataract cliff (former waterfall) between Williams and Badger lakes. Looking south. N47.3373, W117.6572

Mysterious Mima Mounds

One of the most visible and curious features of the Channeled Scabland are groups of regularly spaced hillocks called Mima mounds (Figure 3-27, Plates 15 and 16). Their name is derived from similar-appearing mounds located at Mima Prairie near Olympia, Washington. The circular, measles-like bumps range up to several tens of feet wide and several feet high. Within the Channeled Scabland of eastern Washington, they generally form where a thin cover of loose rubble and windblown silt overlie flat-lying, rocky basalt bedrock. The Mima mounds in eastern Washington are composed of mostly silt. The mounds can also occur atop flood bars underlain with thick piles of coarse gravel and sand. However, they are most abundant upon the flood-swept basalt plateaus and coulees of the Channeled Scabland. In contrast, they are rarely observed in the loess-covered Palouse hills. The fact that they are best preserved in high-energy, flood-swept areas indicate they developed since the last Missoula floods around 15,000 years ago. Had the mounds developed before the last floods, they would have been wiped out by flood erosion or severely molded and streamlined by floodwater, which is definitely not the case.

The origins of Mima mounds have perplexed geologists for years. It appears likely that they form in more than one way, since they are found in a number of different, unrelated environments besides the Channeled Scabland. Among the possible mechanisms are vegetation trapping of windblown silt, burrowing rodents, earthquake shaking or periglacial activity, near the front of a former ice sheet. Scabland Mima mounds lay beyond the farthest extent of the ice sheet, so we can eliminate the possibility they developed directly from glaciation.

Recent investigations by archaeologists (e.g., Jerry Galm and others) discovered an American Indian campfire hearth beneath a Mima mound in the vicinity of Escure Ranch (see Figure 4-43). Several radiocarbon dates on the hearth indicate that it was used as recently as 500 years ago (oldest radiocarbon date is 1,710 years). Because the mound lies above the campfire hearth, it has to be younger and thus suggests some Mima mounds may only be a few hundred years old. If this is the case, wind – one of the few active geologic processes still affecting the scablands – may play a major role in the development of Mima mounds via trapping of windblown silt (loess) by vegetation. Mounds may initiate as loess collects in shallow depressions on a flood-stripped basalt surface. The loess favors the growth of grasses and other vegetation that trap more of the windblown loess into circular mounds.

Geologist R.K. Olmsted described the process in 1963: "As the depression filled, vegetation growing in the accumulated soil continued to gather and hold the dust. Continuation of the same process for thousands of years eventually resulted in the mounds rising above the rims of the original depressions." This same process also appears to apply to elongated low mounds of loess that occur within curvilinear grooves at several places within the Channeled Scabland.

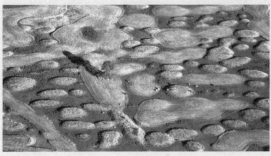

Figure 3-27. Post-flood Mima mounds are ubiquitous within the Channeled Scabland — especially the Cheney-Palouse Tract. For the most part Mima mounds are randomly distributed but sometimes align themselves into elongated low ridges (left).

15. Rock-Bonnie Lakes Cataract Canyon

Features: Steep-walled recessional cataract canyon, rock benches and basins, potholes, flood-etched tectonic fractures, streamlined and scarped Palouse hills, natural bridge, erosional window into underlying, pre-basalt basement rock

Best Observation Points:

Automobile: Rock Lake accessed via Rock Lake Road from Cheney-Plaza Road, 28 highway miles south of Cheney; Hole-in-the-Ground Canyon is accessed via Belsby Road, which turns into Hole-in-the-Ground Road on the east side of the channel, 19 highway miles south of Cheney.

Non-motorized trails (chapter 4): North Rock Lake (Trail P) and Bonnie Lake Steptoe (Trail Q)

Watercraft: Via public launch site at south end of Rock Lake (Washington Discover Pass required). Portable watercraft allows access via Rock Creek to the Bonnie Lake Steptoe (Trail Q).

Elevation of Feature: The surface of Rock Lake lies at elevation 1,725 feet; Bonnie Lake is 70 feet higher, separated by mostly dry, Hole-in-the-Ground Canyon. Rock Lake is up to 400 feet deep, placing the deepest part of the lake at elevation 1,325 feet.

Maximum Flood Depth (Elevation): 975 feet (2,300 feet)

- Rock and Bonnie lakes make up one continuous, flood-scoured rock basin 15 miles long and one to two miles wide along the eastern margin of the Cheney-Palouse Tract (Figure 3-28).

- The continuity of the lakes is broken along a three-mile dry section of the canyon, called Hole in the Ground, which separates Rock Lake (below) from Bonnie Lake (above) (Figures 3-28 to 3-30; see also Figure 4-39, Plate 13).

- A prominent set of northwest-to-southeast-trending tectonic fractures cross the upper ends of both Rock and Bonnie lakes. The weakened rock along the fractures was preferentially removed during Ice Age flooding that strongly controlled the floods' path.

- The great depths of Rock Lake are the result of floods that scoured a deep plunge pool at the head of Rock Lake just beneath a dissected cataract (Figure 3-29). Here, during their maximum, floodwaters were almost 1,000 feet deep!

Figure 3-28. Deep rock basins (Rock and Bonnie lakes) lie along the Rock Creek Coulee recessional cataract canyon. Floodwaters that backflooded Hangman Creek also spilled over (smaller white arrows) into the head of Pine Creek Coulee (No. 16), shown in upper right; these floodwaters emptied into the Cheney-Palouse Tract just above Rock Lake.

Figure 3-29. Linear tectonic fractures (dashed lines) in the basalt bedrock at north end of Rock Lake. Note how the head of Rock Lake terminates along one of these vertical cracks. Ice Age floods eroded through the Priest Rapids Member of basalt into the underlying Roza Member along the fracture lines. Looking southeast. Rock Lake reaches a maximum depth (400 feet) at its head, just below the cataract.

- Streamlined and scarped Palouse uplands line both sides of the deep canyon.
- Pre-basalt Belt rocks crop out in several places along the floor of the canyon, including a steptoe island within the middle of Bonnie Lake (Figure 3-30; see also Figure 4-42).

Figure 3-30. View looking south across Bonnie Lake, Hole-in-the-Ground and Rock Lake canyons. The island within Bonnie Lake is a steptoe composed of Belt-type rocks, once covered by Columbia River basalt. Erosion by Ice Age floods exhumed the island and exposed lava flows of Grande Ronde and Wanapum basalt along the coulee walls.

16. Pine Creek Coulee

"Prominent spillways were eroded across the divide into North Pine Creek Valley."

– J Harlen Bretz (1923)

Features: A mostly solitary, relatively narrow coulee with trenched spurs and flood bars. Multiple spillover channels from Hangman Creek lie at the head of the coulee.

Best Observation Point:

Automobile: Lower Pine Creek Coulee accessed via U.S. Highway 195 to Malden/Pine City Road to Hole-in-the-Ground Road. Spillover channels at the head of the coulee accessed via Spangle-Waverly Road five to six miles south-east of Spangle.

Elevation of Feature: Floor at head of coulee is 2,400 feet; mouth is elevation 1,850 feet.

Maximum Flood Depth (Elevation): 450 feet (2,300 feet) at mouth of Pine Creek Coulee

- 25-mile-long Pine Creek Coulee fed into the extreme east end of the Cheney-Palouse Tract after Missoula floods spilled over a divide from Hangman Creek (Figures 3-28 and 3-14, Plate 12).

- At its downstream end Pine Creek Coulee joined floodwaters that simultaneously flowed south down Rock Creek Coulee (Figure 3-28).

- Along the way floodwaters carved out trenched spurs and deposited massive flood bars filled with bouldery, basaltic debris along Pine Creek (Figure 3-31).

Figure 3-31. Basaltic flood gravel in crescent flood bar (now removed) near Malden-Rosalia Airport in 1976. Size of the boulders, degree of sorting and fabric of the sediment indicates it was rapidly dumped here by colossal floods racing down Pine Creek Coulee.

- A difference of 200 feet existed in the maximum height of the floods between the head of Pine Creek Coulee and its mouth at Rock Creek (Hole-in-the-Ground Canyon) (Figure 3-14). It was this huge difference in hydraulic head that kept the fast-moving floodwaters rushing down coulee.

17. Rock Creek-Cow Creek Scabland Complex

Features: Chaotic channel plexus, coulees, rock basins and benches, potholes, streamlined and scarped Palouse hills, faceted escarpments and flood bars

Best Observation Points:

Automobile: Along State Route 261 from Ritzville south to Benge and Winona. Featured in Road Tour No. 2 (chapter 5)

Non-motorized trails (chapter 4): Escure Ranch to Towell Falls (Trail R) and North Rock Lake (Trail P)

Watercraft: Via public launch sites at Rock Lake (south end) and Sprague Lake. Washington Discover Pass required.

Figure 3-32. The Rock Creek-Cow Creek Scabland Complex comprises most of the Cheney-Palouse Scabland Tract (see also Plate 10).

Elevation of Feature: Flood channels along Rock and Cow creeks descend from about 2,200 feet at the north end of the complex to 1,100 feet at the south end.

Maximum Flood Depth (Elevation): 975 feet (2,300 feet) at Rock Lake

- The Rock Creek-Cow Creek Scabland Complex is a broad, flood-scoured area, up to 30 miles wide, that includes the bulk of the Cheney-Palouse Scabland Tract.

- Today the area is drained by two grossly underfit streams that semi-parallel each other along most of the length of the scabland tract (Figure 3-32).

- The headwaters for Rock Creek come from a collection of flood-scoured, water-filled rock basins in the Turnbull Scabland (No. 13). Cow Creek originates at Sprague Lake.

- A huge island of Palouse loess, 17 miles long by seven miles wide, that lies west of Rock Lake was mostly above the ancient flood level in an upland area that separates Rock Creek from Cow Creek.

- To the southwest Rock Creek and Cow Creek merge to form a single, broad channel plexus that measures an incredible 25 miles wide.

- The town of Benge is centered over a region with the best examples of streamlined and scarped loess islands anywhere in the Channeled Scabland (Figure 3-32).

18. Palouse Loess Islands

"It seems clear that they are but remnants of a once continuous cover of the basalt, and that the scablands have resulted from removal of the Palouse Hills by erosion by some unusual way. The basalt of the scablands is the firm and resistant foundation on which the hills stand."

– J Harlen Bretz (1923)

Features: Eroded, flood-sculpted hills of a once-continuous, thick blanket of windblown Palouse loess.

Best Observation Points:

Automobile: Interstate 90 between Sprague and Fishtrap (chapter 5, Road Tour No. 2); county road between Benge and Winona (Figure 3-32)

Non-motorized trails (chapter 4): Fishtrap Lake Loop (Trail O) and North Rock Lake (Trail P)

Elevation of Feature: Variable – descends from about elevation 2,450 feet in the northern scabland to about 1,200 feet to the south.

- Dozens of teardrop-shaped streamlined hills of Palouse loess (Figures 3-32 and 3-33; see also Figure 2-22, Plates 14 and 15) that are elongated and aligned with the paleo-flood direction particularly in the Rock Creek-Cow Creek Scabland Complex (No. 17).

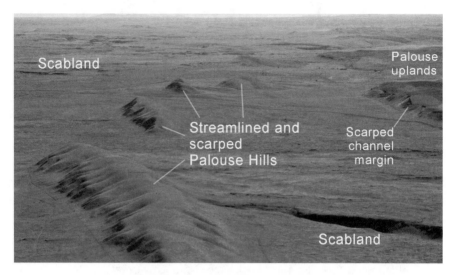

Figure 3-33. Streamlined and scarped Palouse hills within the Cheney-Palouse scablands. Like a flotilla of ships the hills are aligned with the direction of flood flow (toward the viewer).

- Flood-streamlined Palouse islands range from less than one-half square mile to 400 square miles in area.
- The loess islands typically display a prominent, steep, scarped prow at the upstream end and a tapered tail in the downstream direction (see Figure 2-22).
- Steepened escarpments lie along the perimeters of the islands especially along the prow and upstream sides.
- Escarpments are distinctly steeper and straighter than the naturally rolling slopes of the Palouse hills that lag above flood level (see Figure 1-9).
- Eroding floodwaters repeatedly molded the islands into a most hydrodynamically stable shape that provided the least amount of drag to the floodwaters that formed them.

19. Older Scabland Floods

Features: Scattered road and rail cuts expose old flood deposits capped by strongly weathered soils, signifying ancient floods from earlier in the Ice Age going back 1 million years or more.

Best Observation Points:

Automobile: Old flood deposits at Revere (see Figure 1-14) are exposed along east side of Revere Road, 17 miles south of Sprague, near intersection with Lakin Road. Another exposure of extremely old flood deposits (caliche-capped flood gravels) lies along Harder Road (see Figure 5-14). Featured in Road Tour No. 2 (chapter 5).

Elevation of Feature: elevation 1,600 to 1,800 feet

- The evidence for floods from the last glacial cycle (late Wisconsinan Glaciation) between 14,000 to 28,000 years ago is plentiful and widespread.

- Only a handful of sites exist in the Channeled Scabland with a record for older, pre-Wisconsinan floods that go back a million years or more (see Figure 1-8). A few more sites with old flood deposits are known in the Mid-Columbia Basin and other areas downstream (see companion volume).

- The paucity of evidence for the oldest floods is not surprising since the younger cataclysmic floods tended to erode or bury the evidence for the older floods.

- Most old flood localities are located in remote areas of the Cheney-Palouse scablands. One of the best exposures for old flood deposits is displayed at Marengo (Figure 3-34); others include a site near Revere (see Figure 1-14), and along Harder Road (see Figure 5-14, Road Tour No. 2).

- At least one other extremely old flood locality is known in the vicinity of Arbuckle Flat, in the vicinity of Lower Grand Coulee.

- The oldest flood deposits often display a reversed magnetic polarity in combination with caliche paleosols developed atop the flood deposits, suggesting flood ages of 780,000 years or more (age of the last major shift in magnetic polarity). See example in Figure 3-34.

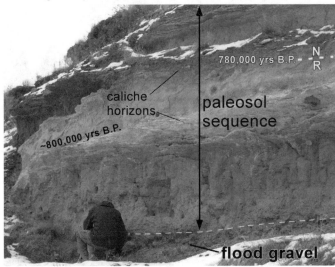

Figure 3-34. Old flood gravels at Marengo are buried beneath a thick sequence of old soil horizons (caliche paleosols). Sediments within the lower paleosols, above the flood gravel, retain a normal (N) over reversed (R) magnetic polarity locked in at the time of sediment deposition. A radiometric age of 800,000 years before present from sediment below the magnetic reversal is consistent with the magnetic-polarity age. Since the flood gravels lie below the dated horizons, it follows that an Ice Age flood that occurred more than 800,000 years ago is preserved at this site. Another well-developed caliche horizon below the 800,000 age date suggests the megaflood gravels at the very base of the exposure may be 1 million years or more in age.

- -

Telford-Crab Creek Scabland Tract

"That all the channels of this Telford-Crab Creek spillway were in operation at one time cannot be gainsaid."

– J Harlen Bretz (1928)

Within a few hours after ice-dam collapse, Missoula floodwaters rapidly overfilled Glacial Lake Columbia and spilled overland via a second set of channelways south of the Columbia Valley into the head of the Telford-Crab Creek Scabland Tract (Figure 3-35, Plates 10 and 11). Similar to the Cheney-Palouse scablands, peak flow through the Telford-Crab Creek Tract occurred after only a single day before beginning to subside. By four days the flow into the Telford-Crab Creek Tract had exhausted itself in favor of a lower flood channel (Grand Coulee) to the west – at least for the last floods.

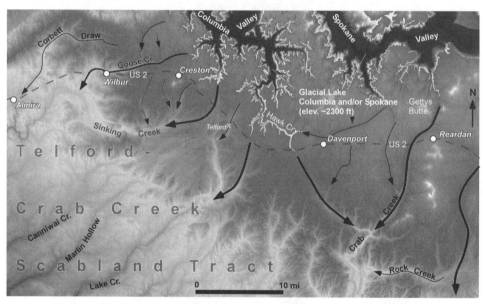

Figure 3-35. Spillover routes for Ice Age floods at the head of the Telford-Crab Creek Scabland Tract. During most earlier floods Glacial Lake Columbia was already filled to near the brim (elevation 2,300 feet) of the Columbia Valley. Incoming megafloods instantly overfilled the valley, spilling over across low divides to the south (arrows).

Telford-Crab Creek Scabland Tract, up to 40 miles wide, is the central of three main flood routes for the Channeled Scabland (see page xii). It formed as floods overtopped low sills to the south of Glacial Lake Columbia and flowed into the heart of the Channeled Scabland east of Grand Coulee and west of the Cheney-Palouse scablands (Plate 10). Here barren, ragged flood channels lie in stark contrast to intervening gentle, rolling Palouse uplands, mantled with golden wheat fields. Similar to the Cheney-Palouse scablands, flood channels to the north are only a few tens of feet deep and only eroded into the uppermost one or two basalt lava flows. Flood channels and coulees farther to the south are associated with recessional cataracts canyons that only partially eroded headward.

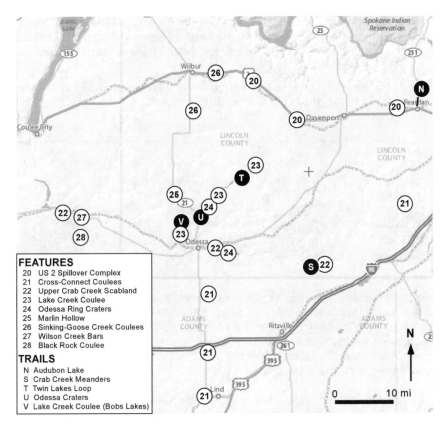

Figure 3-36. Flood features and trails within the Telford-Crab Creek Scabland Tract. Non-motorized trails are described in chapter 4.

20. U.S. Highway 2 Spillover Complex

"About a dozen definite channel heads are distributed along the 85 miles of this divide."

– J Harlen Bretz et al (1956)

Features: Broad spillover complex eroded into low-relief heads of scabland channels; streamlined and scarped Palouse uplands; giant eroded curvilinear grooves

Best Observation Point:

Automobile: U.S. Highway 2 between Reardan and Wilbur. Featured in Road Tour No. 3 (chapter 5)

Elevation of Feature: Lowest spillover points within the Telford-Crab Creek Tract were about 2,300 feet east of Creston.

Maximum Flood Depth (Elevation): 300 feet (about 2,600 feet)

- Ice Age floods spilled over several low divides along south side of the Columbia River Valley and into the heads of a series of scabland coulees that included Crab Creek, Lake Creek, Marlin Hollow, Wilson Creek, Sinking Creek and Goose Creek.

- The lowest spillovers lie at elevation 2,300 feet (Figure 3-37), about the same as those within the Cheney-Palouse Tract. This suggests both tracts were used simultaneously during flooding.

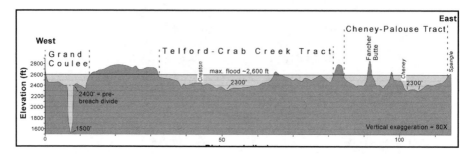

Figure 3-37. An east-west profile across the northern margin of the Channeled Scabland showing relative heights of spillover channels into the main scabland tracts. Based on the cross-sectional area of each of the scabland tracts visible in this diagram, both the Telford-Crab Creek and Cheney-Palouse tracts had the ability to transmit much more floodwater than Grand Coulee, especially before the head of Grand Coulee was breached late in the last cycle of glaciation. A series of the last smaller floods, on the other hand, mostly traveled down a suddenly breached Grand Coulee.

- Maximum flood levels across the spillovers were about elevation 2,600 feet based on trimlines observed along flood channels.

- Spillovers were eroded and deepened during later floods, which simultaneously lowered the maximum level of Glacial Lake Columbia.

- The last Missoula floods may have completely bypassed the Telford-Crab Creek Scabland Tract and the U.S. Highway 2 Spillover Complex after the head of Grand Coulee was breached (No. 29).

- Many interesting curvilinear grooves lie near the head of the Telford Scabland Tract. The curving grooves may represent flood etching of weaker rock within larger-scale fractures or flow bands inherent in the basalt.

21. Cross-Connect Coulees

Features: Low-relief coulees (Rock Creek, Crab Creek, Weber-Bauer, Rocky, Farrier and Lind) connecting the Cheney-Palouse Tract with the Telford-Crab Creek Tract and the Quincy Basin (Figure 3-38)

Best Observation Point:

Automobile: State Route 21 crosses several cross-connect coulees (Rocky, Farrier, Bauer and Lind) between six and 25 miles south of Odessa. Interstate 90 parallels Bauer-Weber Coulee for about 25 miles, starting seven miles west of Ritzville. State Route 231 intersects the Rock-Creek cross-connect coulee 10 miles north of Sprague.

- When the Cheney-Palouse scablands couldn't handle the sudden rush of water, the excess spilled west into the Telford-Crab Creek Tract and/or the Quincy Basin (Figure 3-38) via a series of connecting coulees.

- The cross-connect coulees usually lie at a higher elevation and lack rock benches and vertical walls usually associated with flood coulees (Figure 3-39). Many are almost filled with post-flood windblown sediment.

- Giant current ripples are also more subdued and fainter along the cross-connect coulees.

- Cross-connect coulees appear to be relics of the older and larger floods, which over time have since been partially filled back in with sediments. The younger, smaller floods mostly bypassed these higher cross-connect coulees.

Figure 3-38. Cross coulees connect the Cheney-Palouse Tract with the Telford-Crab Creek Tract and Quincy Basin.

Figure 3-39. Low-relief and subdued Rocky Coulee, looking west. Unlike coulees and bars from the last Ice Age floods, which have steep, tiered coulee walls, most of the cross-connect coulees are gentler and less well-defined. It appears these coulees were used most recently during one or more of the largest floods that occurred earlier in last glacial cycle. Later floods that were smaller with less volume, apparently did not rise high enough to use these higher, cross-connect coulees. While lower coulees were being flushed out by younger floods, higher coulees such as Rocky Coulee were filling in with sediment from non-flood sources such as windblown loess and slopewash off the adjacent uplands.

22. Upper Crab Creek Scabland Complex

Features: Rock benches and basins, flood-scoured ringed craters, dozens of flood bars blanketed with giant current ripples, flood rhythmites

Best Observation Points:

Automobile: 10 miles northwest of Sprague on State Route 23; State Route 21 at Odessa; State Route 28 between Stratford and Wilson Creek

Non-motorized trail: Crab Creek Meanders (chapter 4, Trail S), South Lake Creek Coulee (Trail V2)

Elevation of Feature: 2,500 feet at head of Crab Creek; 1,250 feet at entrance to Quincy Basin

Maximum Flood Depth (Elevation): 350 feet (1,600 feet) at mouth of Crab Creek Coulee near Stratford

- Crab Creek encompasses about 4,000 square miles and is reportedly the longest creek (170 miles) in the United States, and perhaps all of North America.

- The head of Crab Creek lies near Reardan (Plate 10) along the U.S. Highway 2 Spillover Complex (No. 20).

- During Ice Age floods Upper Crab Creek was a major conduit for floodwaters that spilled over along the eastern part of the Telford-Crab Creek Tract.

- Like all other streams on the Scabland, present-day Crab Creek is sluggish and ridiculously underfit in comparison to the terrain it drains (Plate 20, left).

- Some of the best examples of ringed craters and flood bars, blanketed with giant current ripples are preserved near Sylvan Lake (Figure 3-40, see Figure 2-34). This area has the highest concentration of megaripples anywhere in the Channeled Scabland.

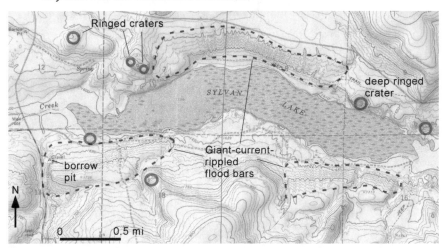

Figure 3-40. Giant flood bars, current ripples, and flood-etched, circular ringed craters along Crab Creek near Sylvan Lake. Megaripples on flood bars (dashed outlines) are recognized by the tight, crenulated contour lines on this topographic map. Flood bar in the lower left is shown in Plate 21 where about a dozen flood rhythmites are exposed in a borrow pit (see Figure 2-29).

23. Lake Creek Coulee

Features: Recessional cataract canyon, rock benches, rock basins, buttes, mesas, flood-etched ringed craters, ice-rafted erratics, flood bars, disappearing lakes

Best Observation Points:

Automobile: State Route 21, six miles north of Odessa (chapter 5, Road Tour No. 3); Coffeepot Road, 14 miles west of Harrington.

Non-motorized trail: Lake Creek Coulee (chapter 4, Trail V)

Watercraft: Via public launch sites at Twin Lakes and Coffeepot Lake

Elevation of Feature: Head of the coulee begins in low-relief scabland southwest of Davenport at approximately 2,100 feet; coulee ends at 1,450 feet where it joins Crab Creek Coulee west of Odessa

Maximum Flood Depth (Elevation): 400 feet (1,850 feet) at Bobs Lakes

- Twenty-five-mile-long Lake Creek Coulee begins modestly in the low-relief scabland west of Davenport (Plate 10).

- As floodwaters gathered they organized into a single, well-defined coulee with recessional cataracts. Inner canyon at the mouth of the coulee is up to 400 feet high (Plate 18b).

- Unusual ringed craters are in abundance along the lower portion of Lake Creek Coulee (Figure 3-43).
- Bobs Lakes, along with Pacific Lake, were a series of lakes that once filled a large part of lower Lake Creek Coulee. Today many of the lakes in the region are dry (see "Disappearing Lakes and Aquifers" sidebar at right).
- In contrast, lakes in the upper part of Lake Creek Coulee, such as deep-blue, three-mile long Coffeepot Lake (Figure 3-41, see Figure 6-9) maintain normal lake levels.

Figure 3-41. Giant current ripples in front of Coffeepot Lake – an elongated rock basin along Lake Creek Coulee. Arrow indicates flow direction (to the southwest), based on asymmetry of the transverse ripples.

24. Odessa Ring Craters

Features: Flood-scoured, circular moats and craters within basalt bedrock

Best Observation Points:

Automobile: Dikes are not easily viewed at road level; they are best viewed from above.

Non-motorized trail: Odessa Craters (chapter 4, Trail U)

Elevation of Feature: Most of the Odessa craters lie at an elevation between 1,600 to 1,800 feet

Maximum Flood Depth (Elevation): 400 feet (2,000 feet)

- Ringed craters are circular features that originally formed in a basalt flow when the molten lava explosively came in contact with surface water.

Disappearing Lakes and Aquifers

Over the last several decades, groundwater levels in the Odessa-Lind area have declined drastically. Since the 1960s water levels in deep wells have dropped up to 400 feet and continue to decline at an average rate of up to 7 feet per year. As a result many once-productive water wells are going dry, and a number of lakes in the region have disappeared (e.g., Pacific and Bobs lakes). Estimates indicate up to two-thirds of the available groundwater has been used up since major pumping began in the 1960s. Water levels in the basalt confined aquifers are declining to such an extent that the ability of some farmers to irrigate their crops may be limited. Domestic, commercial, municipal and industrial uses as well as water quality may also be affected. Under these developing circumstances almost 1 million acres of irrigated farmland and 200,000 people in south-central Washington are at risk of losing their water supply.

Overpumping from irrigation wells (i.e., groundwater withdrawal exceeding natural recharge) in the Odessa-Lind area is the obvious cause of the dropping groundwater levels. Presently all groundwater for irrigation is being pumped from hundreds of wells that produce groundwater from more porous, mostly isolated lenses within laterally extensive, deep lava flows of Columbia River basalt. In 1967 irrigation water was routinely pumped from relatively shallow (less than 1,000 feet) wells within the Wanapum Basalt (Figure 1-1), while only 10 years later most groundwater had to be pumped from much-deeper Grande Ronde Basalt confined aquifers. Recently, farmers have had to deepen wells to 2,000 feet or more in their losing battle with declining groundwater levels. Deep wells are extremely expensive, and few farmers can afford the escalating costs of drilling and the electricity to pump water from such depths.

Recent carbon-14 dating of groundwater collected from deep basalt aquifers indicates the presence of fossil water in excess of 18,000 calendar years. Therefore, much of the groundwater in the deeper aquifers tapped by wells may be derived from pressurized pulses of water associated with discrete Ice Age flood events, perhaps in combination with percolation from Glacial Lake Columbia. Water moves extremely slowly in the basalt bedrock via either vertical cracks (fractures) in the rock or sideways from exposed coulee walls carved into the basalt during flooding. If this hydrologic scenario is accurate, then current, deep well pumping is "mining" limited groundwater supplies that may not be adequately replenished without outside intervention (e.g., aquifer recharge/storage programs).

Potential solutions to the problem of declining groundwater levels within basalt confined aquifers, while continuing to support agriculture in the area, would require: a moratorium on pumping from new irrigation wells, in combination with diversion of surface water from the Columbia Basin Project into the Odessa area, which presently does not supply water to this area, and/or injecting diverted surface water into deep wells to restore depleted confined aquifers. Various alternatives for diverting surface-irrigation water are still under debate, and no concrete measures have been implemented. But even after a preferred solution or strategy is adopted, it may be many decades or generations before the basalt aquifers are restored and the lakes return.

- Years later, after the lava was buried beneath a thick blanket of wind-blown Palouse loess, the lava and ringed craters were exhumed by Ice Age floods (Figures 3-42 and 3-43, see Figures 2-24 to 2-27, 4-53 to 4-55, 4-60 to 4-61, 5-23, 6-7 to 6-8, Plates 21 and 27).

Figure 3-42. Unusual, concentric ringed craters in basalt, up to hundreds of feet in diameter, were etched out during erosion by Ice Age floods.

- Flood erosion etched out the weaker rock between more cohesive, circular ring dikes.
- The Odessa Craters are restricted to a volcanic lava flow, or flows, of the Roza Member basalt, dated at 14.5 million years (see Figure 1-1).
- The majority of the more than 100 visible ringed craters lie along flood-scoured upper Crab Creek and Lake Creek coulees, as well as Marlin Hollow in the vicinity of Odessa (Figure 3-43).

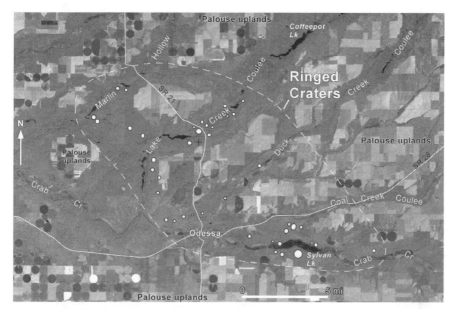

Figure 3-43. Aerial photo showing swarm of visible ringed craters (white circles) exposed along dark-colored flood channels eroded into basalt. Many more of the craters must lie buried beneath the lighter-colored, patch-worked cover of Palouse soil away from flood channels and coulees. Dashed line shows inferred limit for Odessa ringed-dike swarm.

- Many more ringed structures lie buried beneath the protective cover of Palouse loess in between flood coulees of the Telford-Crab Creek scablands.

- Other flood-exposed localities of ringed craters occur near Tokio Station, more than 20 miles to the east-southeast of Odessa (see Figure 2-27, left) and 40 miles to the northwest along the east side of Upper Grand Coulee (Plate 27).

25. Marlin Hollow

Features: Overhanging and undercut potholes, natural bridge, ice-rafted erratics (Plate 20, right), giant current ripples

Best Observation Point:

Automobile: 11 miles north of Odessa on State Route 21 (Road Tour No. 3, chapter 5)

Elevation of Feature: The coulee starts in the Swanson Lakes area at about 2,250 feet; the mouth of the coulee lies at 1,350 feet where it enters Crab Creek Coulee.

Maximum Flood Depth (Elevation): 500 feet (1,850 feet) at junction with Crab Creek Coulee.

- Twenty-five-mile-long Marlin Hollow is a smaller replica of Lake Creek

Coulee, which it parallels a few miles to the north.

- Marlin Hollow begins modestly in the low-relief scabland plains southwest of Davenport (Plate 10) and terminates at Crab Creek, about a dozen miles west of Odessa.

- As floodwaters moved downstream they organized themselves into a well-defined channel with recessional cataracts up to 150 feet high.

- A rare natural bridge (Figure 3-44, Plate 19), and a number of over-hanging and deeply undercut potholes (see Figure 2-13) lie on privately owned land within Marlin Hollow. The natural bridge formed under a special condition – the merging of two undercut potholes.

Figure 3-44. An unusual, flood-sculpted natural bridge lies along Marlin Hollow. The bridge formed in the Roza Member (Wanapum Basalt) where two juxtaposed, overhanging potholes expanded and coalesced during Ice Age flooding. As they grew, the colonnade portion of the basalt flow was preferentially plucked and eroded more than the overlying entablature portion. A suspended span of stronger entablature basalt is all that remained after the two potholes merged. The bridge is located on private land with no public access. See Plate 19 for the same bridge from a different perspective. Looking north.

26. Sinking and Goose Creek Coulees

Features: Interconnected flood-channel network, potholes, rock benches and basins, trenched spurs, ringed craters, flood bars and giant current ripples

Best Observation Point:

Automobile: U.S. Highway 2 follows Goose Creek Coulee through the town of Wilbur (chapter 5, Road Tour No. 3). Sinking Creek Coulee intersects State Route 21, about six miles south of Wilbur.

Elevation of Feature: The head of Goose Creek lies at 2,400 feet, Sinking Creek at 2,430 feet and Sherman Creek at 2,500 feet.

Maximum Flood Depth (Elevation): 200 feet (2,000 feet) in lower Corbett Draw (Figure 3-45)

- Sinking and Goose Creek coulees drained the western margin of the Telford-Crab Creek scabland.
- After overfilling the Columbia Valley, Ice Age floods escaped south via several low divides at Jump, Redwine and Welsh Creek canyons (Figure 3-45).

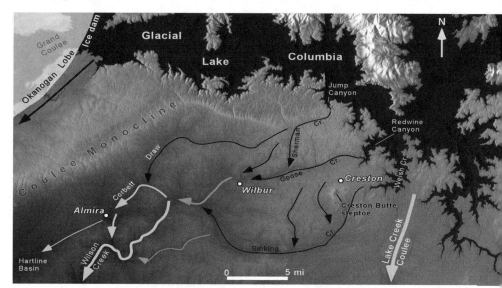

Figure 3-45. Shaded-relief map showing scabland channels (arrows) that developed in the northwestern Telford-Crab Creek scabland. Glacial Lake Columbia, dammed by the Okanogan Lobe, is shown at an altitude of 2,300 feet. The Okanogan Lobe lies near its maximum extent, when only a limited amount of floodwater squeezed through a narrow opening between the ice sheet and the Coulee Monocline. With the ice in this position, the majority of the floodwaters were diverted down the Telford-Crab Creek and Cheney-Palouse scabland tracts.

- Floodwaters gathered a short distance downstream into a single major coulee – Wilson Creek Coulee.
- A heavily potholed spillover channel at the head of Goose Creek, just north of Creston, is shown on an aerial photograph in Figure 3-46.
- Floodwaters that swept down Sinking and Goose creeks were separated from Grand Coulee to the west by a high ridge – the Coulee Monocline (No. 36), which rose well above the highest flood levels (Figure 3-45).

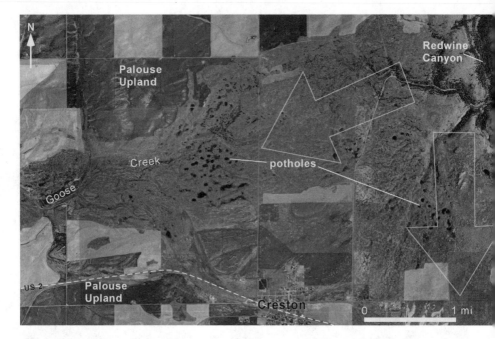

Figure 3-46. Aerial photo showing spillover area at head of Goose Creek. After overfilling Glacial Lake Columbia, Ice Age floodwaters (block arrows) squeezed past Palouse uplands, spilling west into Goose Creek from Redwine Canyon. Along the way several swarms of circular potholes were ground out in the basalt bedrock (Priest Rapids Member). East of Creston, floodwaters also spilled south into the head of Lake Creek Coulee (No. 23).

27. Wilson Creek Bars

Features: Flood bars, giant current ripples, trenched spurs

Best Observation Point:

Automobile: Roadcut through flood bar, which exposes the flood deposits making up the bar, is 0.3 mile off State Route 28 toward the town of Wilson Creek.

Elevation of Feature: Bars rise to an elevation of 1,400 feet.

Maximum Flood Depth (Elevation): 330 feet (1,600 feet)

- Several well-developed flood bars, up to 125 feet tall, lie near the junction of Crab Creek (No. 22) and Wilson Creek coulees (Figures 3-47).
- Many of the bars are covered with acres of giant current ripples with one of the highest concentrations of flood bars and megaripples in the Channeled Scabland.
- The asymmetric shape of the ripples clearly indicate the flow of floodwater was from east to west.
- Wilson and Crab creeks couldn't handle all the floodwater, so some spilled over to the south via the Black Rock Coulee Complex (No. 28).

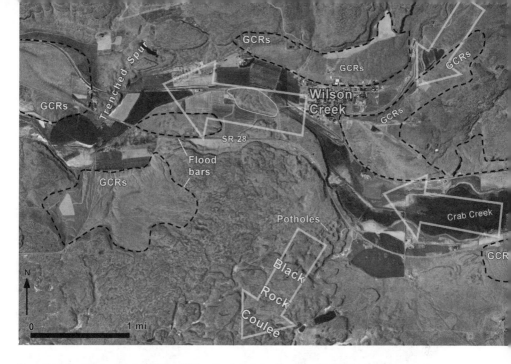

Figure 3-47. Flood features in the vicinity of Wilson Creek, including flood bars (outlined) and a trenched spur. Many of the flood bars are blanketed with giant current ripples (GCRs). Floodwater flow (block arrows) merged where Wilson Creek joins Crab Creek. Together the deep floodwaters eroded several channels across a trenched spur in the upper left. The largest floods overwhelmed the Crab Creek Valley, causing some of the flow to spill southwest via Black Rock Coulee Complex (No. 28), creating a shortcut into the Quincy Basin. Flood-scoured basalt in Black Rock Coulee Complex belongs to the Frenchman Springs Member (lower Wanapum Basalt).

28. Black Rock Coulee Complex

"Crab Creek Valley, below Odessa, received more water than it could carry ... it overflowed southwestward, by way of Black Rock Coulee."

– J Harlen Bretz (1923)

Features: Channels, recessional cataracts, buttes, rock basins and benches, potholes, giant current ripples

Best Observation Point:

Automobile: Two miles east of Wilson Creek on State Route 28, turn right (south) onto Road R NE (Black Rock Road). Continue south for another seven miles to Black Rock Coulee; along the way are views into the rugged north-western portion of the Black Rock Coulee complex.

Elevation of Feature: The head of the Black Rock Coulee complex is 1,350 feet, and the mouth about 1,250 feet.

Maximum Flood Depth (Elevation): 300 feet (1,600 feet) within the central part of the coulee

- Where Wilson Creek joined Crab Creek, the volume of water was more than Crab Creek could handle, so the excess water spilled over into Black Rock Coulee (Figures 3-47 and 3-48).
- Black Rock Coulee itself is about 20 miles long and, in places, less than a mile wide.
- Another wider, unnamed coulee (five miles wide by nine miles long) southwest of Wilson Creek and northwest of Black Rock Coulee is included here as part of the Black Rock Coulee Complex (Figure 3-48).

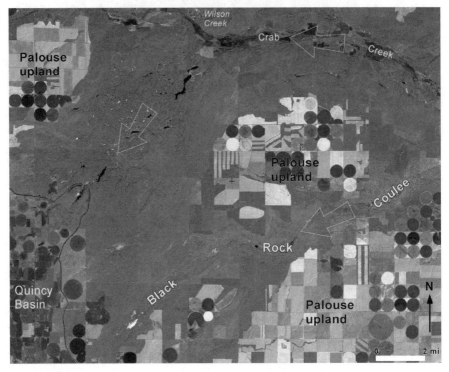

Figure 3-48. Black Rock Coulee Complex. Dark scabland of the Black Rock Coulee complex formed after Ice Age floods overfilled Crab Creek Coulee and spilled southwest, creating a shortcut into the Quincy Basin. Lighter areas with crop circles, covered with Palouse soil, were generally above flood level.

- Two large islands of Palouse loess flank the coulees.
- The coulees lose relief and distinction downstream where they emptied and expanded into the broad Quincy Basin. Here the floodwaters temporarily spread out accompanied by a major loss in speed, power and ability to erode.

Grand Coulee

"It functioned from the beginning of scabland history to become at last the only surviving flood dischargeway. It merits its name, Grand Coulee."

– J Harlen Bretz (1959)

Figure 3-49. Evidently early explorers of Grand Coulee were impressed by its steep, fortress-like walls. Painting by John Mix Stanley, 1853. ARCHIVES AND SPECIAL COLLECTIONS, EASTERN WASHINGTON UNIVERSITY, CALL NO. W7.14:12/1

Fifty-mile-long Grand Coulee, a National Natural Landmark, is one of the longest, deepest and most impressive coulees of the Ice Age. Grand Coulee is a two-tiered, tandem canyon separated by the Dry Falls cataract. The Upper Grand Coulee, composed of mostly Wanapum Basalt, lies northeast of Dry Falls and Lower Grand Coulee (Figure 3-50). The two coulee segments differ greatly in form and history of development. The Upper Grand Coulee is a single coulee that cut across a tilted geologic structure called the Coulee Monocline (No. 36). In contrast, the Lower Grand Coulee formed along the lower segment of the tilted monocline. Upper Grand Coulee is a well-defined, single narrow canyon as little as two miles wide. In contrast, the lower coulee spreads out for 15 miles into an extremely disorganized complex of interconnected, subsidiary spillways.

Compared to other scabland tracts, Grand Coulee has a much more complex history. It evolved from a minor, not-so-grand spillover feature during the earliest floods to the predominant and perhaps last surviving drainageway used during the last (Missoula) floods.

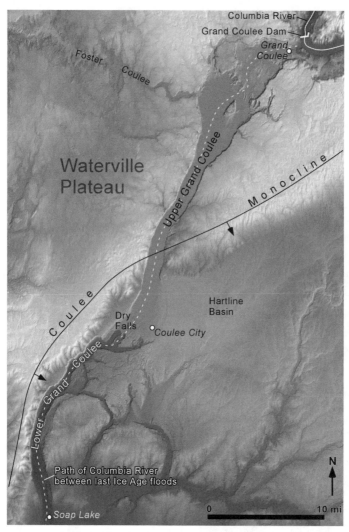

Figure 3-50. Shaded-relief map of Grand Coulee. The upper and lower portions of Grand Coulee are separated by the Coulee Monocline north of Dry Falls. Between Ice Age floods, when glacial ice of the Okanogan Lobe blocked the Columbia River near Grand Coulee Dam, the mighty Columbia River detoured down Grand Coulee (dashed line) following the same path as the last Missoula floods.

So why does Grand Coulee stand out among all the flood coulees as the deepest, longest and most pristine, appearing as if it had formed yesterday? First of all, it was carved by the last floods, which almost exclusively used Grand Coulee after the head of the canyon was breached (No. 29), so it was in fact the "youngest" coulee. Second, Grand Coulee was carved more deeply and faster than the other scabland tracts due to its steeper, higher hydraulic gradient (Figure 3-52). In other words the surface of the floodwater was much steeper through Grand Coulee (average gradient about 20 feet per mile) compared to either the Telford-Crab Creek (15 feet per mile) or Cheney-Palouse (13 feet per mile) tracts. Therefore, the steeper hydraulic gradient through Grand Coulee caused the water to move faster and with significantly greater power and force compared to other flood coulees.

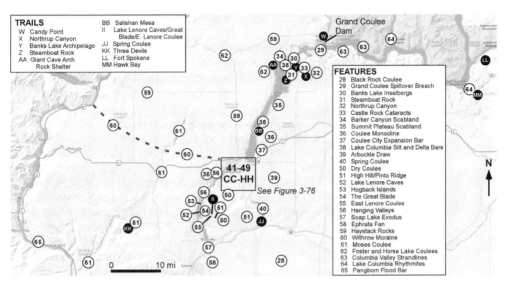

TRALS
W   Candy Point
X   Northrup Canyon
Y   Banks Lake Archipelago
Z   Steamboat Rock
AA Giant Cave Arch
     Rock Shelter

BB Salishan Mesa
II   Lake Lenore Caves/Great
      Blade/E. Lenore Coulee
JJ   Spring Coulee
KK Three Devils
LL   Fort Spokane
MM Hawk Bay

Grand Coulee Dam

FEATURES
28 Black Rock Coulee
29 Grand Coulee Spillover Breach
30 Banks Lake Inselbergs
31 Steamboat Rock
32 Northrup Canyon
33 Castle Rock Cataracts
34 Barker Canyon Scabland
35 Summit Plateau Scabland
36 Coulee Monocline
37 Coulee City Expansion Bar
38 Lake Columbia Silt and Delta Bars
39 Arbuckle Draw
40 Spring Coulee
50 Dry Coulee
51 High Hill/Pinto Ridge
52 Lake Lenore Caves
53 Hogback Islands
54 The Great Blade
55 East Lenore Coulee
56 Hanging Valleys
57 Soap Lake Exodus
58 Ephrata Fan
59 Haystack Rocks
60 Withrow Moraine
61 Moses Coulee
62 Foster and Horse Lake Coulees
63 Columbia Valley Strandlines
64 Lake Columbia Rhythmites
65 Pangborn Flood Bar

41-49
CC-HH

See Figure 3-76

N

0   10 mi

Figure 3-51. Flood features and trails within the northwestern Channeled Scabland. The dashed line represents the Withrow Moraine – the southern limit for glacial ice of the Okanogan Lobe on the Waterville Plateau. See more detailed map (inset) within the Lower Grand Coulee in Figure 3-76 for Feature Nos. 41 to 45 and Trails CC through HH.

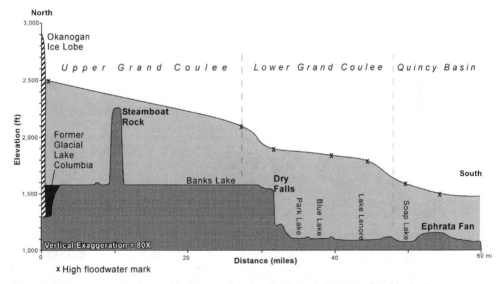

x High floodwater mark

Figure 3-52. Maximum flood-surface profile along Grand Coulee. After being deflected into Grand Coulee by the Okanogan Lobe, megafloods, which approached 1,000 feet deep, flushed down the coulee. The floodwater surface steepened temporarily where floodwaters expanded into the Lower Grand Coulee above Dry Falls and into the Quincy Basin. Note that during the largest floods, even the top of Steamboat Rock was once submerged under as much as 200 feet of floodwater.

Upper Grand Coulee

"Upper Grand Coulee's excavation began at the 800-foot cascade a little north of Coulee City. This cascade shortly steepened to become a waterfall and, as such, it retreated upstream until it finally cut through the divide into the preglacial Columbia Valley."

– *J Harlen Bretz (1959)*

Geologist J Harlen Bretz spent much of his career trying to convince his skeptics that the Channeled Scabland was the product of Ice Age flooding. Nowhere is the evidence for flooding more plentiful, convincing or dramatic than in wondrous Grand Coulee. The history of flooding within Grand Coulee as elsewhere, however, is complex – complicated by repeated advances and retreats of the Okanogan Ice Lobe going back a million years or more. Little is known about the timing and frequency of the older floods and glaciations, except knowing they happened; most of the evidence has been eroded, or buried, under deposits from the last glacial cycle, which lasted from about 14,000 to 28,000 years ago (known by geologists as the late Wisconsinan Glaciation).

Most of the Upper Grand Coulee is lined with a dozen or more flows of 15 million to 16 million-year-old Columbia River basalt. North of Steamboat Rock, however, a ridge of much older (50 million to 100 million years) granitic rock rises above the coulee floor forming a series of irregular rocky knobs we call the Banks Lake Inselbergs (No. 30). South of Steamboat Rock the granitic rock disappears beneath a thickening cover of Columbia River basalt. A major morphological change occurs in the Upper Grand Coulee where granitic rocks disappear under the basalt (Figure 3-53).

Figure 3-53. Upper Grand Coulee narrows considerably south of Steamboat Rock where the granitic rocks disappear below the coulee floor. During some earlier floods the Grand Coulee may have been filled with glacial ice of the Okanogan Lobe, which restricted flood flow to the elevated Summit Plateau Scabland (No. 35) on the left.

Above Steamboat Rock the coulee is up to eight miles wide where granitic rocks crop out along the coulee floor (Figure 3-50). South of Steamboat Rock the canyon quickly narrows to only about one mile wide near where the granitic rocks disappear. Apparently Ice Age floods were less effective at eroding down into the granitic rocks and instead transferred their energy into eroding laterally along the zone of weaker rock that lay atop of the highly weathered granite. No such lateral erosion occurred down coulee where the granite was absent, however.

Evolution of Upper Grand Coulee: Forging a New Path

"The northern, or Upper Coulee, was initiated where the glacial stream cascaded some 800 feet down the steep southeastern slope of the (Coulee) monocline."

— J Harlen Bretz et al (1956)

The cutting of Grand Coulee appears to have taken place mostly, or entirely, during the last glacial cycle (late Wisconsinan Glaciation), which began sometime after 28,000 years ago and ended about 14,000 years ago. While there is scattered evidence for earlier floods, some going back a million years or more, these may have not had much influence on Grand Coulee.

Much of what happened in Grand Coulee was a direct result of the Okanogan Ice Lobe, which migrated many times back and forth across the Waterville Plateau during the Ice Age (Figure 3-54, see Figure 1-11). In fact, 1 to 2 million years ago, before the first Ice Age flood, Grand Coulee didn't exist at all. The present coulee area was just an extension of the broad, elevated Waterville Plateau (Stage 1, Figure 3-54). Not shown in Figure 3-54 is the position of the Okanogan Lobe before it spread out onto the Waterville Plateau early in the late Wisconsin Glaciation (position A in Figure 1-11). This occurred sometime after about 28,000 years ago when the first Ice Age floods rushed down the Columbia River Valley unobstructed by the Okanogan Lobe. This earliest flood, or floods of the last glacial cycle, are also believed to be the largest of the floods. This allowed the floods to travel unencumbered down the western margin of the Columbia Plateau through Wenatchee, perhaps also spilling over across the Channeled Scabland.

Eventually, the Okanogan Lobe blocked the Columbia River along the north edge of the Waterville Plateau, forming an ice dam that created Glacial Lake Columbia (Plates 1 and 11; see also Figure 1-11, positions B through E). Henceforth, ensuing floods that quickly overfilled Lake Columbia spilled over a low divide (2,400 to 2,500 feet elevation) into the head of the ancient Foster Creek basin (Stage 1, Figure 3-54). Before Ice Age flooding, Foster Creek was much longer than it is today – probably extending all the way to the head of present-day Grand Coulee. As the advancing Okanogan Lobe blocked lower Foster Creek, floodwaters spilled over from the Columbia Valley but soon were deflected southwest by the ice lobe. With the ice sheet to the north and the Coulee Monocline uplands to the south, Ice Age floodwaters were forced into the ancestral Foster and McCartney Creek drainages. This initiated the development of Moses Coulee. At least five floods were responsible for the subsequent gouging of Moses Coulee. Some floodwater may have also spilled over into Moses Coulee directly from the north (bold dashed arrow in Stage 1). Keep in mind though, at this early stage, the deep canyon of Grand Coulee did not exist yet. What would someday become Grand Coulee was merely an eastern extension of the broad, low-relief Waterville Plateau.

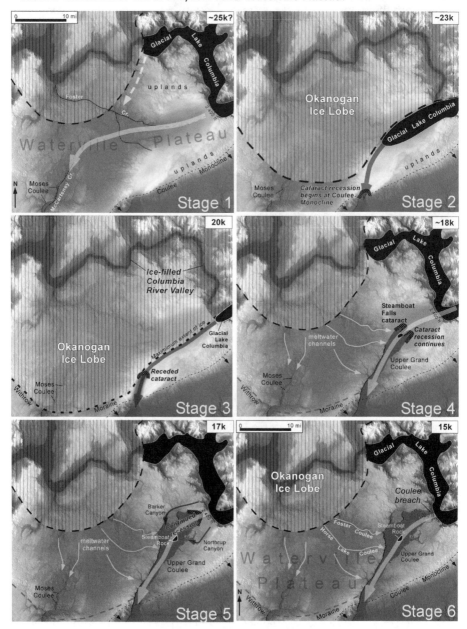

Figure 3-54. Six stages in the evolution for Upper Grand Coulee. Bold arrows indicate flow directions for Ice Age floods.

As the Okanogan Lobe continued to push south and east in Stage 2, the flow of floodwater into Moses Coulee was eventually blocked and cut off by the advancing ice, forcing all the floodwater to squeeze overland through a constriction created by the ice sheet, on one side, and uplands of the Coulee Monocline on the other. At this early stage floodwaters would have been forced to flow over the 800-foot-tall, tilted edge of the Coulee Monocline, located at the mouth of what would become the Upper Grand Coulee (see Figure 3-68). The folded edge of the monocline was riddled with cracks, and openings created when the basalt flows were forcibly bent upward along the structure. The tilted and weakened basalt rock quickly succumbed to the tremendous, erosive forces of the floods and the Upper Grand Coulee cataract canyon was born. Today a large, deep basin located several miles northeast of Dry Falls, filled with 300 feet of flood gravel, lies at the site of the former plunge pool where earlier floods once dropped over the Coulee Monocline.

Commitment and Cataract Recession

With each subsequent outburst megaflood that was blocked by the advancing Okanogan Lobe, the Upper Grand Coulee cataract would recede farther upstream (north). The image in Stage 3 (Figure 3-54) shows a possible position of the recessional cataract when the Okanogan Ice Lobe was at its maximum. The deep freeze of the Ice Age at this stage must have persisted for a long time, based on the size of the Withrow Moraine (No. 60, see Figures 3-107 and 3-108) that extends across the Waterville Plateau. Eventually, after many floods, the cataract migrated into the area where Steamboat Rock is today (Stage 4). The coulee began to widen here when floodwaters encountered granitic rock at the base of the cataract. At least two alcoves with a rock blade running down the middle developed here at former Steamboat Falls.

As Steamboat Falls receded northward, Steamboat Rock was left behind as an isolated goat island (erosional remnant of the rock blade). By the time the cataract had receded to Steamboat Falls, floodwaters were entrenched and fully committed to Grand Coulee, even as the Okanogan Lobe continued to migrate back and forth across the Waterville Plateau. Meltwater radiated out from the front of the ice lobe, some of which drained into the newly created, deep gorge of the Upper Grand Coulee, creating the hanging meltwater channels at Foster and Horse Lake Coulees (No. 62). Meltwater that pooled against the Okanogan Lobe within these west-sloping coulees created temporary Glacial Lake Foster (see Figure 3-113). Once the lake was full, any additional meltwater drained eastward, dropping into the flood-hollowed void of Upper Grand Coulee that now existed below Steamboat Rock.

As the flood cataract continued to recede northward, two more, large, side cataracts, Northrup (No. 32) and Barker (No. 34) canyons, developed on either side of upper Grand Coulee (Stage 5). Even at this relatively late stage, the divide separating Grand Coulee from the Columbia Valley was at least 100 feet higher than the other scabland tracts (see Figure 3-37). Therefore, most Missoula floodwaters spilled across the wider and lower-elevation divides of the Cheney-Palouse and Telford-Crab Scabland Tracts located to the east.

The Grandest Falls Destroyed

At Stage 5, before the cataract retreated all the way to the head of Grand Coulee, a waterfall to dwarf all others in the Channeled Scabland lay just north of Steamboat Rock. The cataract was several miles wide and up to 900 feet tall – more than twice as tall as present-day Dry Falls! With continued retreat, however, the cataract was finally consumed and breached (Stage 6) sometime around 17,000 years ago. The breached divide (Figures 3-55 and 3-56) at the head of Grand Coulee was suddenly lowered an incredible 900 feet. This event would have also rapidly lowered the level of Glacial Lake Columbia an equal amount. The sudden lowering of Lake Columbia upon breaching would have added considerably to the flood volume, producing a flood down Grand Coulee that was unmatched by any other.

In summary, with the head of Grand Coulee breached, the spillway was suddenly 900 feet lower, having dropped from 2,400 to 1,500 feet elevation (Figure 3-55). At its new spillover height at Stage 6, the roles of Grand Coulee versus that of the Cheney-Palouse and Telford Crab Creek tracts were now reversed. For until this time, the lowest flood spillways were to the east – up to 100 feet lower than the Grand Coulee – and thus a greater volume of water was previously transported through these eastern spillways. After breaching, however, Grand Coulee was suddenly 800 feet lower than the other spillways (see Figure 3-37). It's possible that during subsequent floods, most or all of floodwaters were hijacked by the much-lower Grand Coulee. The likelihood of this scenario is strengthened by the fact that the last outburst floods tended to be smaller than their predecessors. During smaller floods the chances of all floodwaters going solely down Grand Coulee was increased. Also, a breached Grand Coulee may cause any future Ice Age floods to be directed solely or dominantly down the Grand Coulee – at least during times when the coulee isn't blocked by a future Okanogan Lobe. However, any especially large floods may still overflow into the Telford-Crab Creek and/or the Cheney Palouse scablands if hydraulic damming and sufficient backup were to occur behind Grand Coulee.

29. Grand Coulee Spillover Breach

"When the cascade migrated north ... it became a typical recessional cataract (Steamboat Falls) nearly 900 feet high. Eventually its retreat extended the lengthening gorge across the divide into the preglacial Columbia River Valley, and thus the cataract destroyed itself."

– J Harlen Bretz et al (1956)

Features: Deep, spillover channel at northern inlet to Grand Coulee that hangs 500 feet above the Columbia River

Best Observation Points:

Automobile: State Route 155 at town of Grand Coulee (chapter 5, Road Tour No. 4)

Non-motorized trails (chapter 4): Steamboat Rock (Trail Z) and Candy Point (Trail W)

Watercraft: Via launch sites along upper Banks Lake at Electric City or Steamboat Rock State Park

Elevation of Feature: Top of spillover lies at 2,400 feet; base of the channel breach lies at 1,500 feet.

Maximum Flood Depth (Elevation): South of the spillover, within Grand Coulee, floodwaters were up to 1,000 feet deep (elevation 2,500 feet). North of the spillover, in the Columbia River valley, floodwater in combination with Glacial Lake Columbia was up to 1,500 feet deep – two and half times the height of Seattle's Space Needle!

- As floodwater eroded the Upper Grand Coulee, the receding 900-foot-high cataract eroded headward a full 25 miles until it broke through into the much deeper Columbia River Valley (Plates 22 and 25).

- Grand Coulee developed when the Okanogan Lobe blocked the Columbia River near present-day Grand Coulee Dam (Plate 11). Ice Age floods were diverted down the Upper Grand Coulee through most of the last glacial cycle when Glacial Lake Columbia formed behind the ice dam, which quickly filled with glacial meltwater.

- Ice Age floods flowed along the edge of the ice sheet over an upland plateau at approximately 2,400 feet in elevation (Stages 2 through 5 in Figure 3-54) and across the Coulee Monocline (No. 36) where the Upper Grand Coulee recessional cataract originated.

- With each successive flood the cataract eroded headward (north) carving out a deep, narrow canyon that lengthened with each flood outburst. Toward the end of the last glacial cycle (about 17,000 years ago) the cataract finally retreated the full 30 miles and breached the head of Grand Coulee (Figure 3-55).

Figure 3-55. A spillover channel, 900 feet deep and two miles wide, breached the head of Grand Coulee as floodwaters spilled south out of the Columbia River Valley and into Upper Grand Coulee (Stage 6 in Figure 3-54; Figure 3-56, Plate 22). This occurred when an ice dam blocked the Columbia River, not far out of view on the right. The spillover channel eroded through layered basalt flows down into the granitic basement rock that today makes up the floor of the upper coulee.

- The two-mile wide breach lowered the spillover channel a full 900 feet across this divide. Today the head of Grand Coulee still hangs more than 500 feet above the natural level of the Columbia River below (Figure 3-56).

- The breached spillover was 800 feet lower than any of the other spillovers into the Channeled Scabland (see Figure 3-37).

- After the head of Grand Coulee was breached, some of the last smaller floods may have traveled entirely down Grand Coulee – bypassing the higher spillovers into the Cheney-Palouse and Telford-Crab Creek Tracts. In essence, the suddenly deepened Grand Coulee may have hijacked most or all the water from subsequent outburst floods toward the end of the last Ice Age.

- With its lower lip into the Channeled Scabland, it became the first coulee to fill and the last to drain.

- Grand Coulee continued to carry floodwaters from Glacial Lake Missoula for more than 10 days during some of the last floods.

- When compared to highly jointed basalt, the granitic basement rocks that make up the floor of the upper coulee were more resistant to erosion by the floods. If not for the more resistant granitic rocks, the floods might have carved an even deeper channel across the Upper Grand Coulee.

Figure 3-56. Spillover breach at the head of Grand Coulee. A 900-foot-deep spillover channel hangs another 500 feet above the Columbia River. Early workings of Grand Coulee Dam construction (1935) appear in the foreground. Looking southwest. ASAHEL CURTIS PHOTO. UNIVERSITY OF WASHINGTON LIBRARIES, SPECIAL COLLECTIONS, IMAGE NUMBER DAM069

30. Banks Lake Inselbergs

"There are numerous pre-basalt hills of granite on the floor between Steamboat Rock and the Columbia, formerly buried in the basalt and later exhumed in the erosion of the coulee."

– J Harlen Bretz (1923)

Features: Old, flood-exhumed granitic rocks underlying Columbia River basalt at the north end of Upper Grand Coulee

Best Observation Points:

Automobile: Along State Route 155 from Steamboat Rock north to Electric City (chapter 5, Road Tour No. 4)

Watercraft: Via launch sites along upper Banks Lake at Electric City or Steamboat Rock State Park

Elevation of Feature: Headlands and islands of granitic basement rock, up to 475 feet high (elevation 2,050 feet), rise out of Banks Lake between Steamboat Rock and Electric City.

Maximum Flood Depth (Elevation): 1,000 feet (2,500 feet)

- Inselbergs as defined here are smooth, rounded rocky knobs of granite that protrude from the coulee floor. The inselbergs also exist as a group of islands within Banks Lake (Figure 3-57).

Figure 3-57. Granitic-inselberg islands of the Banks Lake archipelago. Dark, flat-lying basalt flows on Castle Rock overlie light-colored, irregular knobs of granitic basement rock (inselbergs). Semi-parallel inselbergs in the lower left were molded and elongated by the movement of glacial ice and floodwaters. Looking northeast.

- The granitic rocks slowly cooled within a liquid magma chamber, somewhere between 50 million to 100 million years ago.

- The molten magma slowly crystallized into rock, while thousands of feet of overlying rock slowly wore away. Erosion eventually unroofed the cooled, ancient magma chamber exposing the previously buried granitic rocks to the surface for the first time.

- The granite lay at the surface for eons more until it was reburied beneath several lava flows of Columbia River basalt starting about 16 million years ago.

- Only in recent geologic history did the previously weathered granitic rocks become re-exhumed along the recessional cataract canyon of Grand Coulee – scoured out during the Ice Age floods.

- Cosmogenic-exposure age dates of the granite indicate the inselbergs weren't exhumed by Ice Age floods until about 17,000 years ago.

- The morphology of the granitic inselbergs differs markedly from that of basalt primarily due to the contrasting fracture patterns and lack of layering within the granite rock.

31. Steamboat Rock Monolith

"Steamboat Rock, 880 feet high and a square mile in area, stands isolated out in the Upper Coulee as a 'Goat Island,' where for a time the cataract was divided into two."

– J Harlen Bretz (1959)

Features: Isolated monolith, remnant of a former rock blade located in the middle of Upper Grand Coulee; glacial erratics, moraines and curvilinear grooves on summit plateau

Best Observation Points:

Automobile: From State Route 155, six miles south of Electric City or 19 miles north of Coulee City (chapter 5, Road Tour No. 4)

Non-motorized trails (chapter 4): Steamboat Rock (Trail Z); Northrup Canyon – Wagon Road Grade (Trail X2); Banks Lake Archipelago (Trail Y)

Watercraft: Via public launch sites at Steamboat Rock State Park

Elevation of Feature: Highest point is 2,285 feet. Total height of the monolith is about 800 feet above Banks Lake.

Maximum Flood Depth (Elevation): 1,000 feet (2,500 feet)

Earthcache: Steamboat Rock Glacial Moraine (www.geocaching .com, Code No. GC2EN2R), located along the trail that circles the top of Steamboat Rock (chapter 4, Trail Z)

- Steamboat Rock, an impressive monolith standing prominently in the middle of the coulee, is the quintessential landmark for the Upper Grand Coulee (Figures 3-58 and 3-59, Plates 24 to 26).

- The triangular-shaped monolith measures 2.1 miles long by 0.75 mile wide, rising precipitously 800 feet above the Banks Lake reservoir.

- Steamboat Rock is an erosional remnant of a rock blade (i.e., goat island), created as Steamboat Falls (see Figure 3-54, Stage 4), a dual, recessional cataract, passed by on its way to creating the Grand Coulee Spillover Breach (No. 29) at the head of the coulee (Stage 6).

- The flat-topped summit of Steamboat Rock lies at about the same elevation as the upper surface of the Waterville Plateau and the Summit Plateau Scabland (No. 35) on either side of the coulee, indicating the basalt flows and the Waterville Plateau once continued, uninterrupted, across the entire Upper Grand Coulee (Figure 3-54, Stages 1 and 2).

Figure 3-58. Old postcard of Steamboat Rock before the flooding of Banks Lake in 1951. Devils Lake was one of only a few shallow lakes in the coulee that predated man-made Banks Lake.

- Glacial erratics (Figure 3-59, see Figure 4-77) and moraines (Plate 24, see Figure 4-78) lie atop the summit plateau, indicating glacial ice of the Okanogan Lobe once covered this area.

- Later floods sweeping over the monolith removed some of the glacial debris, especially at the south end of Steamboat Rock, except for the largest erratics, which were too large for even floodwaters to move.

- It is unclear whether the glacial ice covered Steamboat Rock before or after the receding cataract formed Upper Grand Coulee.

- Combined, up to a dozen different lava flows of the Grande Ronde and Wanapum Basalt (see Figure 1-1) are exposed in the steep walls of Steamboat Rock and elsewhere within the Upper Grand Coulee. Older granitic basement rocks are exposed along the base of the monolith on the north side.

- A hanging coulee that crosses the top of Steamboat Rock may be a remnant of ancient Foster Creek – long ago cut off and abandoned during recession of the Upper Grand Coulee cataract.

Figure 3-59. Aerial view over Steamboat Rock. A 100-foot deep, hanging cross coulee divides the Steamboat Rock summit plateau, perhaps a remnant channel of Foster Creek that once flowed westward across the Waterville Plateau (Figure 3-54, Stage 1) before Grand Coulee was laid open by cataract recession across this area (Stages 4 to 6). Ice Age floods may have expanded the cross coulee, but because it lies transverse to flood flow, it probably represents an older, pre-flood feature. The summit plateau is littered with large glacial erratics (circled) carried down by the Okanogan Lobe glacier, not rafted in on icebergs during Ice Age flooding. Note intersecting curvilinear grooves etched out of giant cracks in the basalt bedrock as floodwaters swept over the monolith. Looking north.

32. Northrup Canyon

Features: Recessional cataract canyons, plunge pools, flood bars, exposed contact between basalt and granitic basement rock; adjacent flood-swept, upland plateaus covered with potholes and giant grooves

Best Observation Points:

Automobile: Short access road into mouth of Northrup Canyon off State Route 155. Road ends after 0.6 mile at Northrup Canyon trailhead.

Non-motorized trails: Northrup Canyon (chapter 4, Trail X)

Elevation of Feature: Head of Northrup Canyon lies at 2,340 feet on upland plateau that extends northeastward to the Columbia Valley; scarped Palouse uplands along the margin of the spillover channel rise to 2,460 feet; the mouth of Northrup Canyon joins the Upper Grand Coulee at about 1,600 feet.

Maximum Flood Depth (Elevation): 900 feet (2,500 feet)

Earthcache: Northrup Lake Plungepool (www.geocaching .com, Code No. GC2CH5Q), located along the Northrup Canyon Trail (chapter 4, Trail X1)

- Northrup Canyon is a deep, multi-armed, recessional cataract canyon that splits off east of the Upper Grand Coulee (Figure 3-60; see also Figure 6-21, Plate 22).

Figure 3-60. Northrup Canyon, looking northwest. Adjacent upland plateaus were stripped clean by floods that washed over the entire area. Notice numerous potholes on bench in foreground. Looking northwest.

- Ice Age floods eroded a canyon up to 450 feet deep through the basalt bedrock, exhuming a once-buried ridge of granitic basement rock that parallels the canyon. The basalt flows lapped up onto and around the ridge, eventually burying it in lava about 15 million to 16 million years ago. Since that time the Ice Age floods eroded through the basalt cover, re-exposing the granite rock below.

- Two miles up from the mouth, Northrup Canyon bifurcates into two main arms. One arm goes north and terminates on the upland plateau, only about one-half mile from the edge of Upper Grand Coulee (Figure 3-60). A second arm trends southeast for a mile before bending north-east onto a flood-swept upland plateau that delivered floodwaters spilling over from Spring Canyon (Figure 3-61, Plate 22).

- Northrup Canyon itself is a late-stage flood feature, which didn't form until after the recessional cataract that formed the Upper Grand Coulee had advanced to near Steamboat Rock (Figure 3-54, Stage 5). Once started, however, Northrup Canyon probably receded quickly up valley along the weathered, easily eroded contact between the basalt and underlying granitic rock.

- After the head of Grand Coulee was breached (No. 29), Northrup Canyon was probably cut off from further erosion during the later, smaller floods that were restricted to Grand Coulee inner channel.

northeast

Lake Roosevelt

Spring Canyon

Above flood level

Flood-channel escarpment

Long Lake

Flood-swept upland plateau

Figure 3-61. Flood spillover area in uplands between Spring Canyon and Northrup Canyon. Long Lake fills one of the many, shallow rock basins excavated by high-energy flood currents that swept across this upland plateau. Maximum height of the floods here was about 2,500 feet, based on the height of the eroded, flood-beveled escarpment at upper right. These spillover areas into Northrup Canyon probably developed prior to breaching at the head of Grand Coulee (No. 29). Looking northeast.

33. Castle Rock Cataracts

"Two short semiparallel cataract gorges and alcoves which join the Coulee in the latitude of Steamboat Rock."

– J Harlen Bretz (1969)

Features: Castle Rock mesa, recessional cataract canyons, plunge pools, spillover channels, rock blade, rock basins, grooved upland plateau; exposed contact between basalt and granitic basement rocks

Best Observation Point:

Non-motorized trail: Northrup Canyon – Wagon Road Grade (chapter 4, Trail X2)

Elevation of Feature: Tops of abandoned cataracts are carved into upland plateau at about 2,350 feet. Base of the cataracts merge with Northrup Canyon at about 1,900 feet.

Maximum Flood Depth (Elevation): 600 feet (2,500 feet)

- A pair of short, recessional cataract canyons, about 350 feet tall, are located near the mouth of Northrup Canyon where floods spilled over from the Upper Grand Coulee into Northrup Canyon (Figure 3-62, Plate 26).

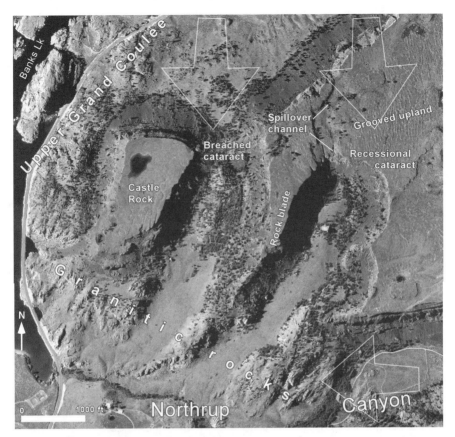

Figure 3-62. Castle Rock cataracts. Vertical aerial photo showing dual cataract canyons just east of Castle Rock. Note shallow, water-filled rock basin eroded into the top of Castle Rock. Cataracts were formed by floodwaters spilling up and over the east side of Upper Grand Coulee. See Plate 26 for an oblique perspective of the cataracts.

- The western cataract, which eroded farther than the eastern one, breached the upland plateau at its head, isolating Castle Rock in the process (Figure 3-62).

- A well-developed plunge pool (Figure 3-63, see Figure 4-68) lies at the base of the unbreached eastern cataract, which has a spillover channel connecting the cataract with the Grand Coulee precipice, now only a short distance (0.2 mile) away.

- Giant longitudinal grooves score the upland plateau adjacent to the cataracts.

- Only a few flows of Columbia River basalt made it here to the edge of the Columbia Plateau where the sequence of basalt lava flows is relatively thin (see Figure 4-71). The bases of the cataracts are eroded into the 50 million- to 100 million-year-old granitic rocks.

- During a future Ice Age flood, as the spillover enlarges and the cataract recedes northward, the eastern cataract will likely become breached as well.

south

rock blade

cataract canyon

plunge pool

Figure 3-63. Water-filled plunge-pool lies at the base of the eastern Castle Rock cataract. This cataract canyon parallels another on the other side of a tall rock blade. Northrup Canyon and Upper Grand Coulee are visible at top center.

34. Barker Canyon Scabland Complex

"Barker Canyon and Northrup Canyon are the same age – products of the Spokane Flood."

– J Harlen Bretz (1932)

Features: Abandoned cataracts, recessional cataract canyon; spillover channels, buttes and mesas, grooved upland plateau; largest rock shelter cave in the Channeled Scabland; delta bars of ancient Glacial Lake Columbia

Best Observation Points:

Automobile: Barker Canyon Road 9.7 miles northwest of the town of Grand Coulee via State Route 174

Non-motorized trail: Giant Cave Arch Rock Shelter (chapter 4, Trail AA)

Watercraft: From one of many public boat launches at north end of Banks Lake

Elevation of Feature: Spillover at head of Barker Canyon lies at 2,150 feet, mouth of coulee fans out onto delta bar at 1,680 feet. Canyon walls flood-eroded up to 2,400 feet

Maximum Flood Depth (Elevation): 800 feet (2,500 feet)

- Barker Canyon is a scabland coulee created by Ice Age floods that ran down the west side of Upper Grand Coulee (Plate 22).

- The head of the canyon begins in low-relief uplands of the Waterville Plateau, where it was blanketed with glacial deposits from the Okanogan Lobe.

- A spillover flood channel rejoins upper Barker Canyon with Grand Coulee a couple miles to the northeast. Tracing the spillover channel to its origin, one can find it 400 feet above the floor of Upper Grand Coulee. The spillover channel and canyon circumvent and isolate a broad, two-mile-wide, flood-swept, upland plateau (Plate 22) covered with multiple mesas, buttes and rock basins.

- The largest-known rock shelter (Big Cave Arch) in the Channeled Scabland is located nearby (see Figure 2-11).

Figure 3-64. Cache Butte at the mouth of Barker Canyon with Steamboat Rock in background. Broad, flat area in right foreground is the top of one of the delta bars from Glacial Lake Columbia (see Figure 3-74) deposited after the last Missoula flood rushed down Grand Coulee. Looking southeast.

- Barker Canyon likely formed about the same time as Northrup Canyon, before the head of the Grand Coulee was breached (No. 29) but after the cataract had receded north of Steamboat Rock (see Figure 3-54, Stage 5).

- Several delta bars protrude out into the Upper Grand Coulee in the vicinity of Barker Canyon; these formed in ancient Glacial Lake Columbia when glacial meltwater drained into the lake from the Okanogan Lobe located on the Waterville Plateau above and to the north (see Figure 3-113).

35. Summit Plateau Scabland

"(Grand Coulee) possesses scabland on the 'rim rock,' above and behind the brink of the cliffs."

– J Harlen Bretz (1928)

Features: Flood-swept basalt plateau along east side of Upper Grand Coulee including giant curvilinear grooves, channels, mesas, buttes, rock basins, potholes, giant current ripples, and an unusually short, side-cataract canyon at Ladds Creek (see Figure 6-20)

Best Observation Point:

Non-motorized trail: Far end of Wagon Road Grade – Northrup Canyon Trail (chapter 4, Trail X2)

Elevation of Feature: The height of the summit scabland rises to 2,400 feet at the north end and 2,150 feet at the south end of the coulee.

Maximum Flood Depth (Elevation): Floodwater was up to 400 feet deep in Whitney Canyon, a side canyon eroded into the summit plateau, but generally less than 100 feet elsewhere (2,350 to 2,500 feet) on the summit plateau.

- Bretz coined the term "summit scabland" for the flood-scoured scabland high above the east wall of the Upper Grand Coulee (Plates 22 and 27).

- This summit plateau scabland was created by floods that flowed along the leading edge of the Okanogan Lobe that once filled all, or most, of Upper Grand Coulee (Figure 3-65). Uplands of the Coulee Monocline further constrained the flow of floodwater to a narrow passageway.

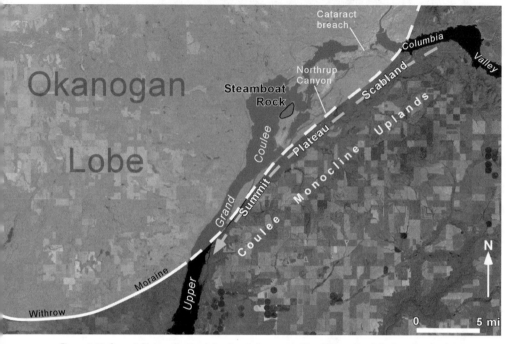

Figure 3-65. Summit Plateau Scabland developed above east side of Upper Grand Coulee when Ice Age floodwaters (arrow) ran between the Okanogan Lobe and uplands of the Coulee Monocline. The floods stripped away all the topsoil up to the trimline (level of highest flood erosion). Above the trimline is a patchwork of croplands that kept their cover of fertile soil.

- The nearly level summit plateau is up to three miles wide where it merges with the flood-scoured plateau above Northrup Canyon (No. 32) while narrowing to less than one-half mile wide at its southern end (Figures 3-65 and 3-66).

- The upper limit for scabland of the summit plateau is marked by what geologists call the "trimline" – the highest level of erosion by the floods. The trimline is 250 feet lower at the southern end of the Upper Grand Coulee compared to the upper end. This is consistent with the drop in surface elevation of the floodwater as they flowed down the coulee (see Figure 3-52).

- Many unusual, giant curvilinear grooves lie near Whitney Canyon along the summit plateau (Figure 3-67, see Figure 1-6). Similar grooves lie atop nearby Steamboat Rock (Plate 24) within the same lava formation (Priest Rapids Member basalt).

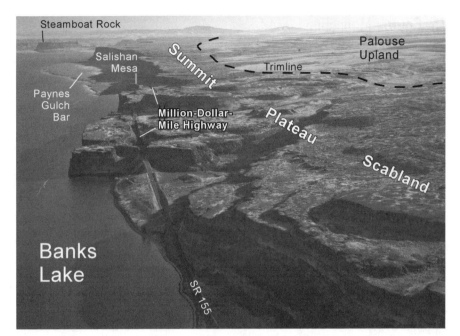

Figure 3-66. Summit plateau scabland along southeast end of Upper Grand Coulee. Trimline marks the upper limit of flood erosion; below that most topsoil was stripped away during megaflooding, exposing the bare basalt rock underneath. The Million Dollar Mile was an expensive two-mile portion of State Route 155 blasted through the basalt in order to relocate the road to higher ground prior to flooding Banks Lake around 1951. Looking northeast.

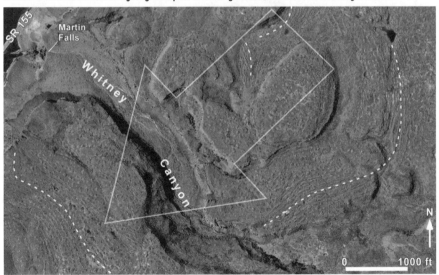

Figure 3-67. Vertical air photo showing sets of parallel curving grooves (dashed lines) atop the summit plateau near Whitney Canyon. Notice how some of the grooves trend semi-parallel to flood flow (block arrow), while most are transverse. This suggests the curvilinear grooves may be large-scale cooling fractures or flow features inherent to the basalt rock, and not solely due to flood scouring. Martin Falls (dry most of the year) drops 400 feet from hanging Whitney Canyon into Grand Coulee below. See another perspective of Whitney Canyon in Figure 1-6.

36. Coulee Monocline

"Upper Grand Coulee was cut through a divide by the stoping of cataracts or cascades down the steep monocline north of the structural Hartline Basin."

– J Harlen Bretz (1928)

Features: Uplifted Waterville Plateau, folded and tilted basalt flows, hogbacks

Best Observation Points:

Automobile: State Route 17 (MP 85.9); State Route 155 (MP 2) (chapter 5, Road Tour No. 4)

Non-motorized trail: East Park Lake (chapter 4, Trail HH)

Watercraft: Visible from Park Lake, accessed via public launch site at Sun Lakes State Park, or from Banks Lake about four miles north of Coulee City boat launch.

Elevation of Feature: Highest point on monocline is 2,820 feet at Jack Woods Butte, 7.5 miles north of Almira; lowest point (1,075 feet) is at mouth of Grand Coulee near Soap Lake.

Maximum Flood Depth (Elevation): 600 feet (2,100 feet) at mouth of Upper Grand Coulee

- A monocline is a geologic term used to describe a single-sided fold in the Earth's crust like that shown in Figure 3-68.

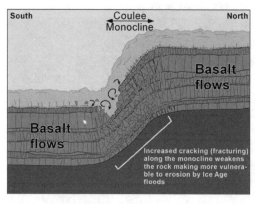

Figure 3-68. Initial flood erosion across the monocline at the mouth of the Upper Grand Coulee produced a cataract that eventually retreated 25 miles northward to the head of Grand Coulee. Notice the increased number of fractures as a result of the brittle basalt flows being forcibly bent along the monocline. The rocks are weakest and prone to erosion where the rocks are the most tilted (up to 45 degrees to 60 degrees from horizontal). Modified after Weiss and Newman (1989).

- The Coulee Monocline was not a feature created by the floods. It was created long before the floods, but it was a key structural feature that strongly influenced the pathway of the floods and development of Grand Coulee; therefore, it deserves special mention here.

- Long before the basalt lava flows were folded, they oozed out of vents and spread out in broad, horizontal sheets across the Columbia Plateau (Plate 2). After cooling, strong, deep forces within the Earth locally squeezed the lava flows, which caused bending and cracking of the hardened, brittle basalt rock.

- One prominent fold – the Coulee Monocline – forms a bounding ridge that runs along the west side of Lower Grand Coulee before crossing the mouth of Upper Grand Coulee and continuing northeast (see Figure 3-50 and Plate 30). The recessional cataract canyon that formed Upper Grand Coulee started here where the monocline crosses the coulee (see Figure 3-54, Stage 2).

- The youngest basalt flows (Wanapum Basalt) are thicker on the downfolded side of the Coulee Monocline, indicating the monocline was actively being folded as the volcanic flows lapped up against this rising ridge.

- In places the rocks on the upper part of the monocline are 1,000 feet higher than the same rocks on the lower part (Figure 3-69).

Figure 3-69. Basalt flows, tilted to the east, are exposed along the Coulee Monocline, Lower Grand Coulee. Looking northwest across Park Lake. Notice how hogbacks in the foreground are tilted in the same direction as the ridge in upper left. The hogbacks are flood-scoured remnants of basalt eroded from the core of the monocline.

- For 15 miles the Coulee Monocline in the Lower Grand Coulee forms the eastern boundary of the elevated Waterville Plateau.

- Many millions of years after the basalt flows were erupted and tilted into a monocline, Ice Age floods started. The rocks along the axis of the fold were more fractured due to the folding, which made the weakened rock along the monocline more vulnerable to erosion by megafloods (Figure 3-68).

- Ice Age floodwaters flowing down the Lower Grand Coulee naturally followed the lower, eastern side of the monocline, preferentially eroding out the weakened rock along the edge of the monocline.

- If the Ice Age Floods and the glacially diverted Columbia River had not carved out Grand Coulee, the Coulee Monocline ridge instead of the Grand Coulee would mark the eastern topographic edge of the Waterville Plateau.

Figure 3-70. Eroded hogback ridges of the Coulee Monocline at southeast end of the Upper Grand Coulee along State Route 155. Shown here are three basalt flows dipping steeply to the right (south). Floodwaters preferentially removed the weaker basalt rock, leaving behind the firmer, more resistant basalt on the hogback ridges. Looking east.

Lake Columbia Floods

Ice Age floods in the Pacific Northwest have long been attributed to sudden outbursts from ice-dammed Glacial Lake Missoula. However, Pleistocene floods were also associated with Glacial Lake Columbia that developed behind another ice dam, the Okanogan Lobe, which dammed the Columbia River somewhere northwest of Grand Coulee Dam (Plate 45). The Okanogan Lobe and Lake Columbia were already in place and survived all the late-glacial outburst floods from Lake Missoula. It wasn't until several centuries after the last Missoula flood that the Okanogan Lobe finally broke apart, releasing one last wall of water, up to 500 feet high, from Lake Columbia. We know Lake Columbia outlasted the Missoula floods by centuries based on hundreds of annual, fine-sand-to-silt varves that overlie the last Missoula flood deposits laid down in ancient Lake Columbia. It appears that the last Lake Columbia flood flowed down the Columbia Valley after the ultimate breakup of the Okanogan Lobe at the very end of the last Ice Age around 14,000 years ago. Flood bars downstream, including the impressive West Bar with its wonderfully preserved giant current ripples (see Figure 3-119), tell of this terminal flood from Lake Columbia.

At least one other flood resulted from Glacial Lake Columbia prior to the final breakup of the Okanogan Lobe. After being hammered by the last Missoula floods, Lake Columbia was finally allowed to rest peacefully for hundreds of years within the Upper Grand Coulee and Columbia Valley. Year after year, one layer after another of silt was laid down over the lake bottom as side streams coming off the Waterville Plateau delivered increasing amounts of meltwater that drained eastward into Grand Coulee (see Figures 3-74 and 3-113). Today, large, untarnished delta bars exist where meltwater plunged into calm waters of Lake Columbia below. The maximum height of Lake Columbia during this time reached 1,850 feet elevation – controlled by the height of an ancient debris dam that existed at the mouth of Upper Grand Coulee (see Figure 3-71, Plate 45). The debris dam, also known as the Coulee City Expansion Bar (No. 37), was created by Missoula floodwaters that fanned out into the broad Hartline Basin, leading to significant sediment buildup at the mouth of Upper Grand Coulee. Over time, after repeated Missoula floods, the expansion bar grew to be 300 feet tall.

At the end of the Ice Age, the debris dam at the south end of the Upper Grand Coulee suddenly failed. Speedy downcutting of the debris dam followed, allowing water to scream through the opening that quickly cut down to bedrock. When the rapidly draining lake reached the elevation of the bedrock beneath the debris dam (elevation 1,540 feet), the spigot to Grand Coulee was suddenly turned off when lake water dropped below the level of the coulee bottom. The resulting debris-dam-outburst flood suddenly lowered the level of Lake Columbia by 300 feet; this translates to a lot of water, considering the expansive size of Glacial Lake Columbia (see Plate 1). All the floodwater escaping through the debris dam would have drained south into the Lower Grand Coulee. This scenario rings true since it allows for the preservation of the Lake Columbia silt and delta bars in the Upper Grand Coulee after the debris-dam flood.

The debris-dam flood from Lake Columbia must have been extremely powerful, on par with a Missoula outburst flood, judging by the underlying bedrock surface that was locally swept clean of any debris that made up the dam. Most of the debris was carried downstream and deposited onto bars of the Lower Grand Coulee including Ephrata Fan (No. 58) at the mouth of Grand Coulee (Plate 30). The final breakup of the Okanogan Ice Lobe, which released the remaining volume of Lake Columbia down the Columbia Valley to the northwest, appears to have occurred during or soon after the failure of the Coulee City debris dam. This is indicated by the complete lack of evidence for a Columbia River channel within Grand Coulee or across the crest of the Ephrata Fan debris dam downstream. The cause of the debris-dam failure is uncertain but could have occurred during an earthquake leading to sediment liquefaction within the dam or a seiche (lake wave like a tsunami) that engulfed the dam.

37. Coulee City Expansion Bar

"The Hartline structural valley became filled with debris from cutting of Upper Grand Coulee before Lower Grand Coulee had been eroded."

– J Harlen Bretz (1923)

Features: Eroded expansion flood bar of coarse gravel and sand that later created a debris dam for Glacial Lake Columbia

Best Observation Points:

Automobile: West bar remnant visible from State Route 17 in hills south and west of Dry Falls Visitor Center. East bar remnant visible near intersection between State Route 155 and U.S. Highway 2, 2 miles north of Coulee City (chapter 5, Road Tour No. 4).

Non-motorized trail: Dry Falls (chapter 4, Trail CC)

Elevation of Feature: East side: Head of expansion bar lies at elevation 1,850 feet and gradually descends southward to about 1,800 feet east of Coulee City. West side: Flood gravels along U.S. Highway 2 similarly go up to 1,800 feet. Just west of Dry Falls, at least two lower flood-cut terraces appear to be along the bar at about 1,700 and 1,750 feet.

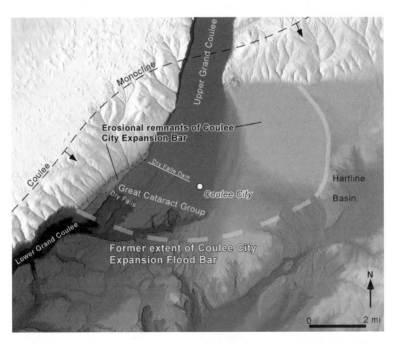

Figure 3-71. Shaded-relief map showing former extent of the Coulee City Expansion Bar (bold line). Sediment within the bar built up where Missoula floodwaters fanned out, slowing temporarily within the broad Hartline Basin after escaping the confines of the Upper Grand Coulee. The expansion bar held back Glacial Lake Columbia for several centuries after the last Missoula flood until the debris dam failed, unleashing one last flood down Lower Grand Coulee. Today, only remnants of the eroded bar are preserved on either side of the coulee.

Maximum Flood Depth (Elevation): 200 feet (2,000 feet)

- A huge expansion bar fanned out into the Hartline Basin at the mouth of Upper Grand Coulee as Missoula floods 500 feet deep and moving up to 70 mph temporarily slowed, causing sediment to accumulate (Figure 3-71).

- A high bouldery surface up to elevation 1,850 feet gently descends from the mouth of Upper Grand Coulee into the Hartline Basin. Coarse boulders at the gaping mouth of the coulee grade into finer debris farther down the fan.

- At one time the total width of the expansion bar must have been an incredible 16 miles!

- The contents of the expansion bar at one location (Figure 2-28, top) is 100 percent basalt clasts – no granitic rock is present. This indicates that at least part of the bar formed during older Ice Age floods at a time before the cataract of the Upper Grand Coulee had receded to Steamboat Falls (former cataract near Steamboat Rock; see Figure 3-54, Stage 4) and exhumed granitic rocks north of there.

- The expansion bar acted as a debris dam that temporarily impounded Glacial Lake Columbia at the southern end of the Upper Grand Coulee for several centuries after the last Missoula flood.

- The center of the expansion bar was removed by later floods when Glacial Lake Columbia broke through the debris dam, releasing a last deluge into the Lower Grand Coulee (see "Lake Columbia Floods" sidebar, page 130).

Figure 3-72. A series of subtle terraces (parallel dashed lines at right) lie at the head of the Coulee City Expansion Bar where the Upper Grand Coulee expands into the Hartline Basin. Note the steeply dipping basalt flows on the left – bent over into hogbacks (same as those in Figure 3-70) along the Coulee Monocline.

38. Lake Columbia Silt and Delta Bars

"There is a widely distributed 'white silt' in this valley and its tributaries above the head of Grand Coulee. It was clearly deposited during the retreat of the latest ice sheet."

– J Harlen Bretz (1932)

Features: Post-flood silt deposits and delta bars once deposited in Glacial Lake Columbia on the floor of Upper Grand Coulee

Best Observation Points:

Automobile: State Route 155, MP 7.7 and between MP 19 and 20 (chapter 5, Road Tour No. 4)

Non-motorized trail (chapter 4): Lake Columbia silt exposed within Banks Lake Archipelago (Trail Y); Delta bar at base of Foster Coulee clearly visible from Giant Cave Arch Rock Shelter (Trail AA)

Watercraft: Tall banks of Lake Columbia silt exposed along much of the Banks Lake shoreline

Elevation of Feature: Base of Lake Columbia silt lies below valley bottom (beneath Banks Lake) at 1,500 feet. Top of the delta bars rise to 1,680 feet.

- A thick deposit of yellowish, laminated silt (Figure 3-73) indicates a long-lived lake (i.e., an arm of Glacial Lake Columbia) occupied the Upper Grand Coulee for several centuries after the last Ice Age outburst flood. The Lake Columbia silt is also known as Nespelem Silt, Nespelem Formation and the Steamboat Rock silt.

Figure 3-73. Glacial Lake Columbia deposits of yellowish silt in the Upper Grand Coulee. Left: Tall bluffs of the well-stratified, post-last-flood lake deposits are exposed in slump faces around Banks Lake, including this one just south of Steamboat Rock. Looking northwest. Right: Scalloped shoreline eroded in the former lake-deposited silt along Banks Lake shoreline viewed from the summit of Steamboat Rock. Glacial Lake Columbia silt blankets flood bars immediately south of Steamboat Rock and below Paynes Gulch (upper right). Notice hanging, side-cataract canyon at Ladds Creek (also shown in Figure 6-20).

- Lake Columbia and the silt deposits did not occupy the Upper Grand Coulee until after Ice Age floods breached the head of the coulee (No. 29) and significantly lowered its elevation.

- Powerful megafloods moving down the coulee earlier eroded and partially scoured the center of the coulee and locally deposited multiple sandy rhythmites beneath the lake-silt sequence.

- The silt deposits are composed of up to hundreds of annual lake varves that blanket the youngest flood deposits, indicating Lake Columbia occupied the valley floor for many centuries after the last outburst flood.

- Lake Columbia silt lies along the floor of the Upper Grand Coulee, up to an elevation of 1,620 feet, although it is reported as high as 1,800 feet elsewhere in the region. Thus, it appears Glacial Lake Columbia filled the coulee to an elevation of about 1,800 feet during deposition of the silt – or about the same height as the Coulee City Expansion Bar (No. 37).

- The silt deposits are highly visible as light-colored bluffs and banks, a few tens of feet tall, exposed along the actively eroding shoreline of Banks Lake. The best exposures of the lake silt lie in broad, flat plains south of Steamboat Rock (Figure 3-73) and along the east side of the coulee along the perimeter of Paynes Gulch flood bar (Plate 27) and around the Banks Lake Inselbergs (No. 30).

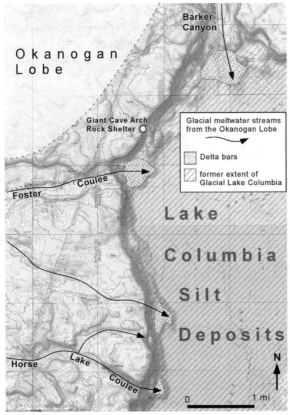

Figure 3-74. Northwestern Upper Grand Coulee showing undisturbed delta bars that prograded into Lake Columbia from several meltwater side streams entering from the north and west. This ancient lake rose at least another 200 feet higher than present-day Banks Lake.

Horse Lake Coulee

Delta bar

Banks Lake

Figure 3-75. A beautifully preserved delta bar at the mouth of Horse Lake Coulee. Here, glacial meltwater drained off the Waterville Plateau via Horse Lake Coulee, over the lip of the hanging coulee, and into the glacial lake below (one time more than 200 feet above level of Banks Lake). Sediment carried by the meltwater stream deposited onto the delta bar as a lobate tongue extending into the former lake. The delta bar protrudes out toward the center of the coulee, suggesting Glacial Lake Columbia outlasted the last Missoula flood. If another large flood followed the growth of the delta bar, rushing floodwaters would have modified or destroyed the bar. Today Horse Lake Coulee hangs 550 feet above modern Banks Lake. Looking northwest.

- The post-Missoula-flood Lake Columbia silt also appears to blanket higher-energy giant current ripples and coarser flood deposits that underlie the flood bars at Steamboat Rock and Paynes Gulch.

- A map produced by J Harlen Bretz in 1932 shows that the silt blankets the entire floor of the coulee, including the area submerged under Banks Lake.

- More evidence for a long-lived glacial lake in the Upper Grand Coulee are features called delta bars, located in several places along the west side of the coulee (Figure 3-74). The elevated delta bars protrude from the mouths of Barker Canyon as well as Foster and Horse Lake coulees.

- Elevated deltas that advanced into the ancient Lake Columbia (Figures 3-74 and 3-75) indicate a lot of glacial meltwater from the Okanogan Lobe was draining off the Waterville Plateau into Upper Grand Coulee via Barker Canyon (No. 34), as well as Foster and Horse Lake coulees (No. 62). The delta bars reflect deposition of sediment by these swollen glacial-meltwater streams into Glacial Lake Columbia.

- Perfect preservation of these delta bars further suggests that Glacial Lake Columbia outlasted the last Missoula floods. Had more floods moved through Grand Coulee, they would have certainly destroyed or modified the delta bars, which is not the case.

Lower Grand Coulee

Features and trails in the vicinity of the Great Cataract Group (Plate 31), located in the northern portion of Lower Grand Coulee, are shown in Figure 3-76. After Missoula floods funneled through the Upper Grand Coulee, they emptied into the expanse of the Hartline Basin (Figure 3-77). During earlier floods the deluges appear to have shot straight south toward the lower gaps that lay on either side of High Hill and Pinto Ridge. At these times the mega-floods eroded Dry, Hudson, Trail Lake and Spring coulees when Dry Falls cataract and its inner canyon had not yet receded far upvalley from its origin near Soap Lake. These eastern flood coulees followed and reamed out older stream valleys controlled by minor flexures in the basalt bedrock at High Hill and Pinto Ridge. Over time Dry Falls cataract receded upvalley, which diverted more of the flood flow westward into the deep inner canyon of Lower Grand Coulee. This shift in flow is attributed to an increased rate of erosion along the highly fractured rock of the Coulee Monocline (No. 36) that parallels the Lower Grand Coulee. Deep erosion of Lower Grand Coulee along the Coulee Monocline left its precipitous western wall almost 1,000 feet high.

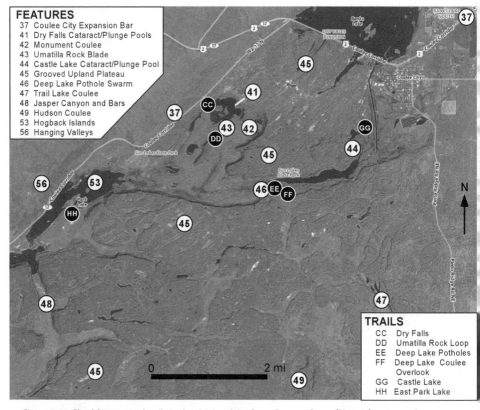

FEATURES
37 Coulee City Expansion Bar
41 Dry Falls Cataract/Plunge Pools
42 Monument Coulee
43 Umatilla Rock Blade
44 Castle Lake Cataract/Plunge Pool
45 Grooved Upland Plateau
46 Deep Lake Pothole Swarm
47 Trail Lake Coulee
48 Jasper Canyon and Bars
49 Hudson Coulee
53 Hogback Islands
56 Hanging Valleys

TRAILS
CC Dry Falls
DD Umatilla Rock Loop
EE Deep Lake Potholes
FF Deep Lake Coulee
     Overlook
GG Castle Lake
HH East Park Lake

Figure 3-76. Flood features and trails in the vicinity of the Great Cataract Group (Plate 31) in the northern portion of Lower Grand Coulee.

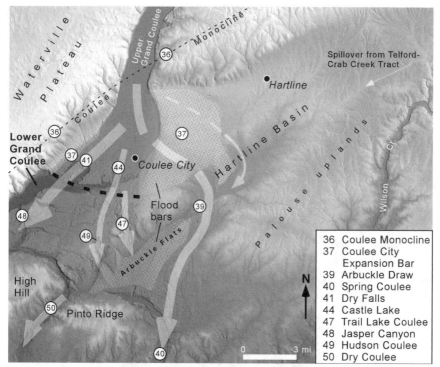

Figure 3-77. After leaving the confines of Upper Grand Coulee via a single channel, Missoula floodwaters spread out and divided into multiple spillways. During earlier floods the deluges continued straight south for gaps on either side of Pinto Ridge. Later floods created the Coulee City Expansion Bar (marked by dark dashed line) and shifted the flow more toward High Hill and the Coulee Monocline after the recessional Dry Falls cataract formed Lower Grand Coulee.

39. Arbuckle Draw

Features: Flow constriction, recessional cataracts, rock benches, potholes, longitudinal grooves, flood bars, giant current ripples

Best Observation Point:

Automobile: While there are no public roads into Arbuckle Draw, one can drive east across the Arbuckle Flats expansion bar and adjacent Palouse uplands via Road 31-NE, accessible from Pinto Ridge Road, five miles south of Coulee City.

Elevation of Feature: The head of the draw is 1,700 feet, the mouth is 1,575 feet.

Maximum Flood Depth (Elevation): 300 feet (1,900 feet)

- Arbuckle Draw, or Bretz's "Deadman's Draw," was carved by earlier floods that came from the north and west via the mouth of Upper Grand Coulee (Figure 3-77).

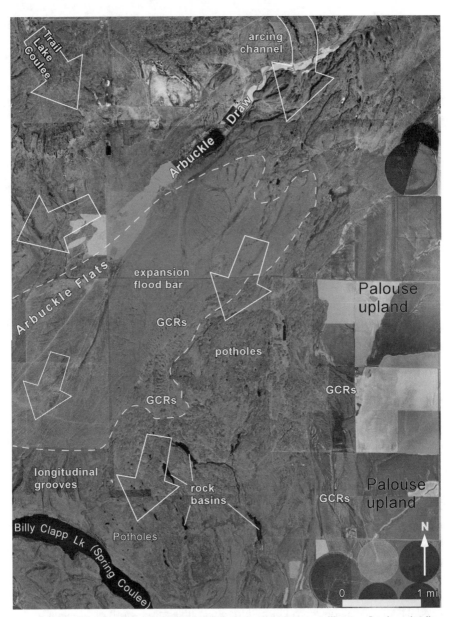

Figure 3-78. Flood features in the vicinity of Arbuckle Draw. Erosional features in Wanapum Basalt are locally buried beneath a cover of flood deposits topped by giant current ripples (GCRs). Bold arrows show the many simultaneous flood-flow directions.

- Before Dry Falls and the other cataracts of the Great Cataract Group had receded into the area, most floodwaters from the Upper Grand Coulee flowed south and east in a broad arc, carving out a series of curving, elongated scabland channels, rock basins and giant grooves all the way to Spring Coulee (Figure 3-78).

- The upper part of the curve is backfilled with flood deposits of the Coulee City Expansion Bar (No. 37), suggesting that Arbuckle Draw was created by an older flood prior to the build-up of sediment over the expansion bar.

- Severely eroded scabland that underlies the margins of the Coulee City Expansion Bar indicates older floods swept through this area prior to deposition of the expansion bar. This is demonstrated in Figure 3-78, where deeply scoured scabland features like grooves, potholes and rock basins, appear to underlie a younger cover of flood debris along the edges of the bars.

- The expansion bar likely formed as Missoula floods eroded the Upper Grand Coulee headward. It wasn't until much later that a portion of Glacial Lake Columbia broke through and removed the central part of the expansion bar.

- As water from the last floods expanded out of Arbuckle Draw, another expansion bar developed immediately downstream along Arbuckle Flats. Only a thin cover of flood sediment overlies this area, barely masking the scarred scabland underneath.

- Only during one or more especially large early floods did a minor amount of floodwater leak over a low divide from the northeast from the Telford-Crab Creek scablands. These floods would have spilled west out of Wilson Creek into the Hartline Basin (Figure 3-77).

40. Spring Coulee (Billy Clapp Lake)

"Spring Coulee is a fine scabland canyon, with castle-like buttes, lateral subsidiary canyons, and cataracts notching its walls."

– J Harlen Bretz (1932)

Features: Recessional cataract canyons, rock basins, potholes, mesas, buttes, hanging coulees, spillover channels, ice-rafted erratics, flood bars, giant grooves and current ripples.

Best Observation Points:

Automobile: Public roads go to either end of coulee. Northwest end is accessed via Summer Falls Park off Pinto Ridge Road (chapter 5, Road Tour No. 4); southwest end is accessed via road to Pinto Dam off State Route 28.

Non-motorized trail: Spring Coulee (chapter 4, Trail JJ)

Watercraft: Via public launch site at Pinto Dam located at south end of Billy Clapp Lake

Elevation of Feature: Scabland features extend from Billy Clapp Lake (1,350 feet) to east slopes of Pinto Ridge at 1,700 feet.

Maximum Flood Depth (Elevation): 450 feet (1,700 feet)

- Spring Coulee is now occupied by man-made Billy Clapp Lake (Figure 3-79, Plate 44).

Figure 3-79. Curving Spring Coulee, now occupied by the Billy Clapp Lake reservoir, wraps around the east side of Pinto Ridge. The trimline on Pinto Ridge marks the highest level of flood erosion. The isolated basalt butte (Frenchman Springs Member) in the middle of the lake became an island after Pinto Dam was constructed as part of the Columbia Basin Irrigation Project (see "The Columbia Basin Project" sidebar below).

- Several smaller lakes, including Long Lake, occupied Spring Coulee prior to the formation of Billy Clapp Lake, dammed by the U.S. Bureau of Reclamation in 1951.

- During Ice Age floods Spring Coulee was fed by floodwater that emerged from the Upper Grand Coulee and flowed down the east side of the spillway complex via Arbuckle Draw (No. 39) and Trail Lake Coulee (No. 47) (Figure 3-77).

- Pinto Ridge, which borders the west side of Spring Coulee was too tall for the floods to flow over, so the converging floodwaters were once again split apart with part of the flow going west down Dry Coulee (No. 50) and the remainder running down Spring Coulee.

Great Cataract Group

J Harlen Bretz was awestruck with what he called "The Great Cataract Group," an abandoned waterfall that stretches out for almost four miles from monstrous Dry Falls eastward to Don Paul Draw (Plate 31). Bretz compared the Great Cataract Group with Niagara Falls, which has similar-shaped cataract alcoves, but is only one-tenth the size. The total rim length of the Great Cataract is close to 10 miles! For short intervals the Dry Falls complex must have been the largest waterfall in the world. Even more amazing is the fact that the width of the flood channel containing the Great Cataract Group only makes up about half the width of the complete flood-channel complex; equally impressive cataract canyons extend another four miles east of the Great

Cataract Group all the way to Arbuckle Draw (Figure 3-77). To imagine a flood channel almost 10 miles wide, up to 1,000 feet deep and moving at speeds approaching 70 mph is almost beyond comprehension.

During maximum flow the cataract would merely show as a standing wave or slight depression on the water surface. However, highly complex and erosive, high-energy currents operated below the water surface, excavating huge amounts of basalt bedrock. The rushing, sediment-choked water was likely a brown, muddy color from suspended material with bobbing icebergs floating on its surface. The shaking of the ground, the roar of the water and sounds of colliding boulders must have been deafening!

41. Dry Falls Cataract/Plunge Pools

"Dry Falls or Grand Falls … was a double fall at the close of the history of this great cataract, with a 'Goat Island' in the middle."

– J Harlen Bretz (1923)

Features: 400-foot tall cataract with three recessional cataract alcoves, plunge-pool lakes (Dry Falls, Red Alkali and Green lakes), Umatilla Rock blade (Bretz's Goat Island), potholes, buttes, grooved upland plateau and flood bars

Best Observation Points:

Automobile: Dry Falls Visitor Center off State Route 17, 19 miles north of Soap Lake or four miles southwest of Coulee City (chapter 5, Road Tour No. 4).

Non-motorized trail: Dry Falls (chapter 4, Trail CC)

Watercraft: Via primitive launch site at Dry Falls Lake accessed from Sun Lakes State Park

Elevation of Feature: The top of the falls are about 1,550 feet and the base about 1,150 feet within the Dry Falls Lake plunge pool – a total drop of 400 feet.

Maximum Flood Depth: Maximum elevation of the floods in this area was 1,900 feet. This translates to a maximum floodwater depth approaching 350 feet above, and 750 feet below, the lip of the falls.

- Dry Falls is perhaps the premier flood feature of all the Channeled Scabland – primarily due to its easy access to a spectacular overview from the precipitous edge of the falls and an informative visitor center (J Harlen Bretz Memorial Museum) (Figure 3-80).

- The Dry Falls recessional cataract began about 15 miles to the south, where floodwaters initially dropped over a basalt ledge into the Quincy Basin near Soap Lake at the mouth of Lower Grand Coulee (Plate 30).

- Amazing as the view is from Dry Falls Visitor Center (Plate 29), one can really only see a portion of the multi-alcoved cataract that makes up Dry Falls. The eastern alcove, called Monument Coulee (No. 42), is mostly obscured by Umatilla Rock (No. 43), a tall blade of basalt that divides the coulee in two, almost-equal segments (Figure 3-81, Plates 31 and 32).

Figure 3-80. Dry Falls and its visitor center are perhaps the most well-known and visited feature of the Ice Age floods. A floods' enthusiast is shown in 1940 (Rufus Woods Collection archived at Central Washington University).

- Two plunge-pool lakes (Dry Falls and Green Lake) are visible from the viewpoint; a third lake (Red Alkali) is hidden against the cataract at the head of Monument Coulee (Plate 35).

- The volume of water racing over Dry Falls is estimated to be 10 million cubic meters per second. Grand Coulee Dam contains 9.2 million cubic meters of concrete. Thus a volume of water approximately equivalent in size to one Grand Coulee Dam would have passed over Dry Falls every second during a large outburst flood!

- So much water flowed here that the falls would have been almost imperceptible, with perhaps only a minor drop in the level of the floodwaters that rushed over the falls.

- Just west of Dry Falls is a long, narrow flood bar perched high up against the side of the coulee (Figure 3-81; see also Figure 3-71). This is the western margin of the eroded Coulee City Expansion Bar (No. 37), which once stretched for 16 miles to the opposite side of the coulee (see Figure 3-77). A flood from Glacial Lake Columbia later cut down into the bar and removed its sediments from the center of the coulee.

- The geology looks much like it did when cataclysmic floods last poured over the falls about 14,000 years ago. The dry, semi-arid climate with slow rates of weathering and erosional modification have helped to preserve flood features here and elsewhere in the scablands.

Figure 3-81. Aerial view looking south over the Dry Falls cataract into Lower Grand Coulee. Floodwaters moving 70 mph and up to 350 feet deep shot over these falls. Notice giant, longitudinal grooves and swarms of potholes behind Dry Falls. Umatilla Rock separates the two main cataract alcoves below the falls. See Plate 32 for color image from slightly different perspective.

42. Monument Coulee

Features: 400-foot tall abandoned cataract, recessional cataract canyon, Umatilla Rock blade, potholes, grooved upland plateau and flood bars

Best Observation Points:

Automobile: Mouth of coulee is visible from Deep Lake Road within Sun Lakes State Park

Non-motorized trails: Umatilla Rock Loop (chapter 4, Trail DD).

Elevation of Feature: The top of the falls are about 1,550 feet and the base about 1,150 feet – a total drop of 400 feet.

Maximum Flood Depth: Maximum elevation of the floods in this area was 1,900 feet. This translates to a maximum depth approaching 350 feet above the falls and up to 750 feet below.

- The recessional cataract canyon at the head of Monument Coulee comprises the middle of three cataract alcoves that make up Dry Falls (Figure 3-82, Plates 31 and 32). The long and narrow Umatilla Rock Blade (No. 43) divides Monument Coulee from the Dry Falls Coulee (No. 41), just to the west.

- Two, unusual, different-colored plunge-pool lakes (Green and Red Alkali lakes) lie at the head of Monument Coulee, below Dry Falls. Ironically, in summertime Red Alkali lake is mostly green and Green Lake is mostly brown (Plate 35). The contrasting colors are likely due to different water chemistry and microbes living within the lakes. Later in the year as the lakes dry up, shallow Green Lake transforms into a white, alkaline playa lake bed (Figure 3-82, top).

- Cataract alcoves and the rock blade at Dry Falls are similar to those observed on the planet Mars (Figure 3-82, bottom), good evidence that similar giant floods have occurred on Mars as well.

The Columbia Basin Project

The multipurpose Columbia Basin Project (CBP) was a bold engineering feat, accomplished by the U.S. Bureau of Reclamation, which began with the generation of hydroelectric power at the 550-foot-high Grand Coulee Dam in 1941 (Figures 3-56 and 6-19; see also Plates 23 and 25). Later, a complex network of canals and siphons were built to distribute life-giving irrigation water from several storage basins. Today the water supports the growth of more than 60 crops within central Washington. The engineered structures took advantage of the many deep coulees and channels carved by megafloods, which conveniently headed southwestward toward the broad Quincy, Othello and Pasco basins, filled with fertile, crop-friendly sediment – the destination for most of the irrigation water. Water delivery, which today irrigates more than 670,000 acres of central Washington, began in 1952.

Coincidentally, the site of Grand Coulee Dam is near the same location as a glacial dam that held back the much-deeper Glacial Lake Columbia and caused megafloods (as well as the Columbia River between floods) to flow down Grand Coulee (Plate 22). Today, 3 percent of the flow from the Columbia River behind Grand Coulee Dam is lifted almost 300 feet by 12 of the world's largest pumps from Lake Roosevelt into the Banks Lake storage reservoir within the Upper Grand Coulee (Plate 25). Altogether, Grand Coulee Dam and other power plants within the storage reservoirs supply almost 7 million kilowatts of electricity into the region's power grid. More than 300 miles of main canals, 2,000 miles of laterals and 3,500 miles of drains and wasteways extend up to 125 miles south of Grand Coulee Dam before rejoining the Columbia River. Besides providing hydroelectric power and irrigation water, the CBP affords recreational opportunities within several reservoirs, increases wildlife habitat, and provides flood control along the Columbia River. Some negative impacts of the CBP include the drowning of American Indian villages, destruction of historic salmon runs and their spawning habitat, and drowning of a vibrant orchard and agricultural industry within the upper Columbia River Valley.

The CBP had many false starts. It took several decades but finally became reality due to the perseverance of local residents Rufus Woods, enthusiastic publisher of the *Wenatchee Daily World*, Ephrata lawyer William Clapp and entrepreneur James O'Sullivan. These original members of the "Dam University," their self-proclaimed lobbyist organization, first met in 1917 to discuss their vision to bring growth and prosperity to the barren, semi-arid desert. To commemorate these earliest supporters of the project, today we have Rufus Woods Lake downstream of Grand Coulee Dam, Billy Clapp Lake within Spring Coulee (No. 40) behind Pinto Dam, and O'Sullivan Dam, which holds back Potholes Reservoir in the Quincy Basin.

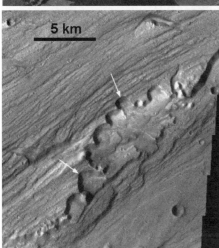

Figure 3-82. Scalloped cataract alcoves are similar on Earth and Mars. Above: Dry Falls. Left: Compare with similarly grooved plateau above cataracts (arrows) on Kasei Valles, Mars. This string of cataract alcoves on Mars is about twice as long as those of the Great Cataract Group shown in Plate 31.
THEMIS VISIBLE LIGHT IMAGE V10081003

43. Umatilla Rock Blade

Features: Tall, narrow rib of basalt that bisects the inner cataract canyon below Dry Falls

Best Observation Points:

Automobile: Dry Falls Visitor Center, MP 94.5 along State Route 17 (chapter 5, Road Tour No. 4); Deep Lake Road in Sun Lakes State Park

Non-motorized trails (chapter 4): Dry Falls (Trail CC) and Umatilla Rock Loop (Trail DD)

Elevation of Feature: High point 1,540 feet, base about 1,270 feet

Maximum Flood Depth (Elevation): 630 feet (1,900 feet)

- Umatilla Rock (also known as Battleship Rock) forms a narrow, flat-topped ridge of basalt between the two cataract alcoves of Dry Falls (Figure 3-81; Plates 31 and 32).

- Before Dry Falls had receded into this area, Umatilla Rock was part of a broad, continuous upland plateau of basalt that extended for more than 10 miles from the Coulee Monocline (No. 36) eastward to the Palouse uplands in Figure 3-77.

- Recession of the cataract to Dry Falls has since eroded and isolated the monolith into a "goat island" that separates two recessional cataract alcoves. An example of such a feature is Niagara Falls' Goat Island, where a narrow rocky ridge lies between the Canadian and American falls.

- A number of hoodoo-like basalt monoliths (see Figure 4-86), some appearing like monuments, that surround Umatilla Rock slumped or rolled away from the edges of the blade during, or since, the last Ice Age floods.

44. Castle Lake Cataract/Plunge Pool

"Castle Lake Falls totals about 300 feet in height above Deep Lake ... the only human uses of this desolate area south of Coulee City are traverses, gravel pits, springs, the main irrigation canal, and perhaps jackrabbit hunting."

– J Harlen Bretz (1969)

Features: Recessional cataract canyon, plunge-pool lake, rock benches, pot-holes, faceted butte escarpment and hanging coulees

Best Observation Point:

Non-motorized trail: Castle Lake (chapter 4, Trail GG)

Elevation of Feature: High point of cataract is 1,620 feet, Castle Lake plunge pool lies at 1,370 feet.

Maximum Flood Depth (Elevation): Nearly 300 feet at the lip of cataract, 530 feet (1,900 feet) over present-day Castle Lake

- The Castle Lake basin lies along the east end of the Great Cataract Group (Plate 31).

- At the base of the cataract is lovely, blue-green Castle Lake plunge pool nestled into the rock bench below (Plate 43).

- Castle Lake lies within a single, recessional cataract canyon eroded down to a flood-swept, pothole-studded rock bench that hangs 100 feet above Deep Lake. This is the same rock bench of Grande Ronde Basalt where dozens of potholes occur at the opposite (western) end of Deep Lake (Deep Lake Pothole Swarm – No. 46; Plate 34, right).

- Castle Rock is an isolated butte along the west side of the Castle Lake basin. It is a faceted butte escarpment neatly sheared off by monstrous flood forces moving across the cataract (Figure 3-83).

Figure 3-83. Castle Lake Cataract Basin. The east face of Castle Rock butte is a faceted escarpment of Wanapum Basalt sheared off as megafloods carved out the basin. Looking southwest.

45. Grooved Upland Plateaus

Features: Giant longitudinal to curving and crisscrossing grooves atop flood-swept plateaus dissected by recessional gorges

Best Observation Point:

Aircraft: Leg 7 of Aerial Tour No. 2

Elevation of Feature: 1,500 to 1,630 feet

Maximum Flood Depth (Elevation): 400 feet (1,900 feet)

- Like a cat's scratching post, flood-swept upland plateaus along Lower Grand Coulee are scored with hundreds of giant, parallel to gently curving grooves (Figure 3-84; see also Figures 2-6, 3-81, 3-82, 3-91, 3-92, and Plate 32).

- The grooves, which are commonly aligned with the direction of flood flow, attest to the tremendous power and speed (up to 70 mph) of deep floodwaters moving over the plateaus.

- One especially large area with grooved uplands occurs in the Lower Grand Coulee, starting just below Dry Falls Dam and extending seven miles downstream to near Blue Lake, and five miles eastward to Hudson Coulee (No. 49).

- Because of their large size and low relief, the grooves are difficult to see from ground level (see Figure 2-6, right); therefore, they are best observed from the air.

Figure 3-84. Grooved upland plateaus in the Lower Grand Coulee developed atop the Priest Rapids Member (Wanapum Basalt). Above: Behind Dry Falls, regular, mostly parallel grooves on the right merge with semi-parallel to crisscrossing grooves on the left. See Figure 3-82 (top) for a different perspective. Looking south. Left: North of Jasper Canyon, looking southeast. Dry Coulee (No. 50) runs across upper right in this image.

46. Deep Lake Pothole Swarm

"Deep Lake, below one of the Grand Coulee abandoned falls, has many associated huge potholes, drilled into the basalt at the foot of the falls as they retreated."

– J Harlen Bretz (1923)

Features: Dozens of deep, closely spaced potholes on a rock bench of Grande Ronde Basalt

Best Observation Point:

Non-motorized trails (chapter 4): Deep Lake Potholes (Trail EE) and Deep Lake Coulee Overlook (Trail FF)

Elevation of Feature: 1,300 to 1,350 feet

Maximum Flood Depth (Elevation): 600 feet (1,900 feet)

- Dozens of closely spaced potholes were drilled into a rock bench of Grande Ronde Basalt at the southwest end of Deep Lake (Figure 3-85, Plate 34, right; see also Figures 4-88 and 4-89).

- Many of the potholes have vertical to overhanging walls and are a cavernous 50 feet deep.
- The potholes likely formed from kolks, underwater tornado-like vortices, that locally developed from extreme turbulence within flood currents.
- Another set of potholes developed on a similar rock bench that occurs within the Castle Lake basin (No. 44) at the opposite end of Deep Lake.

Figure 3-85. Heavily potholed rock bench drilled into the upper Grande Ronde Basalt near Deep Lake, looking south. Truck (circled) for scale. Tom Foster photo.

47. Trail Lake Coulee

Features: Recessional cataract canyon, rock benches, mesas, flood bars; the two-mile-long, man-made Bacon Tunnel at base of cataract cliff within the coulee feeding the Columbia Basin Project's Main Canal

Best Observation Point:

Automobile: Via Pinto Ridge Road, six miles south of Coulee City turn right (north) onto gravel road that heads up Trail Lake Coulee (chapter 5, Tour 4). The head of the coulee and dual outlets of the Bacon Tunnel are 2.5 miles north up this side road.

Elevation of Feature: From 1,460 to 1,700 feet

Maximum Flood Depth (Elevation): 400 feet (1,850 feet)

- Trail Lake Coulee is a recessional cataract canyon that developed after some of the floodwaters that expanded out of the Upper Grand Coulee headed southeast toward Spring Coulee (see Figure 3-77).
- The U.S. Bureau of Reclamation has taken advantage of this natural channelway by diverting irrigation water from the Banks Lake reservoir into the coulee via the two-mile-long Bacon Tunnel. The tunnel begins at Don Paul Draw (Figures 4-92 and 4-93) and emerges from the base of the cataract at the head of Trail Lake Coulee (Figure 3-86).

- From Trail Lake Coulee the Main Canal flows through the turbines of a small hydropower plant at Summer Falls (see Figure 4-104) before entering Billy Clapp Lake (Spring Coulee, No. 40).

Trail Lake Coulee

Cataract cliff

Bacon Tunnel exit

Main Canal

Figure 3-86. Two-mile-long Bacon Tunnel, part of the Columbia Basin Project, empties into and follows Trail Lake Coulee via the Main Canal. Above: After flowing in total darkness for two miles, water from Bacon Tunnel exits from the uppermost Grande Ronde Basalt flow into the Main Canal. Looking west. Cataract cliff formed across the Frenchman Springs Member of basalt. Left: The mouth of first Bacon Tunnel in the late 1940s where it opens up into Trail Lake Coulee. The entrance to the tunnel lies two miles to the north at Don Paul Draw (Figures 4-92 and 4-93). A second tunnel, paralleling the first, was completed in 1979. PHOTO FROM THE RUFUS WOODS ARCHIVAL COLLECTION, CENTRAL WASHINGTON UNIVERSITY

48. Jasper Canyon and Bars

Features: In-and-out coulee, with side canyons containing recessional cataracts; grooved upland plateaus; giant crescent, pendant and eddy flood bars

Best Observation Points:

Automobile: Head of the canyon and a flood bar are visible across Blue Lake along State Route 17 (MP 90.7); (chapter 5, Road Tour No. 4).

Watercraft: Huge flood bar at mouth of Jasper Canyon can be accessed via public launch sites off State Route 17 along Blue Lake.

Elevation of Feature: Jasper Canyon ranges from 1,100 to 1,550 feet

Maximum Flood Depth (Elevation): 750 feet (1,850 feet)

- Jasper Canyon is a deep, narrow coulee carved into the flood-swept basalt plateau of the Lower Grand Coulee (Figure 3-87).

- Jasper Canyon starts out as a cross coulee at Blue Lake, where it trends nearly perpendicular with the direction of the main, overland flood flow, which swept across a Grooved Upland Plateau (No. 45) above (Figure 3-88). Downvalley Jasper Canyon bends to the south and eventually joins Dry Coulee (No. 50) after 2.5 miles.

Figure 3-87. Tall flood bar (arrow) lies at the head of Jasper Canyon along Blue Lake. The 80-foot-tall flood bar partially fills the coulee bottom. The Blue Lake Rhino Cave is located partway up the basalt cliff of Wanapum Basalt on the right. Looking east.

- At Jasper Canyon are a wonderful collection and wide variety of Ice Age flood bars. Because the head of Jasper Canyon lay cross-wise to the main flow, huge flood bars collected within the coulee here (Figures 3-87 and 3-88). A huge pendant-crescent type flood bar developed along the inside of the large bend where Jasper Canyon (No. 48) and Dry Coulee (No. 50) come together (Figure 3-88). This bar almost fills the canyon (Plate 36) and nearly rises to the same level as the upland plateau; here the flood deposits probably approach 400 feet thick!

- Another type of flood bar (eddy bar) formed at the mouths of several of the side cataract canyons leading into Jasper Canyon (Figures 3-88 and 3-89). These bars may have formed from the very last flood down Lower Grand Coulee that came from Glacial Lake Columbia. This flood probably wasn't deep enough to overtop the upland plateaus along Jasper Canyon.

- Jasper Canyon may be a remnant of an older flood coulee that existed before Dry Falls cataract receded into the area.

- The head of Jasper Canyon is also the location of the Blue Lake Rhino Cave. During outpourings of the Priest Rapids basalt flows, the molten lava entered a swamp environment where a dead rhinoceros lay. More than 100 species of Miocene-age trees, shrubs and other plants have been identified from the associated swamp deposits. Trees and the carcass of the animal were engulfed in basalt lava 15 million years ago. Most of the rhino, except for a few bones, has long since disappeared, but the shape of the rhino is reflected in the shape of the remaining cavity. Fluids in the carcass apparently chilled or quenched the enclosing lava, forming a mold of the animal's shape. The rhino rests on its back. The cavity is entered by a small opening in the right hip. The hike up to the cave crosses some treacherously steep walls of the canyon and is not recommended for small children or the timid. Directions to the cave are available at Dry Falls Visitor Center.

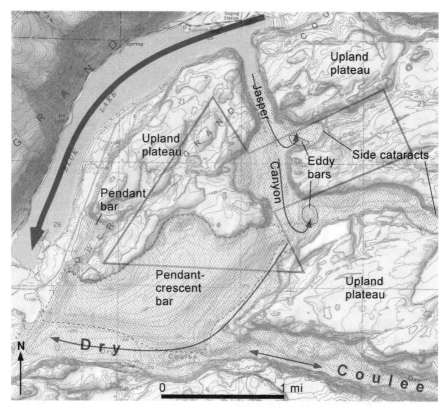

Figure 3-88. Thick flood deposits and tall bars fill a lot of the area between upland plateaus in the vicinity of Jasper Canyon. Large block arrow indicates deep overland flow of the larger and earlier Ice Age floods. Stippled pattern shows area covered with flood deposits and bars. Smaller arrows show the flow of lesser floods or waning stage of the last flood, which built eddy bars (Figure 3-89) at mouths of side coulees and cataract canyons. See Plate 36 for color image of this same area.

Figure 3-89. Eddy bar at mouth of side coulee to Jasper Canyon. This pile of sand and gravel was deposited as floods flowed southeast (left to right) down Jasper Canyon while flood currents swirled around the inside of a side coulee (Figure 3-88). Looking northeast.

49. Hudson Coulee

"The Unnamed (Hudson) Coulee had retreated about 4,000 feet when the last discharge to cross the anticlinal crest subsided. It is a splendid example of an abandoned waterfall with three alcove heads whose cliffs are 100-150 feet high."

— J Harlen Bretz et al (1956)

Features: Abandoned cataract, classic multi-alcoved cataract canyon, rock blade, adjacent grooved upland plateaus and flood bars with giant current ripples

Best Observation Point:

Automobile: Road Tour No. 4 (chapter 5) has a view into the mouth of Hudson Coulee from the crest of Pinto Ridge Road (Figure 5-37). The rest of the coulee is not visible or accessible from any public lands.

Elevation of Feature: Top of cataract 1,700 feet, low point of coulee 1,270 feet; total relief 430 feet

Maximum Flood Depth (Elevation): 630 feet (1,900 feet)

- Hudson Coulee is a classic recessional-cataract canyon, about 1.5 miles wide and three miles long originally referred to by Bretz as the "Unnamed" Coulee (Figure 3-90).

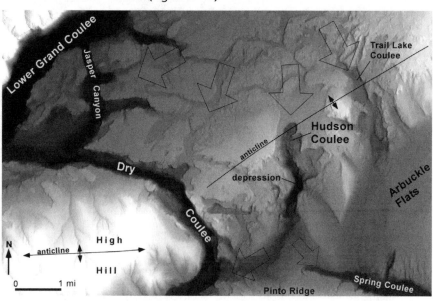

Figure 3-90. Shaded-relief map in the vicinity of Hudson Coulee. Block arrows show directions for flood flow. The entire area north and east of High Hill was submerged during the largest Ice Age deluges. The floods ran up and over the folded basalt surface (anticline) that lay near the head of Hudson Coulee. Floodwaters were forced to go around another taller anticline at High Hill to the west.

- Two alcoves are divided by a narrow rock blade at the head of the coulee; a third alcove, slightly removed from the other two, was gouged out to the east.

- Hudson Coulee is one of several cataract canyons that developed after floodwaters radiated out from the mouth of Upper Grand Coulee (see Figure 3-77).

- A few miles south of Hudson Coulee, flood flow split again as the flood-waters plowed into Pinto Ridge. From here some of the flow headed west, emptying into Dry Coulee (No. 50), with the remainder turning east into Spring Coulee (No. 40).

- An elongate, closed depression (partially erosional and depositional in origin) more than 120 feet deep occurs in the lower part of Hudson Coulee (Figure 3-90). Such depressions are common where high-energy currents encounter gentler slopes. The process is analogous to the "garden hose effect" where the nozzle is pointed towards the ground and the powerful jet of water excavates a depression while debris accumulates on the lateral and down current sides.

Figure 3-91. Hudson-Upper Dry Coulee scabland complex. Apparently eastward flow down Dry Coulee captured some of the overland flow moving in the opposite direction, causing a giant flow reversal (white arrow) near the center of this image.

- As the floodwaters encroached and started to pile up against High Hill, some unusual and dramatic changes in flow direction occurred (Figure 3-91). This is interpreted from the orientation of channels and cataract canyons, elongated rock basins, as well as some beautifully preserved giant grooves and current ripples. Momentum carried most of the flow southward into Dry Coulee through a gap that separated High Hill and Pinto Ridge (Figure 3-90). However, some of the flow was also diverted eastward into Spring Coulee. Simultaneously some of the flow traveled west across upland plateaus toward upper Dry Coulee, as indicated by orientation of some well-developed, giant, linear grooves (Figure 3-92). Along the way some of the flow made an almost 180-degree turn (central arrow in Figure 3-91). Incredibly, it appears floodwater flow was moving simultaneously in opposite directions; flow was moving west across the upland plateaus while moving in the opposite (east) direction down Dry Coulee only one mile away!

50. Dry Coulee

Features: In-and-out coulee; potholes, rock benches and basins, side-cataract canyons, flood-swept upland plateaus with giant grooves and flood bars

Best Observation Point:

Automobile: Via Dry Coulee Road off Pinto Ridge Road, which follows the lower segment of Dry Coulee for 10 miles. Road ends at south end of Dry Coulee near intersection with the Quincy Basin and State Route 28 along Crab Creek.

Elevation of Feature: 1,190 to 1,740 feet; total relief 550 feet

Maximum Flood Depth (Elevation): 650 feet (about 1,850 feet)

- Dry Coulee is a remote in-and-out coulee similar to Jasper Canyon.

- Dry Coulee (also known as Lenore Canyon) is divided into two segments. An upper segment, inaccessible to the public, begins along the east side of the Lower Grand Coulee near Lake Lenore and wraps around the north side of High Hill (Figure 3-90). The lower segment of Dry Coulee, accessible via Dry Coulee Road, trends southwest through the gap between High Hill and Pinto Ridge before it opens up onto Ephrata Fan (No. 58) and the Quincy Basin about 12 miles to the south (Plate 30).

Figure 3-92. Giant longitudinal grooves eroded in upland plateau of Wanapum Basalt between Dry Coulee and Jasper Canyon. The grooves in foreground were created by floods flowing west toward Lower Grand Coulee. Trimline in upper left shows the highest level of erosion by megafloods against High Hill. Looking southwest.

- The walls of Dry Coulee are nearly vertical and locally more than 300 feet high. The sediment-covered floor of the coulee lacks surface streams and displays a number of bars and shallow depressions.

- Fewer than a half dozen ranches are located along the coulee. Farms in the lower coulee draw unlimited groundwater from the productive aquifer contained in permeable flood deposits that underlie the coulee floor. This water is used to irrigate the expansive alfalfa fields within the coulee.

- The lowest point along the Dry Coulee is not at the mouth as one would expect from a "normal" stream channel. Instead a low-point depression, several tens of feet deep, actually lies toward the head of the canyon near the intersection with Jasper Canyon (see Figure 6-24). Here the added force of water from Jasper Canyon was capable of locally hollowing out this depression within flood deposits, which cover most of the coulee floor.

51. High Hill/Pinto Ridge

Features: Two broad, soil-covered, dome-like uplands (anticlines) that lay above flood level and caused floodwaters to divert around them

Best Observation Points:

Automobile: Chapter 5, Tour No. 4 along Pinto Ridge Road between the Summer Falls turnoff and intersection with State Route 28

Non-motorized trail (chapter 4): Spring Coulee (Trail JJ), located on east side of Pinto Ridge; good view of High Hill visible from The Great Blade along the East Lenore Coulee Trail (II)

Elevation of Feature: High Hill rises to 2,075 feet and Pinto Ridge about 2,000 feet. These were two dry islands that protruded above the maximum level of the floods, which in this area rose to about elevation 1,850 feet.

- Pinto Ridge and High Hill are two dome-shaped, anticlinal ridges east of the Lower Grand Coulee that deflected floodwaters around and between them (Figure 3-77, Plate 30).

- High Hill, located along the east side of the Lower Grand Coulee, is separated from Pinto Ridge by lower Dry Coulee.

- Both High Hill and Pinto Ridge are capped by fertile windblown loess that today supports agriculture, unlike the lower slopes where similar soils were totally stripped away below the flood trimline.

- East-west trending geologic faults lie along the north sides of both High Hill and Pinto Ridge. The broken-up, weaker rock along these faults made it easier for the floods to carve deep coulees (i.e., Dry and Spring coulees) here.

52. Lake Lenore Caves

Features: Flood-plucked, overhanging, rock shelters in basalt

Best Observation Points:

Automobile: From State Route 17 (MP 85) along Road Tour No. 4 (chapter 5)

Non-motorized trail: Lake Lenore Caves to The Great Blade (chapter 4, Trail II)

Elevation of Feature: 1,250 feet

Maximum Flood Depth (Elevation): 550 feet (about 1,800 feet)

- The Lake Lenore Caves are natural rock shelters where floods preferentially hollowed out the colonnade portion from the base of a Grande Ronde Basalt flow, leaving behind the stronger, overhanging entablature above (Figure 3-93). The caves lie midway up the west wall of The Great Blade (No. 54), just east of Lake Lenore.

Figure 3-93. Lake Lenore Caves, plucked out of weaker rock at the base of one of the upper Grande Ronde Basalt lava flows by Ice Age floods. The younger Wanapum Basalt makes up the crest of The Great Blade (No. 54) above in background. A trail leading from Lake Lenore Caves to East Lenore Coulee via a notch in The Great Blade is described in chapter 4 (Trail II). Looking north.

- The caves functioned as rock shelters used for temporary overnight camps and storage by American Indian hunters and gatherers for at least 5,000 years.

- Lake Lenore lies below the caves and is one of four large lakes present in the Lower Grand Coulee. It is also an alkaline lake but fresher and less saline than Soap Lake, its downstream neighbor.

53. Hogback Islands

Features: Isolated, erosional remnants of once-continuous, tilted basalt flows along the Coulee Monocline protruding out of the Lower Grand Coulee lakes

Best Observation Points:

Automobile: State Route 17 from Lake Lenore to Park Lake along Road Tour No. 4 (chapter 5)

Non-motorized trails (chapter 4): East Park Lake (Trail HH) and Lake Lenore Caves (Trail II)

Watercraft: Via public launch sites at Lenore, Blue and Park lakes

Elevation of Feature: Hogbacks rise up to 90 feet above modern lake levels in the Lower Grand Coulee

Maximum Flood Depth (Elevation): 700 feet (1,800 feet)

- Small, isolated, flood-scoured rocky protrusions, called hogbacks, lie within lakes (Park, Blue and Lenore) of the Lower Grand Coulee (Figures 3-94 and 3-95; Plates 37 and 38).

- The islands of tilted basalt are part of the flood-ravaged core of the Coulee Monocline (No. 36).

Figure 3-94. A hogback island of Grande Ronde Basalt in foreground is composed of a tilted basalt flow slightly more resistant to attack by the floods along the Coulee Monocline (No. 36). Notice how the hogback is tilted at nearly the same angle as flows in the monoclinal ridge in the background. Looking northwest.

- Basalt rock naturally contains numerous shrinkage cracks (i.e., fractures) that formed as the once-molten lava cooled and contracted (see Figure 1-2). Even more fractures formed as the hardened, brittle basalt was bent and folded along the monocline. For this reason flood erosion was most effective along the more fractured axis of the one-mile-wide Coulee Monocline, which coincides with the Lower Grand Coulee (Plate 30). The hogbacks that remain in the coulee bottom expose ancient lava flows that were slightly more resistant to the floods' erosional forces.

54. The Great Blade

"There were a few double falls each member of which receded at approximately the same rate, so that the island in mid-channel became very much elongated, like a great blade, as the falls receded and the canyons lengthened."

— J Harlen Bretz (1928)

Features: An unusually long, tall, narrow, gently curving, flood-sculpted ridge of basalt

Best Observation Points:

Automobile: From State Route 17 along Lake Lenore, (Road Tour No. 4, chapter 5)

Non-motorized trail: Lake Lenore Caves to The Great Blade (chapter 4, Trail II)

Watercraft: Via primitive launch sites at Lake Lenore

Elevation of Feature: 1,100 to 1,660 feet; total relief 560 feet

Maximum Flood Depth (Elevation): 700 feet (1,800 feet)

Earthcache: Great Blade Notch (www.geocaching .com, Code No. GC2BX9T), located along the Lake Lenore Caves to The Great Blade and East Lenore Coulee Trail (chapter 4, Trail II)

- A tall, narrow basalt ridge, coined "The Great Blade" by Bretz, parallels Lower Grand Coulee east of Lake Lenore (Figures 3-95 to 3-97, Plate 39).
- The basalt blade is an erosional remnant left behind from the recession of two, closely spaced, parallel, cataract canyons that migrated northward.
- On the west side of the blade is Lower Grand Coulee, which migrated northward all the way to Dry Falls (No. 41). On the other side of the blade is the shorter East Lenore Coulee (No. 55), which only receded to the vicinity of Dry Coulee (No. 50).
- Like a giant rib The Great Blade is tallest and narrowest (800 feet) at its south end (Figure 3-95), widening to the north. The blade extends for almost four miles south of Dry Coulee.
- The Lake Lenore Caves (No. 52) were eroded along the west wall of The Great Blade about 1.5 miles from the south end of the rocky rib.

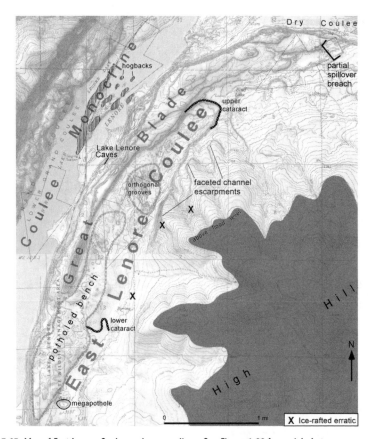

Figure 3-95. Map of East Lenore Coulee and surroundings. See Figure 4-99 for aerial photo.

Figure 3-96. The Great Blade rises above a rock bench within East Lenore Coulee. At eye level is the eroded remnants of the Roza Member, capped by the Priest Rapids Member of Wanapum Basalt – the youngest basalt unit in this area and the same basalt that makes up the lip of Dry Falls. Looking southwest.

55. East Lenore Cataract Canyon and Potholes

"A subfluvial cataract alcove and its recessional gorge at the truncated western end of High Hill are separated from the main coulee by a remarkable bladed ridge."

— J Harlen Bretz (1969)

Features: Recessional cataract canyon, crisscrossing giant grooves, rock benches, potholes and ice-rafted erratics

Best Observation Point: No public roads go into East Lenore Coulee, and since it hangs above the Lower Grand Coulee, it is out of view except via non-motorized trails or aircraft.

Non-motorized trail: Lake Lenore Caves to The Great Blade and East Lenore Coulee (chapter 4, Trail II)

Elevation of Feature: Head and sides of canyon 1,750 feet, mouth of coulee at 1,350 feet; total relief 400 feet

Maximum Flood Depth (Elevation): 450 feet (1,800 feet)

- Just east of Lake Lenore and The Great Blade is a 5.3-mile-long hanging coulee referred to here as East Lenore Coulee (Figures 3-95 and 3-97; see also Figures 6-25 and 4-99, Plates 39 to 42). Bretz called this now completely dry coulee "the synclinal valley," since the structure on the basalt surface dips slightly here between the Coulee Monocline and High Hill.

- The cataract canyon may have started out as a stream valley that followed the trough of a geologic syncline (downwarped trough). This valley appears to line up with Jasper Canyon, another hypothesized pre-flood stream valley to the north (see Figure 3-88).

- Ice Age floods naturally followed this ancient valley, carving scabland along its reach. Like stair steps, two basalt tiers and cataracts occur, one each in the upper and lower ends of the coulee.

- However, the enormous volume of floodwater descending through the area simultaneously flowed along the edge of the monocline to the west (Lower Grand Coulee). The more fractured bedrock along the tilted edge of the monocline was easier to erode and thus the Lower Grand Coulee was deepened faster than in the East Lenore Coulee. In this way the dominant flood channel eventually shifted west into the Lower Grand Coulee.

- East Lenore Coulee is bounded on the west by The Great Blade (No. 54) and on the east by High Hill (No. 51), where several faceted escarpments were eroded along the channel, which is up to 0.75 mile wide (Figure 3-95, Plate 41).

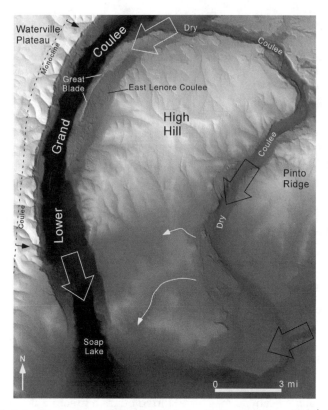

Figure 3-97. Shaded-relief map between the Lower Grand Coulee, East Lenore Coulee and Dry Coulee. East Lenore Coulee developed as floodwaters scoured the northwest flank of High Hill. Block arrows indicate major flood-flow directions.

- The head of East Lenore Coulee ends at the divide crossing with another coulee – Dry Coulee (No. 50). During the last, or one of the last, Ice Age floods the East Lenore head began to breach the spillover into Dry Coulee, reminiscent of the breached head of Grand Coulee with the Columbia Valley (No. 29). This is apparent from the hanging channel at the head of the coulee that today is perched high above the floor of Dry Coulee (Figure 3-95).

- An elevated, rock bench of Grande Ronde Basalt lies along either side of the lower East Lenore Coulee. The bench is riddled with dozens of beautifully developed, deep potholes (Plate 41; see Figures 2-9, 2-10, 4-99). Many of the potholes coalesced into channels after repeated flooding.

- Some of these potholes are beveled and smoothed on the downstream side, a product of intense abrasion by the floods (see Figure 2-9, right).

- A megapothole, 800 feet in diameter and more than 60 feet deep, lies at the southern end of East Lenore Coulee (Figure 3-98, Plate 42) and stands out as the largest in this region.

Figure 3-98. An 800-foot wide megapothole eroded into Grande Ronde Basalt at the south end of East Lenore Coulee. Looking northeast.

- A large group of giant, crisscrossing grooves in Grande Ronde Basalt lies midway within the East Lenore Coulee (see Figure 4-99, Plate 41). The grooves intersect in an orthogonal pattern. One groove direction is north-northeast in line with floodwaters coming down the coulee. The other groove direction curves to the north-northwest.

- One set of grooves was likely formed solely by floodwaters coming down the coulee while the second group appears to be associated with a set of large-scale fractures (cooling or tectonic) that dip steeply to the southwest. Ice age floodwaters rushing over these fractures apparently etched out the weaker rock along the fractures that align transverse to the flood-flow direction.

56. Hanging Valleys

"Tributary furrows on the monoclinal slope to the west, expressing the general maturity of the Plateau, hang hundreds of feet above the surface of the lakes on the coulee floor."

– J Harlen Bretz (1928)

Features: Truncated, old stream valleys, perched high above west wall of Lower Grand Coulee, suddenly falling away into the flood-gouged void

Best Observation Points:

Automobile: State Route 17 and Sun Lakes State Park Road (Tour No. 4, chapter 5)

Non-motorized trail: Lake Lenore Caves (chapter 4, Trail II)

Watercraft: Via Lenore, Blue and Park lakes

Elevation of Feature: Stream valleys gently descend off uplands of the Waterville Plateau from as high as 2,600 feet. Upon reaching the edge of Lower Grand Coulee, the valleys drop out of sight for hundreds of feet into the coulee bottom (about elevation 1,100 feet).

Maximum Flood Depth (Elevation): Only the lower parts of some of the hanging valleys were backwashed during megafloods; gabled headlands between the valleys were generally above maximum flood level (1,800 feet)

- More than two dozen hanging valleys are perched high above the valley floor along the west wall of Lower Grand Coulee (Figure 3-99; see also Figure 2-23, right).

- Early geologists witnessing these features assumed a glacier once filled the valley, since hanging valleys are a classic landform in glaciated mountainous terrain where glaciers widen and shear off the sides of valleys, leaving the tributary valleys hanging. However, today we know glacial ice never extended as far south as Lower Grand Coulee; therefore, they must be a product of Ice Age floods.

Figure 3-99. Illuminated hanging valleys lie perched high above the west wall of Lower Grand Coulee. Looking southwest.

- Before the Ice Age floods, tributary streams drained east down the sloping Coulee Monocline (No. 36) off the elevated Waterville Plateau. The tributaries emptied into a trunk stream that flowed south, down a synclinal valley, near the location of today's East Lenore Coulee (Figure 3-95).

- Ice Age floods later eroded out the weaker rock along the Coulee Monocline. The most powerful flood currents, which lay on the outside of the bend in the Lower Grand Coulee, sheared off and faceted the western wall (see Figure 2-23, right). In the end this produced the same result as if a glacier had once scoured out the valley. Today tributary valleys hang hundreds of feet above the coulee floor.

- The remnant hanging valleys are generally above maximum flood level. However, floods roaring down the coulee repeatedly swept its west wall, maintaining its near-vertical slope. All the loose, basalt talus along the walls today has developed since the last Ice Age flood about 14,000 years ago.

57. Soap Lake Exodus

Features: Starting point for the 17-mile-long recessional cataract canyon of Lower Grand Coulee to Dry Falls; breakout location for floods entering the Quincy Basin; south end of Lake Bretz, a debris-dammed, post-floods lake that extended almost all the way to Deep Lake at the end of the Ice Age

Best Observation Points:

Automobile: Along State Route 17 in Soap Lake (Road Tour No. 4, chapter 5)

Watercraft: Via public launch sites around Soap Lake

Elevation of Feature: The highest elevations (2,350 feet) are just west of Soap Lake in the Beezley Hills that were mostly above maximum flood level. The lowest elevation is about 980 feet at the bottom of Soap Lake. Maximum relief 1,370 feet. The surface of Soap Lake presently lies at 1,075 feet.

Maximum Flood Depth (Elevation): 600 feet (about 1,600 feet)

- Soap Lake today fills a two-mile-long, flood-scoured depression up to 90 feet deep. It is the southernmost of a series of lakes occupying the Lower Grand Coulee (Plate 30). In 1882 Lieutenant Thomas Symons, who was surveying the area for U.S Army Corps of Engineers, wrote: " ... a succession of lakes, the northern ones being clear, white, sweet water filled with fish; toward the south the lakes become more and more strongly impregnated with alkali, until the one at the end of the coulee is of the most detestable unpalatable nature."

- As intimated by Symons the alkalinity in the Lower Grand Coulee increases to its maximum at Soap Lake where waves can whip the surface into a frothy, soap-like foam along the lakeshore, hence the name Soap Lake. High concentrations of calcium and sodium carbonate account for its "soapy," alkaline condition.

Figure 3-100. The view from Soap Lake looks up into the "gun barrel" for outburst floods coming down Grand Coulee. Light area along the shoreline are mineral salts that have precipitated out of this highly alkaline lake in modern times. Looking northwest.

- Soap Lake lies at the muzzle of the "gun barrel" where floodwaters up to 600 feet deep shot out of the Grand Coulee at tremendous speed before suddenly expanding into the Quincy Basin. This sudden spreading caused the floodwaters to slow down dramatically, leading to the deposition of massive apron of sediment debris – the Ephrata Fan (No. 58) just south of Soap Lake.

- After the last Ice Age flood that created Ephrata Fan, a new lake (Lake Bretz) remained behind the debris dam (Plate 30). The original level of Lake Bretz rose to elevation 1,160 feet, the same level as a lake-spillover channel eroded at the head of Ephrata Fan. Silt deposits laid down in ancient Lake Bretz also blanket the basin up to this elevation.

- Being more than 80 feet deeper than the modern-day Soap Lake, Lake Bretz extended for 20 miles along Lower Grand Coulee all the way to Deep Lake Coulee (Plate 31). The remains for this lake are still visible today as lake-silt deposits and a white-mineral precipitate that coats the valley walls up to an elevation of 1,160 feet (Figure 3-101). The ancient nature of Lake Bretz is told by a volcanic ash from Glacier Peak, which erupted 13,800 calendar years ago, that locally lies within these post-last-flood lake deposits.

Figure 3-101. Layers of stratified silt deposited in Lake Bretz that once occupied the Lower Grand Coulee at the end of the Ice Age. These fine-grained sediments are locally plastered against the valley walls up to an elevation of 1,160 feet. Note ski pole for scale.

- At the end of the Ice Age, the melting of all glacial ice off the Waterville Plateau and increased aridity caused the level of the groundwater to gradually drop. Due to evaporation and lowering of groundwater levels since the Ice Age, Lake Bretz eventually disappeared, leaving behind the series of smaller lakes (Soap, Lenore, Blue and Park) present today. Over time dissolved chemicals from the surrounding basalt and sediment have become concentrated into these alkaline lakes with the lowest (Soap Lake) being the most saline.

Eccentric Soap Lake

Soap Lake, at the extreme southern end of Grand Coulee (Plate 30) is a unique mineral lake that has long been known for its therapeutic properties. At the turn of the last century, Soap Lake, which gets its name from the frothy foam that whips up along the southern shoreline, was home to one of the most well-known mineral spas in the country. The water has a soapy, slippery feel because of the high concentration of mineral salts. Referred to by American Indians as "Smokiam" (healing waters), Soap Lake soothed the aches and pains of generations of weary travelers. The healing waters were believed to have curative powers for treating Buerger's Disease and psoriasis. With advancements in medicine, however, the flow of visitors waned, and the town of Soap Lake shrank from as many as 5,000 inhabitants to around 1,700 today.

With the warming at the end of the Ice Age, a single Lake Bretz stretched along the length of Lower Grand Coulee (see Plate 30); it segregated into a series of smaller, lower lakes as groundwater levels dropped and evaporation rates increased. The now-separate lakes feed one another from the north via an underground aquifer. Evaporation concentrates the natural salts of the groundwater that flows into the lakes; salinity of the water increases with each lake, ending in Soap Lake.

As the Columbia Basin Project (CBP) began to transfer irrigation water through this area in the early 1950s, the level of Soap Lake rose and the salinity of the lake dramatically dropped. Soap Lake became less "soapy," and locals became concerned that the lake might lose its unique qualities. To alleviate these problems seven wells were drilled by the U.S. Bureau of Reclamation below the level of the lake, and fresh groundwater entering the lake was intercepted and pumped back into the irrigation canal before it could reach Soap Lake. This action appears to have returned the lake to pre-CBP levels, but the salinity and alkalinity of the lake continues to decrease.

Within the 90-foot-deep lake are two distinct zones – a stagnant, high-density, mineral-rich layer at the bottom 15 to 20 feet of the lake, which lies beneath a fresher, less-alkaline lake layer. Unlike most lakes, however, these two layers have not overturned and mixed for perhaps thousands of years. Thus, the mineral-rich layer lies trapped at the lake bottom. Scientists describe non-mixing lakes like this as meromictic. Only 11 meromictic lakes are known to exist in the United States, and Soap Lake may be the most extreme of them all. All sorts of unusual substances and life forms may reside in the cold, dense and dark lowermost lake layer.

The conditions of Soap Lake are considered so extraordinary, the National Science Foundation awarded a grant to study the rich microbial diversity that exists within the lake. In 2004, a new genus of bacteria was discovered along the shore of Soap Lake. And the lower levels of the lake are believed to host a variety of extremophiles – microorganisms that have evolved and adapted to living under the especially harsh conditions that exist at the lake bottom. Some believe these microorganisms could someday be applied by the pharmaceutical industry to treat medical ailments or by engineers to clean up hazardous waste. The Soap Lake Conservancy, established in 2000 to preserve and protect the special qualities of Soap Lake, has been instrumental in the study and protection of these microorganisms for possible future medical and engineering applications.

Figure 3-102. Today's sleepy Soap Lake was once a popular tourist destination. UNIVERSITY OF WASHINGTON LIBRARIES, SPECIAL COLLECTIONS, IMAGE NUMBER WAS0051, DATE AND PHOTOGRAPHER UNKNOWN

58. Ephrata Fan and Monster Rock

"Grand Coulee water, on emerging from its rock-bound course, spread widely in Quincy basin, and the extensive gravel deposit there records a great decrease in transporting ability."

– J Harlen Bretz et al (1956)

Features: Giant expansion flood bar with huge basalt- and granitic-bedload boulders

Best Observation Point:

Automobile: Along State Route 17, 14 to 18 miles northwest of Moses Lake (Road Tour No. 4, chapter 5), and along State Route 282 southeast of Ephrata. Monster Rock is about one mile east of State Route 17 on Trout Lodge Road NE.

Elevation: 1,100 to 1,300 feet

Maximum Flood Depth (Elevation): 400 feet (1,500 feet)

- Ephrata Fan is an immense expansion flood bar with many low-lying, interconnected channels and closed basins located at the mouth of Grand Coulee (Soap Lake Exodus, No. 57).

- The huge bar formed as floodwaters burst out of the confines of Grand Coulee and expanded into the Quincy Basin (Plate 30). Water and debris exploded from the mouth of the Grand Coulee, sending debris in a wide swath like pellets from the barrel of a shotgun. The fan is composed of up to 130 feet of bouldery flood sediment.

- Larger boulders at the head of the fan (see Figure 5-36) indicate higher current velocities closer to the fire-hose nozzle, which was Grand Coulee. Farther downstream only smaller pebbles and sand grains were deposited onto the debris fan as floodwaters continued to expand and slow.

- Large boulders of basalt (about 95 percent of the total) that cover the head of the fan were ripped out of Grand Coulee and other scabland channels upstream. The other approximately 5 percent of boulders are granite, mostly derived after the Ice Age floods had breached the head of Grand Coulee and exposed inselbergs along the coulee floor (Nos. 29 and 30).

- The roundness and size of the boulders suggest they were mostly carried as bedload – rolled and tumbled into place along the base of the flood torrent. This is especially true of the granitic boulders that were transported long distances (at least 40 miles) by the floods, from where they originated at the opposite end of Grand Coulee (see Banks Lake Inselbergs, No. 30).

- Neither the granite nor the basalt boulders are technically considered erratics since they weren't carried to their resting place via glacial ice or icebergs. Even if some of the especially large basalt boulders were carried in icebergs they would still not be erratics since the bedrock in this area is also basalt. The strict definition for an erratic is an out-of-place rock carried by ice that is different from the underlying bedrock.

- Most boulders are only a few feet or less in diameter. A few especially large boulders (all basalt) dwarf the others. The largest of these is Monster Rock (Figure 3-103) that weighs more than 1,500 tons! Monster Rock and other extra-large basalt boulders may have been partially buoyed by glacial ice; otherwise, it is difficult to imagine how such huge boulders could have survived transport as intact blocks so far out onto the fan.

Figure 3-103. NASA scientist Matt Golombek, who helped choose landing sites for the 2004 Mars Exploration Rover Mission, stands in front of Monster Rock. This oversized boulder represents the tilted entablature portion of a basalt flow, ripped from the walls of Grand Coulee during megaflooding. A crescent-shaped scour hole occurs in the underlying flood sediment on the upstream side of the boulder, out of view in this photograph. The dimensions of the boulder are 60 by 35 by 25 feet.

- Some of the extremely large basalt boulders, such as Monster Rock, have large depressions upstream and downstream of the boulders. Called scour holes, they formed after the boulders stopped moving; floodwaters continued to flow and sculpt the loose, finer sediment around them.

- The National Aeronautics and Space Administration (NASA) has studied Ephrata Fan as an analog for megafloods on Mars. The geologic processes, landforms and flood deposits geologists have found in the Ephrata Fan are similar to those found along Martian outflow channels. (See "The Mars Connection," page 22 in volume 1 of *On the Trail of the Ice Age Floods: A geological field guide to the Mid-Columbia Basin*).

Waterville Plateau

The Waterville Plateau (Figure 3-104) is a broad, basalt-covered, dish-shaped upland basin that extends west from Grand Coulee to the Columbia River that overall dips gently northward. During most of the last Ice Age floods, the Waterville Plateau was partially covered by the Okanogan Lobe. It was this same ice sheet, up to 1,000 feet thick and 40 miles wide that effectively sealed off most flows of water down the Columbia River Valley, thus creating Glacial Lake Columbia (see Figures 1-11 and 3-54, Plate 1). The plateau is a rich geological showcase of landforms and other features produced by continental glaciation.

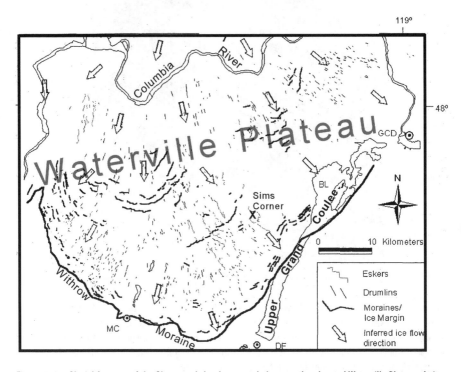

Figure 3-104. Glacial features of the Okanogan Lobe that extended across the elevated Waterville Plateau. At its maximum the ice lobe was thickest (up to 2,000 feet) over the Columbia River Valley and thinned to less than 100 feet along the edge of the ice sheet at the Withrow Moraine. The oscillating glacier deflected the path of Ice Age floods and appears directly responsible for the formation of Moses and Grand coulees. At its farthest advance the ice probably filled the uppermost Grand Coulee (see Figure 3-65, Plate 22). The Withrow Moraine marks the farthest extent of the ice; up to 13 parallel moraines developed as the ice lobe receded. DF = Dry Falls; BL = Banks Lake; MC = Moses Coulee; GCD = Grand Coulee Dam. Modified after Easterbrook 2003.

Glaciers are like conveyor belts, always advancing forward, carrying their load of rock, soil and other debris that was picked up along the way. At the base of the ice sheet is a zone of ice containing a jumbled mixture of rubble mixed with silt and clay, squeezed under the massive weight of an overlying sheet of ice. This material laid down at the base of the glacier is called glacial "till." As the glacier inched southward, eventually the rate of ice advance equaled the rate of melting along the ice front. When the climate was stable the ice front remained stationary. When this happened a landform called an end, or terminal, moraine developed as the ice-carried sediment piled up at the melting front of the glacier. Such a landform, the Withrow Moraine (No. 60), was created on the Waterville Plateau when the Okanogan Lobe reached its maximum extent around 20,000 years ago. The ice lobe stayed in this position long enough for a well-defined ridge of glacial debris to pile up at the front of the glacier (Figures 3-104 and 3-105).

The age of the Withrow Moraine is based on an analysis by scientists Terry Swanson and Marc Caffee who dated six ice-transported boulders deposited atop the moraine. They dated the time since the boulders came to rest on the moraine using a sophisticated exposure-dating technique (i.e., cosmogenic chlorine-36 isotope). During its full advance, the Okanogan Lobe effectively blocked megafloods from the Waterville Plateau (Figure 3-54, Stage 4). Instead, all floodwaters were forced down other coulees (Grand Coulee, Telford-Crab Creek and/or Cheney-Palouse tracts) to the east. Because of the Okanogan Lobe, the record of Ice Age flooding is spotty and incomplete on the Waterville Plateau.

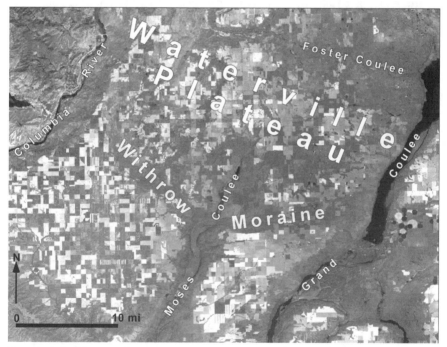

Figure 3-105. Satellite image showing distinct boundary for the Okanogan Lobe as defined by the Withrow Moraine. The boundary separates the more fertile and productive farmlands to the south from darker, less productive, stony farmlands that underlie the former ice sheet north of the moraine.

As the Okanogan Lobe advanced and retreated, Ice Age floods occasionally found their way onto the uplands of the Waterville Plateau. The paths of the floodwaters across the plateau were strongly controlled by the location of the leading edge of the ice sheet. For example, as ice advanced early in the last cycle of glaciation (Figure 3-54, Stage 1), some Ice Age megafloods were diverted southwest toward Moses Coulee.

Most or all the floods that swept over the Waterville Plateau, however, probably only did so until the recessional cataract approached its breaching point at the head of the coulee (No. 29). After the breaching event, most or all of the floodwaters spilled out of the Columbia Valley and naturally followed the path of least resistance, which was down the freshly cut inner canyon of Upper Grand Coulee. With this breach, the coulee was suddenly 900 feet lower than the adjacent plateau. Because of this spillover breach channel, it appears that future Ice Age floods will be permanently cut off from ever again occupying flood routes of the Waterville Plateau.

59. Haystack Rocks

Features: Huge basalt boulders transported across the Waterville Plateau via glacial ice of the Okanogan Lobe, after the last flood swept across the Waterville Plateau

Best Observation Point:

Automobile: Yeager Rock (Figure 3-106) located four miles east of Mansfield along State Route 172

Elevation of Feature: 1,850 to 2,350 feet

- Unusually large, ice-transported boulders of Columbia River basalt called "Haystack Rocks" are spread out across the Waterville Plateau, carried south by the Okanogan Lobe (see Figures 3-107 and 5-47).

- From a distance Haystack Rocks appear like large piles of hay scattered about the mostly flat, expansive farmlands of the Waterville Plateau. Most were dislodged from the Columbia Valley or other coulee walls (e.g., Foster and Horse Lake coulees) where large outcroppings of basalt rock were exposed to the advancing ice sheet.

- Most Haystack Rocks are from the more tightly fractured entablature portion of basalt flows (see Figure 1-2), which hold together better as cohesive blocks. The colonnade portion, on the other hand, tended to break apart into smaller, individual basalt columns as they were plucked away and moved by the ice.

- Even though Haystack Rocks were undoubtedly transported by glacial ice, they are technically not erratics. That is because they are composed of basalt, which also forms the bedrock in this region. To be a true erratic, an ice-transported boulder needs to be different than the underlying bedrock.

Figure 3-106. Yeager Rock – perhaps the most renowned Haystack Rock of the Waterville Plateau. A roadcut along State Route 172 exposes the base of the huge boulder of basalt entablature, which rests on a bed of glacial till (close-up in inset). The glacial till here was laid down at the base of the glacier and is characterized by gravel-sized pieces floating in a poorly sorted, massive matrix of mostly light-colored, compacted, powdery silt. The till agglomeration was compressed and bound together under the tremendous weight of up to a thousand feet of now-absent glacial ice. Yeager Rock was deposited over the till as the ice sheet melted back toward Canada. Looking north.

60. Withrow Moraine

"The Withrow moraine crossing of Moses Coulee is unique in all scabland. It is a very strongly expressed ridge or series of ridge hills of glacial drift marking the extreme southern limit ever reached by the northern ice sheet on this part of the plateau."

– J Harlen Bretz (1959)

Features: Low, broad ridge of bouldery glacial till marking the farthest limit of the Okanogan Lobe and Haystack Rocks

Best Observation Point:

Automobile: Upper Moses Coulee, two miles southwest of Jameson Lake; one mile north of Withrow along State Route 172 (Road Tour No. 5, chapter 5)

Elevation of Feature: 1,800 feet along the floor of Moses Coulee to 3,000 feet north of Withrow

Figure 3-107. Huge basalt boulders (Haystack Rocks) line the distinct edge of the Withrow Moraine (dashed line). The smooth, cultivated fields on the left lay just beyond the former edge of the Okanogan Lobe, which achieved equilibrium here (i.e., rate of glacial melting equaled rate of ice advance) for an extended period of time. Like a conveyor belt, the Okanogan Lobe continued bringing bouldery debris to the glacier's edge before coming to rest onto the moraine about 20,000 years ago. Location: 10 miles west of Mansfield, N47.8304, W119.8712. Looking north.

- While the Withrow Moraine wasn't created by nor did it come into contact with megafloods, it does reflect the location of the Okanogan Lobe, which had a major impact on flooding.

- The moraine is a hummocky low ridge of glacial till up to one mile wide and 250 feet high that marks the farthest extent of the glacial ice on the Waterville Plateau (Figures 3-104, 3-107 and 3-108; see also Figures 5-44 and 5-47).

- The moraine can be continuously traced for 35 miles from the west side of the Waterville Plateau to the Upper Grand Coulee on the east (Figures 3-104 and 3-105).

- The moraine is highly visible from the air because of the distinct contrast between the type of sediment present on either side of the moraine (Figure 3-105). Soils on the moraine and northward are composed of mostly bouldery glacial till – a stony soil that is not crop-friendly and difficult to cultivate – as well as dispersed Haystack Rocks (Figure 3-107; see also Figure 5-45). Just beyond the moraine, however, lies finer-grained and better-sorted sandy loess and glacial outwash, laid down as a blanket beyond the edge of the ice sheet (Figure 3-107; see also Figure 5-46). Because the sediment deposited in front of the glacier is more evenly graded, and contains virtually no stones, it is more fertile and much easier to cultivate. Visible on aerial photographs, then, beyond the moraine is a rich, heavily cultivated, continuous patchwork of farmlands; north of the moraine is a more sparse patchwork of less-productive farmlands (Figure 3-105).

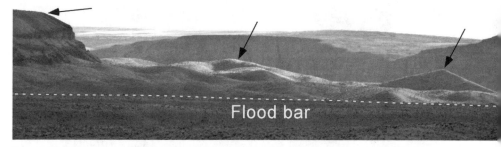

Flood bar

Figure 3-108. The hummocky Withrow Moraine (arrows) where it crosses upper Moses Coulee. Glacial till of the moraine is superimposed onto a crescent-type flood bar, more proof that advance of the ice sheet came after the last outburst flood poured down Moses Coulee. Looking west. An exposure of the interior of the moraine is shown in Figure 5-45.

- Since the Withrow Moraine is preserved in an undisturbed state where it crosses Moses Coulee (Figure 3-108), this suggests that the Okanogan Lobe must have advanced over the coulee after the last megaflood ran down Moses Coulee. If any post-moraine floods had used Moses Coulee, they would have destroyed or at least severely modified the moraine, yet the moraine is pristine and undisturbed.

- Today, glacial deposits of the moraine are absent within Grand Coulee itself, after being washed away during outburst floods that used Grand Coulee after the Withrow Moraine was formed about 20,000 years ago.

61. Moses Coulee

"The empty canyons and dry cataracts of the plateau are easily the most conspicuous scabland forms. Among the canyons Grand Coulee takes precedence, followed by Moses Coulee."

– J Harlen Bretz (1928)

Features: Abandoned cataracts, plunge pools, recessional cataract canyons, hanging coulees, rock basins, potholes, mesas, buttes, rock benches and flood bars

Best Observation Points:

Automobile: Along U.S. Highway 2, 18 miles west of Coulee City; and along Palisades, Moses Coulee and Jameson Lake roads, which run most of the length of Moses Coulee (Road Tour No. 5, chapter 5).

Non-motorized trails: Two trails within the Three Devils Scabland Complex (chapter 4, Trail KK)

Watercraft: Via public launch sites in upper Moses Coulee at Jameson and Grimes lakes

Elevation of Feature: Descends from 2,200 feet at its head to 800 feet at the mouth over nearly 50 miles

Maximum Flood Depth (Elevation): 1,100 feet (1,900 feet) within the lower coulee; 300 feet (2,500 feet) in the upper coulee

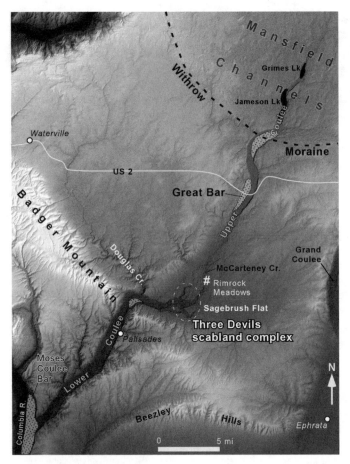

Figure 3-109. Shaded-relief map of 50-mile-long Moses Coulee on the Waterville Plateau. Stippled areas represent flood bars along the coulee.

- Next to Grand Coulee, 50-mile-long Moses Coulee, with its 800-foot-tall walls, is the longest and deepest of the scabland coulees. The more remote Moses Coulee begins high up on the Waterville Plateau and makes a long, 1,400-foot descent southwest to the Columbia River (Figure 3-109; see also Figure 6-13).

- Floodwaters coming down upper Moses Coulee fanned out into the Rimrock Meadows area before descending into a complex maze of channels and coulees along McCarteney Creek, referred to here as the Three Devils scabland complex (Figure 3-110; see Figures 4-105 to 4-107 and 6-26, Plate 46). The scabland complex ends just above the Billingsley Ranch in a series of hanging coulees and cliffs that drop into the flat-bottomed lower Moses Coulee (see Figures 4-106 and 5-42). Below the Three Devils scabland complex, lower Moses Coulee returns to a single deep channel, up to 800 feet deep all the way to the mouth of the coulee where it joins the Columbia Valley (Figure 3-109; see also Figures 5-41, 6-13 and 6-27, Plate 49).

Figure 3-110. Looking down Three Devils Coulee toward a bifurcating hanging coulee, which drops precipitously into the lower Moses Coulee beyond.

- Moses Coulee was created by outburst floods that followed the ancestral McCarteney Creek, once a "normal" stream valley. This is indicated by the many wonderful examples of hanging valleys that feed and drop into the flood-deepened coulee. These hanging valleys formed in a similar way as those along the Lower Grand Coulee (No. 56) – from lazy tributary streams that drained off the higher ridges prior to the mega-floods. Outburst floods quickly over-deepened and -widened the coulee, which left the side valleys hanging up to 600 feet above today's valley floor (Plate 49).

- Near the head of Moses Coulee lies Grimes Lake where it merges with the Mansfield Channels, a broad network of low-relief channelways. The Mansfield Channels may be relict megaflood channels that were later partially backfilled with glacial debris and modified by meltwater streams draining off the front of the Okanogan Lobe.

- At least five separate Ice Age flood events are known to have occurred based on an analysis of flood deposits at the mouth of Moses Coulee by geologist Richard Waitt.

- The lack of caliche, or other signs of soil development, on the moraine or flood deposits within the coulee appears to suggest that Moses Coulee formed from outburst floods that occurred earlier in the last glacial cycle (late Wisconsinan Glaciation) but probably not during one of many older, pre-Wisconsinan glacial cycles (see Figure 1-8).

- The age of the last flood down Moses Coulee is estimated at greater than 20,000 years ago – the age of the Withrow Moraine that partially blocks the floor of Moses Coulee (Figures 3-108 and 3-109). Today the Withrow Moraine lies undisturbed on the valley floor; had more floods come down Moses Coulee after the last glacial maximum, they would have surely wiped out or severely modified the moraine.

- Floods in Moses Coulee apparently occurred during a time when the Waterville Plateau extended, uninterrupted, many tens of miles to the east over the area where Grand Coulee lies today (Figure 3-54, stage 1). A higher ridge (i.e., Coulee Monocline) separated this area from the Hartline Basin south of the plateau. Prior to the floods, lazy streams (Horse Lake and Foster creeks) flowed west across this basalt upland. With the advance of the Okanogan Lobe and blocking of the Columbia River, these streams and any megafloods would have been diverted along the ice front and forced to flow southwest over the low divide near the Mansfield Channels and into the head of McCarteney Creek.

- All this must have happened before the carving of cavernous Grand Coulee; otherwise, most (or all) the floodwater would have simply flowed down the much-deeper Grand Coulee. In fact, this is exactly what happened during later floods when the Grand Coulee cataract canyon had receded to the vicinity of Steamboat Falls (Figure 3-54, Stage 4), which permanently cut off the flow of floodwater across the Waterville Plateau and Moses Coulee.

- The Great Bar of Moses Coulee, an immense flood bar and an established National Natural Landmark, lies four miles downstream of the Withrow Moraine (Figures 3-109 and 3-111, Plate 47). This giant bar, 250 feet tall, three miles long and 0.75 mile wide, hugs the inside of the broad bend in upper Moses Coulee just below a basalt headland. As such, it can be considered a combination pendant-crescent-longitudinal flood bar (see Figure 2-32).

Figure 3-111. The immense Great Bar of Moses Coulee. An outwash train or network of the braided stream channels was derived from glacial melting of the Okanogan Lobe, once located only a few miles upvalley to the right. Notice that floods spilled over onto the tall plateau surface on either side of the coulee. Bar is located in Figure 3-109.

- Just upstream and around the edge of the Great Bar, along the coulee floor, lies a network of abandoned braided-stream channels (Figure 3-111, see Figure 6-14). The braided channels lie within an outwash train formed by melting of the Okanogan Lobe that once filled Moses Coulee only a few miles to the north. Multiple, surging meltwater streams drained out of the front of the glacier, carrying lots of suspended sediment, which spread out across the valley bottom as a braided stream.

- A huge, hammerhead-shaped expansion flood bar built up at the mouth of Moses Coulee where it emptied into the Columbia Valley (Figure 3-109). The bar temporarily blocked the Columbia River with flood debris, creating a transient lake several hundred feet deep that backed up towards Wenatchee. The evidence for this lake lies in varve-like sediments exposed just above Rock Island Dam, at the north end of the flood bar (see Figure 3-118). Later floods coming off the Channeled Scabland to the east backflooded the Columbia Valley from the south via Potholes Coulee (see Figure 3-118). In this ancient lake, flood-deposited beds of sand are sandwiched in between layers of lake-deposited silt. A last outburst flood that came down the Columbia Valley from Glacial Lake Columbia at the end of the Ice Age (14,000 to 15,000 years ago), after the last Missoula flood, breached Moses Coulee bar and drained the lake.

- Most geologists have assumed Moses Coulee was carved by outburst floods from Glacial Lake Missoula. However, another possibility for the origin of Moses Coulee may be floodwaters coming from a subglacial outburst flood from beneath the Okanogan Lobe itself. A number of Canadian geologists, including John Shaw and Jerome Lesseman, have argued in favor of subglacial outburst floods for a number of years for at least some of the megafloods that created the Channeled Scabland, including Moses Coulee.

62. Foster and Horse Lake Coulees

Features: Two stream valleys that originally drained the Waterville Plateau and perhaps later used to deliver Ice Age floodwater into Moses Coulee

Best Observation Point:

Automobile:

    Foster Coulee: State Route 17 west of Leahy and Foster Road east of Leahy
    Horse Lake Coulee: Hawks Cliff Road that heads east off State Route 17

Elevation of Feature: Floor of Foster Coulee ranges from 1,200 to 2,100 feet; Horse Lake Coulee ranges from 2,230 to 2,280 feet. Coulee walls are up to several hundred feet tall.

- Foster and Horse Lake coulees form east-west trending valleys that cross a portion of the Waterville Plateau (Figures 3-112 and 3-113).

Figure 3-112. Foster and Horse Lake coulees hang above Upper Grand Coulee. Foster (background) and Horse Lake (foreground) coulees were last used to drain meltwater off the Okanogan Lobe. Note prominent delta bars that protrude out into Banks Lake reservoir; these formed when the glacial meltwater flowed over the hanging coulees into the Glacial Lake Columbia that once rose another 200 feet above present-day Banks Lake. Sediment transported by meltwater streams from the Okanogan Lobe accumulated onto the once-submerged delta bars below. Before the floods and Upper Grand Coulee became a recessional cataract canyon, the now-hanging Foster and Horse Lake coulees were shallow and gentle, west-flowing stream valleys when not occupied by glacial ice. The excavation of Grand Coulee by cataract recession during Ice Age floods came later.

- Horse Lake Coulee lies several miles south of Foster Coulee, which it parallels for seven miles before bending north to join Foster Coulee. The Horse Lake Coulee splits into two channels about three miles west of Grand Coulee (Figure 3-113).

- Foster and Horse Lake coulees existed before the first Ice Age floods carved out Moses Coulee. Both coulees were originally normal, north-west-flowing stream valleys that drained the much-broader Waterville Plateau that once existed before the formation of Grand Coulee (Figure 3-54, Stage 1).

- Today the heads of Foster and Horse Lake coulees hang precipitously about 500 feet above the west wall of the Upper Grand Coulee (Figures 3-112; see also Figure 3-75). Both coulees descend to the west; the heads of these channels originally may have extended farther east but were consumed and destroyed during recession of the cataract that formed the precipitous, inner canyon of the Upper Grand Coulee.

- A cross channel preserved atop Steamboat Rock (see Figure 3-59), which roughly lines up with Foster Coulee, may be a preserved remnant of the ancestral Foster Creek at a time before the Upper Grand Coulee was incised into the Waterville Plateau (see Figure 3-54, Stage 1).

- At least five floods responsible for development of Moses Coulee (No. 61) may have been routed through Foster and Horse Lake coulees earlier in the last glacial cycle. Once the Grand Coulee cataract had receded to near Steamboat Falls (Figure 3-54, Stage 4), however, overland flow of floodwaters to Moses Coulee, as well as Foster and Horse Lake coulees, was cut off in favor of the suddenly much-deeper Grand Coulee created by ensuing cataract recession.

- From then on the upper ends of Foster and Horse Lake coulees served as channels that transported glacial meltwater in a reverse direction (eastward) from underneath and/or away from the front of the Okanogan Lobe (Figure 3-113; see also Figure 3-54, Stages 4 through 6, and Figures 3-74 and 3-75). During the maximum extent of the ice sheet, marked by the Withrow Moraine (No. 60), the area of Foster and Horse Lake coulees was deeply buried beneath glacial ice (Figure 3-54, Stage 3). Therefore, it may have been only during intermediate stages of ice advance and retreat that these coulees were used to transport meltwater from the Okanogan Lobe like that shown in Figure 3-74.

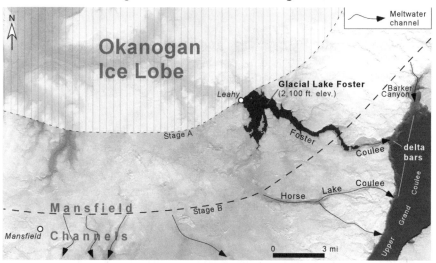

Figure 3-113. Shaded-relief map of Waterville Plateau in the vicinity of Foster and Horse Lake coulees. Ice-dammed Glacial Lake Foster rose to an elevation of about 2,100 feet at Stage A, before spilling east over a divide into the Upper Grand Coulee and Glacial Lake Columbia. By the time ice had advanced to Stage B, glacial meltwater also drained into upper Grand Coulee from Horse Lake Coulee and Barker Canyon. Glacial meltwater also drained south into Moses Coulee via the late-glacial Mansfield Channels (Figure 3-109).

- The last activity in Foster and Horse Lake coulees was the transfer of glacial meltwater from the melting Okanogan Lobe into Upper Grand Coulee. This is indicated by the preservation of lake deposits in Foster Coulee and lake-delta bars within Upper Grand Coulee (Figure 3-113).

- Lake deposits formed in ancient Glacial Lake Foster (2,100 feet elevation) when the Okanogan Lobe blocked west-flowing Foster Creek (Figures 3-113). Lake Foster then overflowed and drained eastward before dropping 500 feet into Glacial Lake Columbia, which occupied the Upper Grand Coulee at the close of the Ice Age.

- Where the hanging meltwater streams dropped into Upper Grand Coulee, beautifully preserved delta bars (No. 38) prograded into the Lake Columbia (see Figures 3-74). No more Ice Age floods occurred after this time; otherwise, the delta bars would have been severely modified or destroyed. Glacial Lake Columbia must have persisted for many more centuries after the last Ice Age flood as indicated by hundreds of silty Lake Columbia varves that cover the floor of Upper Grand Coulee.

- Glacial Lake Columbia drained suddenly from the Upper Grand Coulee at the very end of the Ice Age when the debris dam at the Coulee Expansion Bar (No. 37) failed (see "Lake Columbia Floods" sidebar on page 130).

Columbia Plateau Perimeter

63. Columbia Valley Strandlines and Terraces

Features: Wave-cut benches and terraced sediment bars of former Glacial Lake Columbia

Best Observation Points:

Automobile: Strandlines most visible along Spring Canyon Road, 3.6 miles east of intersection with State Route 174 (Figure 3-114), and across the Columbia River into the Swawilla Basin another 1.5 miles farther east. More strandlines are visible under good lighting conditions south of State Route 174 from four to seven miles east of the town of Grand Coulee. Multiple terraces visible where State Route 25 and State Route 21 (Keller Ferry) cross the Columbia Valley.

Non-motorized trail: Several terrace levels visible from Fort Spokane Trail (chapter 4, Trail LL)

Watercraft: Via Lake Roosevelt about seven river miles west of Keller Ferry

Elevation of Feature: Visible strandlines rise from about 1,900 to 2,400 feet; as many as 10 different sediment terraces are found up to elevations of 1,900 feet.

Maximum Flood Depth (Elevation): More than 100 feet (2,500 feet)

- Mountains of ice, hundreds to thousands of feet thick, advanced southward into the Pacific Northwest, blocking stream valleys and creating hundreds of lakes, big and small. Glacial Lake Missoula was the "granddaddy" of them all, but other large lakes such as Glacial Lake Columbia formed when ice of the Okanogan Lobe blocked the Columbia River near and downstream of Grand Coulee Dam (Plates 11 and 22). Manmade Lake Roosevelt behind Grand Coulee Dam today is a much smaller version of Lake Columbia (see Figure 6-19, Plate 50). Another ice-dam blockage occurred, apparently during an earlier glacial cycle, when the Columbia Lobe came down the Columbia River valley from the north and blocked the Spokane River to form Glacial Lake Spokane (Plate 11). At their highest levels Glacial Lake Columbia, along with Lake Spokane, backed up all the way to the edge of the ice dam for Glacial Lake Missoula near present-day Lake Pend Oreille (Plate 3).

- Waves created by surface winds blowing across the glacial lakes eroded dozens of faint, parallel wave-cut strandlines that reflect former levels of the glacial lakes (Figure 3-114). The highest strandline (elevation 2,400 feet) represents the highest level of Lake Columbia against the shoreline. Most strandlines lie beneath the 2,300-foot level, however, and a few stand out more than others. Today the strandlines are only visible in a few protected places where flood, or post-flood, erosion didn't destroy them, which is mostly at the western end of the ancient Glacial Lake Columbia, near Grand Coulee Dam.

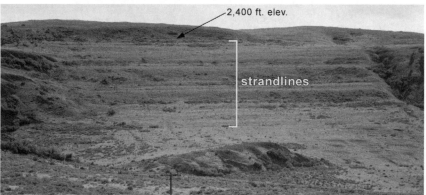

Figure 3-114. Horizontal wave-cut benches (strandlines) etched into the high, south wall of the Columbia River valley between Spring and Neal canyons (N47.9346, W118.8825). Strandlines go up to elevation 2,400 feet, marking the highest level for Glacial Lake Columbia. These strandlines were etched into the hillside prior to the last floods, which are known to have breached the head of Grand Coulee (No. 29) and suddenly lowered the outlet for Lake Columbia from elevation 2,400 feet to 1,500 feet. Looking southwest.

- The lowest spillover channels for the last floods to enter the Cheney-Palouse and Telford Crab-Creek scablands lie at an elevation of about 2,300 feet. Strandlines in ancient Glacial Lake Columbia, however, rise at least another 100 feet. Therefore, it appears spillover channels into the Channeled Scabland were lowered by at least 100 feet, probably from flood erosion, since Lake Columbia attained its maximum height.

- Another revealing feature of Glacial Lake Columbia are remnants of up to 10 nested terraces along the valley margins (Figure 3-115, Plate 50). These terraces signify a complex history of changing lake levels related to advance and retreat of Okanogan Lobe and the changing height of the bedrock spillway at the head of Grand Coulee (No. 29).

- The highest terrace (about elevation 1,900 feet) is oldest – and the lowest (about elevation 960 feet) is youngest. Each terrace once continued across the valley, but was later incised and partially backfilled with megaflood rhythmites (No. 64) associated with lowered levels of Glacial Lake Columbia and/or Lake Spokane.

- The upper terraces likely formed when the glacial lakes were at their highest level (about elevation 2,400 feet); this was apparently before spillovers incised far into heads of the scabland channels leading into the Cheney-Palouse and Telford-Crab Creek tracts. Lower terraces formed after the lake was suddenly lowered by 900 feet with a spillover breach at the head of Grand Coulee (No. 29) late in the last glacial cycle. The lowest terraces probably formed behind the dwindling, latest-glacial Okanogan ice dam and/or glacial-debris dams within the Columbia River Valley.

Figure 3-115. Terraces of ancient Glacial Lake Columbia. Top: Four nested terraces preserved at multiple levels along modern-day Lake Roosevelt. Of these, the highest terrace (No. 4) is the oldest and the lowest terrace (No. 1) is the youngest. Looking northwest toward the confluence of the Columbia and Spokane valleys. Bottom: Multiple terraces (arrows) along the lower Spokane River Valley in 1940. Looking east. UNIVERSITY OF WASHINGTON COLLECTION

64. Lake Columbia Rhythmites

Features: Dozens of rhythmite beds composed of Ice Age flood sediment separated by still more dozens of varves from Glacial Lake Columbia

Best Observation Points:

Note: Rhythmite exposures in the Sanpoil Valley are located on land owned by the Colville Tribes of the Colville Reservation and not accessible by land via any public roads or trails. However, excellent exposures of rhythmites are visible along the shoreline of Lake Roosevelt – a public waterway.

Automobile: Hangman Creek Rhythmites (No. 11) are visible along U.S. Highway 195, about six miles south of Interstate 90.

Non-motorized trails (chapter 4): Campion Park (Trail H) and Hawk Bay Rhythmites (Trail MM)

Watercraft: Sanpoil Arm of Lake Roosevelt, one to seven river miles north of the Keller Ferry landing and Hawk Bay Arm two to four river miles south of Seven Bays Marina

Elevation of Feature: 1,290 to 1,330 feet

Maximum Flood Depth (Elevation): 1,600 feet (2,500 feet)!

- Rhythmite sequences along the Hawk Creek and Sanpoil River arms of Lake Roosevelt display a record of multiple Ice Age floods, separated by dozens of years of quiet-lake varve deposition within Glacial Lake Columbia (Figure 3-116; see also Figures 4-112, 4-113 and 2-36). Today, some of these rhythmites are visible along the shores of Lake Roosevelt (1,290 feet elevation) reservoir, the much lower, modern equivalent to Lake Columbia (Plate 11).

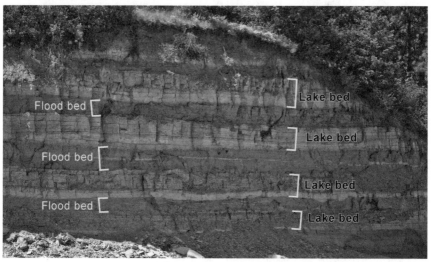

Figure 3-116. Rhythmite-lake beds exposed along the Sanpoil Arm of Lake Roosevelt. Three dark layers are sandy rhythmites, each laid down in a matter of hours during Ice Age flooding. In between rhythmites are lighter-colored, varved lake beds, laid down over dozens of years between outburst floods within Glacial Lake Columbia.

- Considerable landsliding along the banks of Lake Roosevelt (see Figure 4-111) has occurred, due to seasonal and man-made fluctuations of the lake behind Grand Coulee Dam. Fortuitously, slumping along these land-slides has created many excellent exposures of these ancient deposits that have revealed some formerly hidden secrets of Ice Age flooding.

- During most outburst floods, prodigious Lake Columbia already occu-pied the Columbia River Valley behind an ice dam created by the Okanogan Lobe (Plate 11). Apparently every few dozen years or so, the relatively quiet lake was violently overrun by an outburst flood from Lake Missoula. The deep waters of Lake Columbia buffered and protected the lake bottom during the sudden deluge, allowing a sediment pulse to be deposited and preserved along the lake bottom. Sediment deposition from megafloods is especially well-preserved in more protected arms of Lake Columbia, such as Hangman Creek (Figure 3-20), Hawk Creek (Figure 4-112) and the Sanpoil Valley (Figure 2-36).

- The scenario for the depositional record follows. First deposited was all the suspended sediment (mostly sand) in the turbulent floodwater. Within a few days after a flood, all the sand would have settled out of suspension, leaving behind still-floating fine particles of silt and clay. These particles took weeks to months to slowly sink to the bottom of the lake, which remained after each flood event. In the wake of each out-burst flood, normal lake sedimentation resumed, depositing a sequence of silt-clay varves (see Figure 2-30) derived from glacial meltwater drain-ing into Lake Columbia from the north. Most of these varves are only fractions of an inch thick.

- Like tree rings each varve represents a single, annual cycle of lake depo-sition. A maximum of 55 varves, and an average of about a few dozen, have been observed between flood beds in the Sanpoil Valley, suggest-ing as many years separated each flood outburst for at least the last glacial cycle.

- At times the depth of the floodwaters that formed the rhythmites could have been up to 1,600 feet deep up against the Okanogan Lobe ice dam (Plate 11)!

65. Pangborn Flood Bar

Features: Giant pendant-crescent flood bar, giant current ripples and signifi-cant archaeological remains

Best Observation Point:

Automobile: State Route 28 south of East Wenatchee (Road Tour No. 5, chap-ter 5); between Grant and Batterman roads east of East Wenatchee atop the flood bar

Elevation of Feature: Bar ranges from 600 to 1,200 feet

Maximum Flood Depth (Elevation): 1,000 feet (1,700 feet), based on the height of ice-rafted erratics just north of Pangborn Bar

- Pangborn Bar is a gigantic 600-foot-tall, combination pendant-crescent bar four miles long and two miles wide that underlies East Wenatchee along the east side of the Columbia River (Figures 3-117 and 3-118).

- The bar naturally accumulated in the slightly slower flow of floodwaters that developed along the inside of a broad bend in the Columbia Valley (crescent-bar position) and just downstream of an ancient, pre-flood landslide complex (pendant-bar position). Locally atop of the bar are giant current ripples and ice-rafted erratics.

- The massive Pangborn Bar probably formed early in the last glacial cycle during one or more of especially large Ice Age floods, which traveled down the Columbia Valley before the Okanogan Lobe had fully advanced across the Columbia River (see Figure 1-11, position A). The flood(s) that created Pangborn Bar must have occurred sometime between 25,000 to 28,000 years ago, since after that time the Okanogan Lobe blocked the Columbia Valley from the largest floods.

Figure 3-117. Aerial view onto the huge, flat-topped Pangborn flood bar. Looking south over East Wenatchee.

- A giant eddy scar lies at the downstream end of Pangborn Bar where a huge, one- to two-mile-wide whirlpool formed from floodwaters that swirled around the outside of the valley near Jumpoff Ridge (Figure 3-118). This is similar to an eddy scar that developed at the downstream end of the Priest Rapids Bar (see Volume 1 of *On the Trail of the Ice Age Floods*), another crescent-type bar, after floodwaters were forced around a curving flow path.

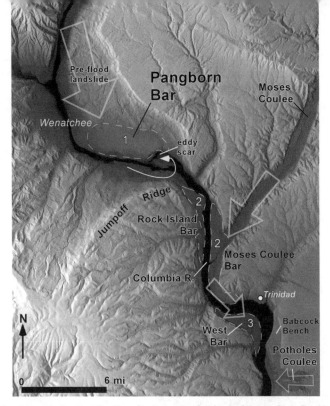

Figure 3-118. Pangborn and other giant flood bars (dashed outlines) along the Columbia River. Flood bars were formed by three very different sizes and ages of giant floods. 1) Pangborn Bar was deposited from an especially large flood that came down the Columbia Valley early in the last glacial cycle (about 25,000 to 28,000 years ago) from the north before the Okanogan Lobe advanced onto the Waterville Plateau (see Figure 1-11, position A). 2) This was followed by at least five floods that came down Moses Coulee after the flow of floodwater was diverted onto the Waterville Plateau by the Okanogan Lobe but prior to the development of Grand Coulee. The last Ice Age flood also came solely down the Columbia Valley associated with the breakup of the Okanogan Lobe and drainage of Glacial Lake Columbia around 14,000 years ago. 3) This last flood created West Bar with its wonderfully preserved ripple surface (Figure 3-119). This last outburst flood, from Glacial Lake Columbia, cut into and modified the older Pangborn and Moses Coulee bars.

- Most of the later floods, including those from Glacial Lake Missoula, were diverted across the Channeled Scabland when the Okanogan Lobe advanced across the horn of the Columbia Valley (see Figure 1-11, positions B through E).

- Outburst flooding down the Columbia Valley through Wenatchee also occurred at the very end of the Ice Age (about 14,000 years ago). This was during the final breakup of the Okanogan Lobe, which suddenly released the contents of Glacial Lake Columbia. Flood features from this last flood, however, do not extend far up the valley walls, so it appears this last flood was volumetrically much smaller than the earlier flood(s).

- This last Glacial Lake Columbia flood was probably not deep enough to overtop Pangborn bar (elevation 1,200 feet). This is indicated by high bars from Channeled Scabland floods downriver at Babcock Bench, along the east side of the Columbia River, that show no sign of erosion by a Glacial Lake Columbia outburst flood above 1,000 feet.

- The evidence for this last flood (i.e., Lake Columbia) lies in the giant bed-load boulders atop younger flood bars (see Figure 5-50) lower in the valley, as well as giant current ripples atop West Bar (Figure 3-119). These clearly show that a last outburst flood could have only come down the Columbia Valley from the north.

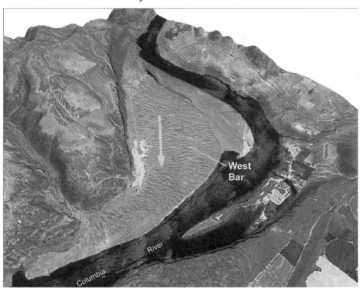

Figure 3-119. Giant current ripples atop West Bar, looking north. The character of the ripples indicates the flow of water that created them was directly down the Columbia River valley from the north (arrow) at the very end of the Ice Age (i.e., the breakup of Glacial Lake Columbia).

- In between the earlier, largest flood(s), and the smaller, Lake Columbia flood that came directly down the Columbia River Valley, there was a series of other floods that affected the Wenatchee area. These other floods cut across the Waterville Plateau via Moses Coulee when the horn of the Columbia was blocked by the Okanogan Lobe (see Figure 1-11, positions B and C) but prior to the development of Upper Grand Coulee (Figure 3-54, Stage 1), or perhaps from subglacial outpourings from directly beneath the Okanogan Lobe. At least five floods flowed down Moses Coulee during this time. However, Moses Coulee was eventually cut off from the Missoula floods by cataract recession and drastic deepening of the Upper Grand Coulee later in the last glacial cycle.

- A cache of American Indian, Clovis-age spear points was discovered in an excavation atop Pangborn Bar in 1988 (since backfilled). The age of the spear points is estimated at 13,100 years based on the presence of radiocarbon-dated Glacier Peak volcanic ash adhering to one of the spear points. This is direct evidence that native peoples occupied this area within at least one or two thousand years of the last Ice Age floods. The extraordinary spear points are presently on display at the Burke Museum in Seattle.

Figure 4-1. Several trails, including the Pine Lakes Loop Trail (Trail L) shown here, wander through the flood-ravaged wetlands of the Turnbull National Wildlife Refuge.

Part II: Trails and Tours

"The elephantine character of the channeled scabland demands more than cursory inspection, more than detailed study of limited portions."

— *J Harlen Bretz et al (1956)*

The best way to appreciate the power and magnitude of the Ice Age floods is to get out and see the features they left behind. Like a giant maze, the floods created a complex network of interconnected pathways across the region. Because the scale of the floods is so huge, their evidence can be witnessed from a variety of distances and viewpoints, each providing a different perspective. Depending on time, budget and physical ability, you can experience flood features by 1) off-road trails via horseback, mountain bike or on foot; 2) public roadways via automobile or bike; or 3) aircraft. A few of the features also can be viewed up close via boat from the Columbia River or from one of the hundreds of lakes and other waterways within the region.

Chapter 4 focuses on more than 40 non-motorized trails. The five road tours and two aerial tours, described in chapters 5 and 6, are designed to cover the most and best flood features in the least amount of distance and time. Most flood features included in this guide are visible from public lands. However, some important features are also located on private lands that are not accessible to the public. These features cannot be ignored, however, because they, too, sometimes provide important pieces in the puzzle of the floods' story. Specific directions to features on private lands have been intentionally omitted to protect the rights and privacy of landowners. While exploring flood features, please stay on road right-of-ways, respect the rights of private-property owners and obey all posted signs.

Summit of Castle Rock, Upper Grand Coulee, looking south

4

Trails of the Ice Age Floods

This chapter describes more than 40 non-motorized, off-road trails on public lands within the region that are accessible by foot, mountain bike, horse, and/or watercraft. Each trail is designated by a one- or two-letter code used throughout this book (Figure 4-2).

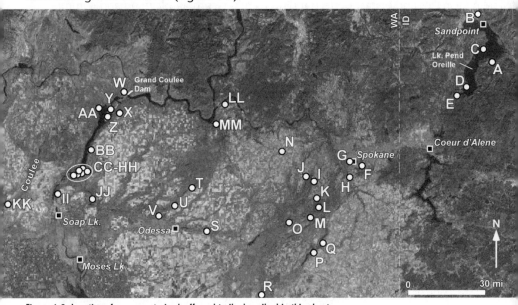

Figure 4-2. Locations for non-motorized, off-road trails described in this chapter.

Geographic coordinates (latitude, longitude) for specific key locations are sometimes provided in parentheses after the features of interest. These points may be entered into a Global Positioning System (GPS) receiver for easier navigation and location. Before using the coordinates, be sure to set the reference datum of your GPS unit to WGS84.

Get a Permit

Recreational-use permits are required to support facilities managed by Washington state agencies including Washington State Parks, the Washington Department of Fish and Wildlife (WDFW) and Department of Natural Resources. Vehicle-use permits from the WDFW automatically come with the purchase of fishing or hunting licenses; however, for all other state lands, a Discover Pass is required to recreate in and park on state lands. Discover Passes are available online at www.discoverpass.wa.gov or by phone at

866-320-9933; in person from one of 600 recreational license vendors where Washington State fishing and hunting licenses are sold; when you renew your vehicle license; at state parks headquarters and regional offices; and at state parks when staff is available. Both annual and one-day passes are available.

Safety Considerations

The trails highlighted in this book are designed for those with a sense of adventure and personal responsibility. Exploring any of the trails described has inherent risks, some of which are hidden. These risks and warnings include, but are not limited to, vehicular traffic, inclement weather, including extreme heat and cold, waterways, wildfire, cliffs, waterfalls, animals, plants, insects, uneven footing, treacherous obstacles, slippery or unstable surfaces, and poisonous snakes and plants. Understanding warnings, proper planning and common sense are required before undertaking outdoor activities.

Figure 4-3. Most of the trails featured in this book receive little or no maintenance; as such many trails are overgrown and poorly marked, or unmarked altogether. Shown here is one of the trail markers along an underused and overgrown U.S. Bureau of Land Management trail to the Odessa Craters (Trail U).

Many of the trails are poorly marked or not marked at all, especially in the sparsely populated, infrequently visited areas of the central Channeled Scabland. Some of the trails require cross-country travel along part or most their length; these are automatically classified as "difficult." For these trails be sure to carry and know how to use a map and compass, or a GPS unit – solo travel is not recommended. Be especially aware of rattlesnakes, which can be expected anywhere in the Channeled Scabland any time of the year. Beware of ticks when walking through brush in spring to early summer. Because most trails are dry with no potable water or shade, it is best to avoid midday exposure during the summer; early or late in the day is usually best. Carry plenty of drinking water to stay hydrated during all times of the year. To avoid the nuisance of cheatgrass seeds clinging to socks and boots, wear gaiters if hiking in spring through late summer.

Also be vigilant to "leave no trace" while traveling through the fragile and delicate shrub-steppe habitat of the Channeled Scabland region. Whenever possible use existing trails or pathways so as not to "bust the crust." Over time a slightly consolidated cryptobiotic crust develops on the surface of shrub-steppe environments; this helps to hold the soil together and reduces the potential for surface erosion as well as noxious-weed invasion. Animal traffic, including humans, can break apart the crust and leave the soil vulnerable.

Geocaching

Geocaching is a modern-day equivalent of hide-and-seek or orienteering, except explorers use an electronic GPS receiver to hone in on a specific location. At the time of this writing, hundreds of geocaches have been hidden by outdoor enthusiasts within the Channeled Scabland, and the number keeps growing. The locations of geocaches, most of which require some hiking to find, can be found at www.geocaching.com.

Three special geocaches, called Earthcaches, have been located within Grand Coulee by the authors. Earthcaches identify features of special geologic significance and are a virtual type of geocache – no cache container or any other man-made object is present. The three geocaches (and identification codes) are: 1) Northrup Lake Plungepool (GC2CH5Q), 2) Steamboat Rock Glacial Moraine (GC2EN2R) and 3) Great Blade Notch (GC2BX9T). From these Earthcaches the evidence for the Ice Age floods and desolate beauty of the region is especially striking. To access information and descriptions for these Earthcaches, just enter the GC codes listed above within www.geocaching.com, enter the coordinates into your GPS and go. The authors plan to place more Earthcaches at more spectacular viewpoints for Ice Age floods' features in the future.

Trails in the Vicinity of Ice-Dam Breakout

Modern Lake Pend Oreille is situated in about the same position as the ice dam that created Glacial Lake Missoula (Plate 3). The modern lake sits in an intermontane valley, which was filled with thousands of feet of ice as recently as 15,000 years ago. After each ice dam failure and ensuing flood, portions of the Clark Fork Valley (Plate 4) would be ice free for only a few years before more ice flowed south down the Purcell Trench, rapidly refilling the valley and creating a new ice dam against Green Monarch Ridge – setting the stage for yet another cataclysmic Lake Missoula flood.

Trail A. Green Monarch Divide

Flood Feature Nos. 1, 2

Hike to the summit of Green Monarch Mountain, the second-highest point on the buttress-ridge that once stood above a tight glacial seal for Lake Missoula.

Geologic Highlights: High rock ridge that acted as a buttress for the Purcell Trench Lobe and temporary seal for Glacial Lake Missoula

Length: 3.1 miles one-way to Green Monarch Mountain summit

Elevation (Relief) Along Trail: 4,650 to 5,075 feet (425 feet)

Difficulty: Moderate

Best Observation Point: Open, burned-off areas on Green Monarch Mountain

Best Mode of Travel: Hike

Management/Ownership: U.S. Forest Service (Kaniksu National Forest)

USGS 1:24,000 Scale Map: Packsaddle Mountain, Hope, Clark Fork

Idaho Geological Survey Map: Sandpoint 1:100,000 Scale Digital Web Map (DWM)-94

Warnings: No potable water

Directions: In downtown Clark Fork, Idaho, turn southwest off Idaho State Highway 200 onto Stephen Street next to gas station. The road crosses railroad tracks and bears left to the bridge over the Clark Fork River. At the south end of the bridge, turn right. Continue about 2.5 miles to Johnson Creek Road No. 278. Cross the cattle guard and creek and follow this road seven miles to Johnson Saddle. Stay on Road 278 to the right, but go only 100 feet or less to a spur road that goes a short ways to the Trail No. 69 trailhead. There is parking here for up to six vehicles.

Trail Log

0.0   Starting at Johnson Saddle ascend trail going north through an overgrown clear-cut. N 48.09849 W116.29121

0.5   Follow skid road into a lodgepole pine forest.

0.7   Trail undulates through dense forest along Green Monarch Ridge.

2.2   Begin steep ascent to Green Monarch Mountain.

2.9   Spectacular vistas of Lake Pend Oreille, Mineral Point, the Purcell Trench and the Cabinet Mountains open up in burns from a 1991 forest fire.

3.1   Green Monarch Mountain summit (elevation 5,076 feet) (Figure 4-4). Green Monarch Ridge is underlain by Precambrian Belt rocks and therefore may be the source for many of the distinctive argillite and quartzite, ice-rafted erratic boulders found along the paths for the Missoula floods downstream. Retrace route to the trailhead or continue west along the ridge crest another 2.5 miles to Schafer Peak (elevation 5,210 feet). Imagine thousands of feet of ice lay directly below, pushing hard against this ridge. The flowing ice crept east up the Clark Fork Valley and west into the Pend Oreille trench, shearing off the steep north face of Green Monarch Ridge (see Figure 3-4).

Figure 4-4. Lake Pend Oreille from Green Monarch Mountain. Glacial ice moved down the Purcell Trench before plowing into Green Monarch Ridge (in foreground). This obstruction split the glacier forcing one sublobe east to Clark Fork on the right and the other sublobe down the valley to the left occupied by present-day Lake Pend Oreille.

Trail B. Mickinnick   Flood Feature Nos. 1, 2, 7

Climb to a ridgetop above Sandpoint for a spectacular 270-degree overview of the Purcell Trench and Lake Pend Oreille as well as the Pend Oreille and Clark Fork River valleys, which once held back Glacial Lake Missoula with thousands of feet of creeping, glacial ice.

Geologic Highlights: Glacially scoured and smoothed rock walls along the margin of the glacier that created Lake Missoula. Overview of former Purcell Trench Ice Lobe (No. 1) location and the Pend Oreille River valley, one of the northern escape routes for Ice Age floods.

Length: 7 miles round-trip

Elevation (Relief) Along Trail: 2,150 to 4,300 feet (2,150 feet)

Difficulty: Difficult due to a long, continuous elevation gain

Best Observation Point: Several panoramic viewpoints along the trail that only improve with height

Best Mode of Travel: Hike

Management/Ownership: U.S. Forest Service, U.S. Bureau of Land Management, City of Sandpoint

USGS 1:24,000 Scale Map: Sandpoint, ID

Idaho Geological Survey Map: Sandpoint Digital Web Map (DWM-76)

Warnings: No potable water

Directions: From Sandpoint go 2.5 miles north on U.S. Highway 95 (Figure 4-5). At MP 477 turn left (west) at stoplight onto Schweitzer Cutoff Road. After 0.5 mile turn right (north) on North Boyer Road. Go one mile, turn left onto Schweitzer Mountain Road and go 0.5 mile to Woodland Drive. Turn left and go 0.5 mile to the well-marked trailhead for Trail No. 13 on the right.

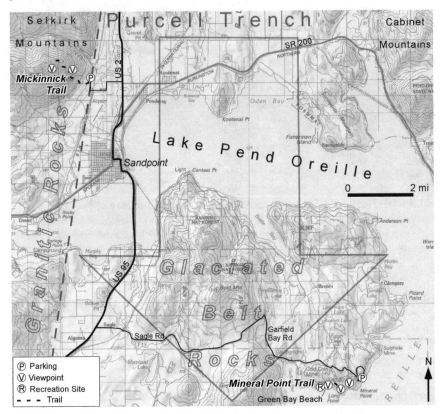

Figure 4-5. Upper Lake Pend Oreille showing locations of the Mickinnick (B) and Mineral Point (C) trails. Large block arrow indicates flow direction for the Purcell Trench Ice Lobe (No. 1), which once covered this area with thousands of feet of glacial ice, forming a portion of the ice dam for Glacial Lake Missoula.

Trail Log

0.0   Parking and informational signs located at trailhead. Follow trail southwest across the flat, glacial-valley floor.

0.2   Begin ascent up the Selkirk Mountain front, which continues for hundreds of miles north into the heart of British Columbia, forming the western boundary of the Purcell Trench (see Figure 3-2, top).

1.2   Sitting benches are located at the first panoramic view of the Pend Oreille valley below.

1.5   Several aligned and streamlined rock knobs of 100 million-year-old granitic rock molded by glacial ice that pushed against the valley walls. These granitic rocks are part of what geologists call the Kaniksu Batholith.

2.0   Another sitting bench with spectacular view.

2.8   Trail levels off as it approaches mountain summit. Note rounded slopes (Figure 4-6), smoothed by the passage of thousands of feet of glacial ice of the Purcell Trench Lobe slowly grinding across this side of the valley (Plate 3).

Figure 4-6. This rock surface was smoothed and rounded by the grinding action of glacial ice, which once filled this valley. Looking southeast.

3.5   Trail ends at sitting benches with a spectacular 270-degree view to the north, east (Figure 4-7) and south. The present-day outlet for Lake Pend Oreille is to the southwest via the Pend Oreille River Valley. When the ice sheet was not fully advanced, some of the floodwater from Glacial Lake Missoula escaped down this valley, although most of the torrent ran straight south via the Rathdrum Prairie Outburst Plain (No. 3, see Figure 3-11). Retrace route back to trailhead.

Figure 4-7. Telephoto view of Clark Fork Valley from the Mickinnick Trail. Looking east.

Trail C. Mineral Point   Flood Feature Nos. 1, 2

A well-maintained, lightly forested, friendly trail makes an undulating descent from several high overlooks to a Forest Service recreation site, ending at an enchanting argillite-pebble beach along Lake Pend Oreille.

Geologic Highlights: Directly across Lake Pend Oreille from Mineral Point is the Green Monarch Ridge Buttress (No. 2), which was instrumental in deflecting a sublobe of glacial ice up into the Clark Fork Valley and damming Glacial Lake Missoula. Ancient (1.4 billion to 1.6 billion year old) Belt rocks exposed, once overridden by thousands of feet of ice belonging to the Purcell Trench Lobe.

Length: 5 miles round-trip

Elevation (Relief) Along Trail: 2,100 to 2,500 feet (400 feet)

Difficulty: Moderate

Best Observation Points: Several high viewpoints occur along the trail (Figure 4-8); these include great views west and south to Green Monarch Ridge (No. 2) as well as Bernard and Cape Horn Peaks (Figure 4-9) that bounded the ice sheet to the south.

Best Mode (other modes) of Travel: Hike (mountain bike, horse)

Management/Ownership: U.S. Forest Service (Trail No. 82)

USGS 1:24,000 Scale Map: Talache, ID

Idaho Geological Survey Map: Talache Geologic Digital Web Map (DWM-75)

Warnings: No potable water

Directions: Six miles south of Sandpoint, turn east onto Sagle Road from U.S. Highway 95 between MP 468 and 469 (Figure 4-5). Continue on Sagle Road 7.2 miles, then turn right onto Garfield Bay Road. Drive 1.4 miles into Garfield Bay before turning left onto Green Bay Cutoff Road, which bears left and uphill. Take a right onto Mineral Point Road No. 532 after 0.3 mile. A turnoff to Green Bay (FS 2672) is 1.2 miles ahead; do not turn onto Forest Service Road 2672, but continue straight on Forest Service Road 532 for 1.9 miles. Take a last right onto Forest Service Road 532A, which arrives at trailhead (Trail No. 82) after 0.5 mile.

Figure 4-8. Former subglacial landscape. Outcropping of platy, argillite Belt rock at overlook onto Lake Pend Oreille. Looking southeast. Since being deposited about 1.5 billion years ago, these ancient, deep-sea sediments have been tilted steeply downward to the left (east) by jostling Earth movements since that time. Sites like this were the source for ice-rafted erratic boulders found hundreds of miles away, some as far away as west-central Oregon.

Trail Log

0.0   Head south from the trailhead next to vault toilet. N48.1810, W116.3882. All the rocks exposed along this trail belong to the 1.4 billion- to 1.6 billion-year-old, ancient-sea sediments, which belong to a grouping of rocks known to geologists as the Pritchard Formation of the Belt Supergroup (Figure 4-8).

0.1   Great overlook toward Clark Fork where a once 2,000-plus-foot high wall of ice pushed up against Green Monarch Ridge (No. 2). A sublobe of the ice backed up 10 miles into the Clark Fork River Valley to near the Idaho-Montana border, thus sealing the sole outlet for Glacial Lake Missoula (Plate 3). The area underfoot does not appear to have been scoured by the last Missoula floods, suggesting it remained covered by the ice during most or all Missoula flooding.

1.0   At a short turnout off the main trail stands a good exposure of gray to rust-orange argillite (hardened mudstone) Belt rocks that are tilted almost vertically (Figure 4-8). These rocks were laid down horizontally on an ancient seabed about 1.5 billion years ago! After being buried under thousands of feet of younger sediment, over the eons they hardened into rock onto the ancient continental margin of North America. After many shifts in movement, the rocks were tilted on edge and exhumed by many more eons of erosion to be visible today. In the distance, white stripes on Bernard Peak are post-glacial landslides that have shed off its steep, ice-scoured, north flank (see Figure 3-5). Right of Bernard Peak is Cape Horn Peak near Bayview, Idaho, a high ridge that bounded the west side of the ice lobe (see Figure 3-8).

1.4   Green Monarch Ridge (No. 2) looms ahead (Figure 4-9), a mere five miles to the south. This feature was the buttress for the glacial lobe of ice that pushed up into the Clark Fork Valley (Plate 3).

Figure 4-9. Looking south across Lake Pend Oreille from Green Bay Beach onto site of former ice dam. See Figure 3-4 for a different, aerial view of the Green Monarch Ridge, which deflected a lobe of ice up the Clark Fork River Valley, creating Glacial Lake Missoula.

2.0   Trail makes final descent to idyllic Green Bay beach with a walk-in campground. The flat, smooth beach pebbles (great for skipping) are mostly platy Belt rocks rounded by millennia of lapping waves onto this exposed beach.

Trail D. Cape Horn   Flood Feature Nos. 1, 3, 4

Ascend Forest Service roads above the former terminus of the Cordilleran Ice Sheet to a sweeping view of Lake Pend Oreille and its steep, glacially beveled valley walls. Deepest point of Lake Pend Oreille (1,150 feet deep) lies just offshore to the north.

Geologic Highlights: Glacial- and flood-beveled valley walls, Rathdrum Prairie Outburst Plain (No. 3). Exposures of glacial till up to elevation 3,150 feet. Occasional views southwest onto the glacial terminus at Bayview and the Hoodoo Channel.

Length: 5 miles round-trip

Elevation (Relief) Along Trail: 3,180 to 4,100 feet (920 feet)

Difficulty: Moderate

Best Observation Point: High on north side of Cape Horn Peak, looking north into Lake Pend Oreille at trail's end

Best Mode of Travel: Mountain bike or hike

Management/Ownership: U.S. Forest Service

USGS 1:24,000 Scale Map: Bayview and Cocolalla, ID

Idaho Geological Survey Map: Coeur d'Alene 30X60 Minute Quadrangle (GM-33)

Warnings: No potable water. Watch out for dirt bikes along the narrow, single-track Bayview-Blacktail Trail No. 230 near the upper end.

Directions: From U.S. Highway 95 at Athol, Idaho, head east onto Idaho State Highway 54. After 4.4 miles turn left (north) onto Perimeter Road that follows the west boundary of Farragut State Park. After 2.5 miles Perimeter Road turns right (east) toward Bayview, Idaho; go 2.1 miles farther, and at the Bayview Post Office, turn left onto Cherokee Road (Figure 4-10). Cherokee Road turns to gravel and becomes Forest Service Road 297 as it switches back and forth up the south side of Cape Horn Peak. At 2.8 miles from the Post Office, park in one of several wide spots along Forest Service Road 297 at the upper end of a septic-leach field, about 2.2 miles before the Bayview-Blacktail Trail No. 230 trailhead.

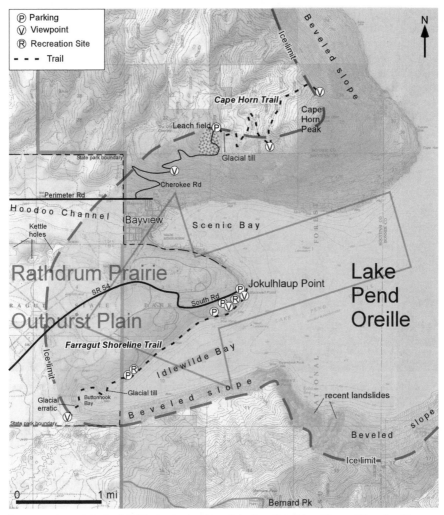

Figure 4-10. Lower Lake Pend Oreille showing locations of the Cape Horn (D) and Farragut Shoreline (E) trails. The ice lobe east of Cape Horn was up to 2,500 feet thick but thinned rapidly towards its terminus near Bayview, Idaho (Plates 5 and 9). Large block arrow indicates flow direction of ice for the Lake Pend Oreille sublobe and outburst floods from Glacial Lake Missoula.

Trail Log

0.0 Park in one of several wide spots along Forest Service Road 297 and continue along the road via a series of climbing switchbacks. Low clearance vehicles should not attempt to drive farther since there are many deep ruts and washouts in the road above here. Washouts expose brown, gray and maroon-colored quartzite Belt rocks. Cape Horn is capped with quartzite, which is a very hard rock that resists weathering and explains why this peak stands out above others in this area.

0.1 Glacial till is exposed in a roadcut. Glacial till consists of a mostly massive, poorly sorted sediment mixture that formed at the bottom or sides of a glacier. This is the highest exposure of till (elevation 3,150 feet) observed on this hike, indicating the glacier at times filled the valley at least to this height. The bottom of Lake Pend Oreille, the world's 13th deepest lake, lies at elevation 910 feet just a few miles north of here. The lake bottom contains more than 250 feet of post-flood lake sediments, thus putting the ice sheet base as low as 660 feet above sea level at one time (see Figure 3-3). This indicates that the Lake Pend Oreille sublobe, even here, near its southern terminus was about 2,500 feet thick!

Figure 4-11. Cape Horn Peak Trail. Panoramic view of Lake Pend Oreille to the north from spectacular viewpoint at the upper end of the trail.

0.3 White rock in road bed is a Cambrian limestone that once formed in a warm sea more than 500 million years ago!

1.3 Wonderful view to the south of the outburst point for the Missoula floods at Scenic Bay (Bayview) and the Rathdrum Prairie Outburst Plain (No. 3) beyond (see Figure 3-5, Plate 6).

2.1 Road forks. Right fork is a dead end – continue left onto the more used road marked as Trail 230.

2.3 Forest Service Road 230 transitions into an ATV-designated trail. (Watch for all-terrain vehicles!) The single-track trail winds up through dense trees to the ridge crest north of Cape Horn Peak. (In late summer this would be a good place to find huckleberries.)

2.5   Gain ridgetop with a panoramic view looking north up Lake Pend Oreille, which occupies the valley over 2,000 feet below (Figure 4-11). The steep, even slope below was planed off and beveled by glacial ice slowly moving and grinding its way across this slope for millennia. Retrace route back to trailhead.

Trail E. Farragut Shoreline   Flood Feature Nos. 1, 3

Hike along the scenic shoreline of Lake Pend Oreille from Jökulhlaup Point where a wall of ice more than 2,000 feet thick once towered along the edge of the glacier. The trail lies within Farragut State Park, a peaceful 4,000-acre park, established in 1964 that lines the southern tip of Lake Pend Oreille. During World War II this site was home to almost 300,000 sailors who received their basic training at the Farragut Naval Training Station.

Geologic Highlights: Glacial valley and terminus of Purcell Trench Ice Lobe (No. 1). Beveled glacial and flood-scoured slopes, erratics and glacial till. Many enormous, rounded boulders of granite and Belt rock, tossed about by the turbulent floods, have been reorganized into parking borders by state-park personnel.

Length: Up to 5.6 miles round-trip

Elevation (Relief) Along Trail: 2,070 to 2,220 feet (150 feet)

Difficulty: Easy

Best Observation Points: Jökulhlaup Point, Willow Day-Use Area

Best Mode of Travel: Hike, mountain bike

Management/Ownership: Idaho State Parks

USGS 1:24,000 Scale Map: Bayview, ID

Idaho Geological Survey Map: Coeur d'Alene 30X60 Minute Quadrangle (GM-33)

Warnings: Entrance fee required to access and use the facilities within Farragut State Park.

Directions: At the Farragut State Park Visitor Center, turn off Idaho State Highway 54 onto South Road. Continue 3.4 miles to Jökulhlaup Point (Figure 4-10) where a set of interpretive signs (including description of a jökulhlaup) is found at the gated end of South Road. On foot, continue 200 feet past blocked road, turn right down short, steep slope to Shoreline Trail connection below. The hike can be shortened by starting at any of the other access points for the Farragut shoreline. These include the Willow Day-Use Area, Eagle Boat Launch or Beaver Bay Beach. A maze of other trails crisscross Farragut State Park, in addition to one that starts inside the park and takes hikers outside its boundary to vantage points high above the lake's south side. Scout Trail No. 37 affords stunning views of Buttonhook and Idlewilde bays and all the way up the lake to Mineral Point from the rocky ledge that deflected the ice dam and flood torrents. For more information obtain a trail guide at the Visitor Center.

Trail Log

0.0   From the Jökulhlaup (Blackwell) Point peninsula (N47.9702, W116.5398) travel a short distance down to the shoreline and head south along Idlewilde Bay (Plate 5). With the breakup of the ice dam floodwaters moving at up to 65 mph, the ice would have been more than 2,000 feet deep here.

0.3   Willow Day-Use Area viewpoint with coin-op binoculars.

0.5   Eagle Boat Launch. Continue southwest along single-track trail that follows the shoreline. Hiking is recommended along the Shoreline Trail; mountain biking is better along a parallel upper trail.

0.6   Riprap boulders along shoreline are composed of unusual, zebra-like-striped rocks of Cambrian-age (about 550 million years) limestone. These rocks appear to have been artificially placed here as riprap to prevent erosion along the lakeshore. They were probably barged here from a limestone quarry (Plate 5) exposed at the base of Cape Horn Peak near Bayview, located 1.5 miles north of here.

Figure 4-12. Farragut Shoreline Trail near Beaver Bay Beach.

1.8   Beaver Bay Beach. A clear, blue-green sparkling lagoon of Lake Pend Oreille. Great place for a refreshing dip in the lake or a picnic on the beach.

2.2   Buttonhook Bay – extreme south end of Lake Pend Oreille (Plate 6). An outcrop of fine, powdery, pale-brown glacial till lies along Shoreline Trail just northeast of Buttonhook Island (N47.9524, W116.5735). Highpoint Trail continues along the north edge of Buttonhook Bay and the Rathdrum Prairie Outburst Plain (Figure 4-10).

2.7   Glacial erratic at edge of Rathdrum Prairie Outburst Plain (Figure 4-13). The presence of undisturbed glacial erratics and till here at the outburst point for the Missoula floods suggests that the ice sheet advanced over this site at least one last time after the last Missoula flood. If a Missoula flood had followed, the glacial deposits would have been obliterated.

Figure 4-13. Farragut Shoreline Trail. An 8-foot diameter, angular, granitic glacial erratic (N47.9515, W116.5807) is located along the upper edge of the Rathdrum Prairie Outburst Plain (No. 3), a suggestion that glacial ice of the Lake Pend Oreille sublobe occupied this spot after the last Missoula flood moved through this area.

2.8   Here at the top of the Rathdrum Prairie Outburst Plain (No. 3) is an overlook with an interpretive sign for Pen d'Oreille City, an old settlement that once existed in Buttonhook Bay below. This location is at or near the maximum extent of glacial ice and the start of the Rathdrum Prairie Outburst Plain, an expansive sediment apron that spread out for many miles downstream (Figure 4-10, see Figure 3-6; Plates 5 to 7).

Trail F. Dishman Hills

Flood Feature Nos. 3, 9

Ascend through the flood-ravaged Dishman Hills to a panoramic view across the broad, flat-bottomed Spokane Valley toward Rathdrum Prairie.

Geologic Highlights: The Dishman Hills Natural Area protrudes northward into the Spokane Valley like a sore thumb. Here the full force of west-flowing Lake Missoula floodwater rode up and over this transverse ridge of more resistant rock. This flood-scoured ridge of old granitic and metamorphic rocks shows erosional forms that are distinctly different from those scoured out of basalt on the Channeled Scabland.

Length: 1.2 miles one-way to Eagle Peak, longer hikes possible

Elevation (Relief) Along Trail: 1,960 to 2,425 feet (465 feet)

Difficulty: Easy to moderate

Best Mode of Travel: Hiking only

Best Observation Point: Eagle Peak summit

Management/Ownership: Spokane County Parks and Recreation, Dishman Hills Natural Area Association, Washington Department of Natural Resources, and the Nature Conservancy

USGS 1:24,000 Scale Maps: Spokane NE and Spokane SE, WA

Warnings: No potable water; trails continue beyond public lands where permission from private landowners is advised; trail signs are generally lacking; carry a compass or GPS and obtain a trail map online at www.dhnaa.org to aid in navigation.

Directions: From Interstate 90 take Exit 285 (Sprague Avenue), merge onto Appleway Boulevard (one way) and travel 1.5 miles east. Turn south (right) on South Sargent Road and park at Camp Caro Community Park (Figure 4-14). Other entrances (with limited street parking) are from 8th Avenue on the west and 12th and 16th avenues on the east.

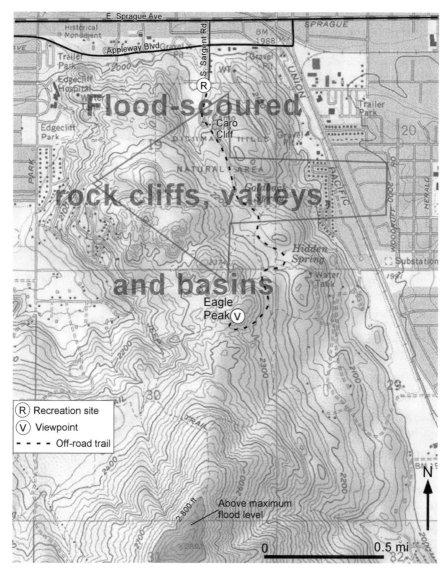

Figure 4-14. Map of the Dishman Hills area. Only the highest elevations, above 2,800 feet, escaped the Missoula floodwaters. Block arrow indicates westerly flow of Missoula floodwater that smashed into this rocky spur. Notice that the typical rock benches, buttes and mesas, common to flood terrain in the Channeled Scabland are absent here; that's because this rock is granite, which eroded very differently than basalt rock to the west.

Trail Log

0.0   Park at end of road at the Camp Caro Community Park (N47.6531, W117.2895). Trail heads south via entrance through a log structure. Old metamorphic rocks here are some of the oldest (over 1 billion years old!) in Washington state. Some younger granitic rocks also occur here, which are a mere 50 million to 70 million years old.

0.2   A complex of northwest-trending ravines, cliffs and basins were eroded out along zones of weakness in the bedrock by the west-flowing Missoula floods. Caro Cliff (Figure 4-14) and other rock walls follow these weak zones in the bedrock, etched out by Missoula floods. Continue an upward ascent following any of the maze of trails that leads to the south.

1.2   Hike to the high point, an eroded rock knob called Eagle Peak (N47.6397, W117.2860). From here is a panoramic view to the east looking toward the source of the Missoula floods. The surface soil layer is shallow to absent in flood-eroded areas but thicker in the higher hills that lay above maximum flood level (greater than 2,800 feet in elevation) located not far south of here (Figure 4-14).

Trail G. Spokane Falls/Riverfront Park   Flood Feature No. 9

Come stroll through downtown Spokane's Riverfront Park to witness flood-borne Spokane Falls and environs.

Geologic Highlights: Basalt-ledge knickpoint; Canada Island – a goat island-like flood feature

Length: Up to one mile via interconnected trail and city-street network

Difficulty: Easy

Best Mode of Travel: Walk

Best Observation Points:

Automobile: Monroe Street or Post Street bridges in Spokane (Figure 4-16)

Non-motorized trail: Various views and perspectives along the Riverfront Park trail system

Management/Ownership: City of Spokane

Elevation of Feature: Top of Spokane Falls cascade equals 1,800 feet; base equals 1,720 feet; total drop about 80 feet

Warnings: Beware of city traffic around park perimeter.

Directions: On Interstate 90 at Spokane take the Division Street exit north. Turn left (west) onto Spokane Falls Boulevard just before crossing bridge over the Spokane River. Park and head north via one of several paths leading into Riverfront Park (Figure 4-15).

Figure 4-15. Map of Spokane's Riverfront Park (outlined) showing network of streets and trails. The falls descend across a rocky ledge of Grande Ronde Basalt.

The main route for the Missoula floods followed the Rathdrum Prairie into the Spokane Valley where hundreds of feet of coarse gravel and sand were deposited. Earlier in the last glacial cycle, the valley was flooded up to elevation 2,300 feet or more by Glacial Lake Columbia (or Spokane) (Plate 3), placing a glacial lake up to 550 feet deep over Riverfront Park. During periodic outburst floods from Glacial Lake Missoula, up to an additional 500 feet of floodwater was added to the already flooded valley before spilling south across the Channeled Scabland. The last Missoula floods ran over dry ground in the Spokane Valley, after the head of Grand Coulee was breached (No. 29), which suddenly lowered the level of Glacial lake Columbia by 900 feet.

Thus, the floor of the valley lay unprotected from the onslaught of the last Missoula megafloods, which swept across the desiccated valley bottom, reworking and redepositing the bouldery flood deposits (see Figure 3-16). Today, groundwater fills the voids within these coarse flood deposits to form the prolific Rathdrum-Spokane Aquifer (No. 9), a plentiful source of fresh water for Spokane – eastern Washington's largest city – and Kootenai County in Idaho.

With the end of the Ice Age about 14,000 years ago, after the rivers were finally free of glacial and lake impediments, the Spokane River began to erode into hundreds of feet of lake and Missoula flood sediments that partially filled the valley. Post-glacial downcutting by the river was slowed considerably, however, upon hitting a resistant ridge in the vicinity of Riverfront Park. Here, the lowering river encountered a narrow ridge of hard, basalt bedrock that extends across the valley. Spokane Falls is the result of the river that today continues to slowly grind its way into the bedrock ridge (Figure 4-16).

- -

Spokane Falls is actually a cascade or series of shorter waterfalls over basalt that descends a total of about 80 feet.

Spokane Falls represents what is known as a "knickpoint," where the slope of the riverbed steepens abruptly. Behind Spokane Falls the sluggish river has a gradient of only about 7 feet per mile, but below the falls knickpoint the river races along a gradient of almost 25 feet per mile. Upstream of the falls erosion of the sediments has been arrested and will continue to be so until the falls eventually erodes headward (east) through the basalt ridge. When this occurs, perhaps thousands of years from now, more of the sediment fill will be removed from the floor of the Spokane Valley upstream, and the level of the Rathdrum-Spokane Aquifer will drop accordingly with downcutting of the bedrock ridge.

Figure 4-16. Spokane Falls is actually a cascade or series of rapids and waterfalls that descends across an eroded, rocky ledge of basalt. Footbridge (in foreground) passes over the lower end of the falls to Canada Island located at left. Looking east from the Post Street Bridge.

The slowly retreating Spokane Falls is split into two sets of falls where the river cuts into the bedrock ridge (Figure 4-16). In between the two incised bedrock channels lies Canada Island, a small-scale version of a "Goat Island" reminiscent of massive flood erosion at other places within the Channeled Scabland, such as Dry Falls (No. 41) and Steamboat Rock (No. 31).

Trail H. Campion Park

Flood Feature No. 11

Examine and unravel some of the complex Ice Age floods' history preserved in slackwater sediments exposed in a steep cut bank of Hangman Creek.

Geologic Highlights: Recent landslides have exposed Hangman Creek Rhythmites (No. 11) that reveal a long record of repeated Missoula flood events. Also revealed is evidence for landslide slumping events between some floods.

Length: 0.25 to 0.5 mile round-trip

Elevation (Relief) Along Trail: 1,850 feet (few feet)

Difficulty: Easy

Best Mode of Travel: Walk across a flat meadow to an overlook across Hangman Creek.

Best Observation Point: West side Hangman (Latah) Creek

Management/Ownership: Spokane Parks and Recreation, Washington Department of Natural Resources

USGS 1:24,000 Map: Spokane SW, WA

Warnings: Proceed with caution if making a U-turn on U.S. Highway 195. Traffic entering from Hatch Road will be turning both right and left onto U.S. 195. If coming from the north it may be safest to exit onto Hatch Road, turn around, and then return to U.S. Highway 195 northbound. Views are best on the west side of Hangman Creek; standing below the steep cliffs along the east side of Hangman Creek could be dangerous, and it is not public land.

Directions: From the Interstate 90 intersection with U.S. Highway 195, proceed south 5.2 miles to the intersection with Hatch Road on the left (east) side. U.S. 195 is a divided highway and traffic moves swiftly – proceed with caution. At Hatch Road make a U-turn and proceed north on U.S. 195 for 0.4 mile. Pull off into a wide area with large boulders blocking a dirt road on the right side of the highway between MP 91 and 92.

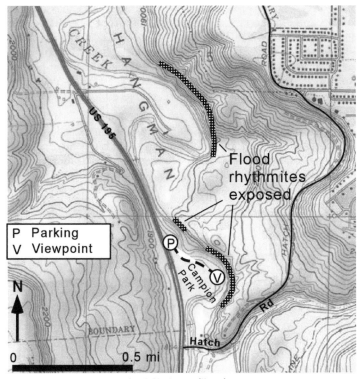

Figure 4-17. Campion Park and Hangman Creek Rhythmites (No. 11).

This trail hugs Hangman Creek, also known as Latah Creek. In 1882 Lieutenant Thomas Symons shed light on how this schizophrenic stream got its name: "This beautiful creek took its detestable appellation from the fact that on its banks in 1858 Colonel Wright caused to be hung the Indians captured by him who had been guilty of murder and other crimes. ... It would be commendable to the people of the section if they would change the name from Hangman's to Lah-too (Latah) or Nedlewhauld Creek." Apparently the locals only halfheartedly took Symon's advice, for today the creek still goes by Hangman Creek.

Trail Log

0.0   Note imposing cliff to the east is undercut by Hangman Creek. Hike southeast across meadow paralleling Hangman Creek.

0.1   Across the creek are slackwater flood rhythmites exposed in the tall embankment by recent slumping. The fine (silt and clay) layers, called varves, were deposited in Pleistocene-age lakes impounded by the Cordilleran Ice Sheet, which blocked the Columbia (or Spokane) River to the west (Plate 11). Intervening coarse sand and gravel layers were deposited when Missoula floods emptied into the glacial lake en route to the Channeled Scabland.

A steep gully divides the cliff into two sections. The section to the north (left) contains a prominent discontinuity in the orientation of the layers (Figure 4-18). The relationship of these strata suggests that an ancient landslide occurred here some 30,000 to 40,000 years ago, based on a study by Scott Meyer in 1999. Stream erosion by an ancestral Hangman Creek then cut into the sediments and exposed a cliff similar to the present one. Subsequently the upper cliff slid over the lower layers. Another Ice Age lake formed, which was again periodically invaded by outbursts from Glacial Lake Missoula. Sediments from these later flood events covered over and buried the lower part of the valley and the old landslide. Over the last 15,000 years, post-glacial stream erosion in Hangman Creek has once again uncovered the older deposits, including the ancient landslide.

Modern road construction has forced Hangman Creek to locally cut into the valley sides. As a result, today the exposed steep bluffs are unstable and susceptible to landsliding as seen here. Engineering stabilization with large logs at the base of bluff is slowing the rate of slope retreat but is probably only a temporary solution.

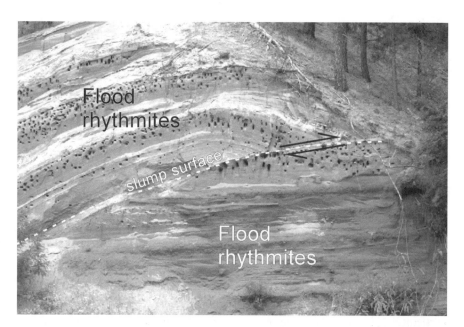

Figure 4-18. Missoula flood rhythmites exposed along Hangman Creek (No. 11). Each rhythmite consists of a layer of gray sand or pebbles deposited during an outburst flood, which grades up into silt to clay varves. This top part represents dozens of years of quiet deposition within Glacial Lake Columbia between Missoula floods. Post-glacial downcutting of Hangman Creek and its forced position against the valley wall have led to undercutting and slope failure, much to the detriment of homes above. Irrigation water added from above percolates downward and moves laterally along the tops of impermeable clay layers; this further destabilizes and accelerates slumping along the bluff. Shown here is a close-up of an Ice Age landslide that occurred between 30,000 to 40,000 years ago along the slump surface. Downcutting by Hangman Creek over the last 15,000 years has since exposed and revealed the history of these ancient events. See also Figures 3-19 and 3-20.

The lower rhythmites have up to 53 silt-clay lake varves atop each rhythmite, deposited in the stillness of Glacial Lake Columbia (or Spokane) between Missoula floods. This suggests up to a half century elapsed between some outburst floods. The upper 12 rhythmites here, however, do not have any lake varves between flood-laid beds, indicating the glacial lake did not exist here during the last dozen Missoula floods. Being at elevation 1,800 feet here, this site would have been above the level of Lake Columbia after Grand Coulee was breached (No. 29) and the level of the lake suddenly dropped 900 feet (from elevation 2,300 feet to 1,500 feet). This explains why no lake varves are present between the last Missoula floods preserved at Hangman Creek.

Trails in the Vicinity of the Cheney-Palouse Scabland Tract

Trail I. Riddle Hill Steptoe

Flood Feature Nos. 10, 12

"Islandlike hills of much older crystalline rocks project above the plane surface."

– J Harlen Bretz et al (1956)

Ascend a well-maintained road to the top of Steptoe Ridge that protruded above and impeded the flow of outburst megafloods into the head of the Cheney-Palouse scablands.

Geologic Highlights: Streamlined steptoe hills, spillover channels, lake-filled rock basins, West Plains basalt plateau, drainage divide

Length: 3 miles round-trip

Elevation (Relief) Along Trail: 2,350 to 2,750 feet (400 feet)

Difficulty: Easy, except for two metal gates that must be climbed over

Best Mode of Travel: Hike

Best Observation Point: Radio towers on Riddle Hill summit

Management/Ownership: Washington Department of Natural Resources

USGS 1:24,000 Scale Maps: Four Lakes, Medical Lake, WA

Warnings: No potable water, hunters in fall

Directions: From Interstate 90 take the State Route 904 (Cheney) exit. Turn south in Four Lakes onto the Four Lakes-Medical Lake Road (Figure 4-19). At three miles turn south (left) onto the Silver Lake Road. Proceed about 0.2 mile, park in wide area on left side of road and walk to nearby metal gate with a "No Fireworks" sign.

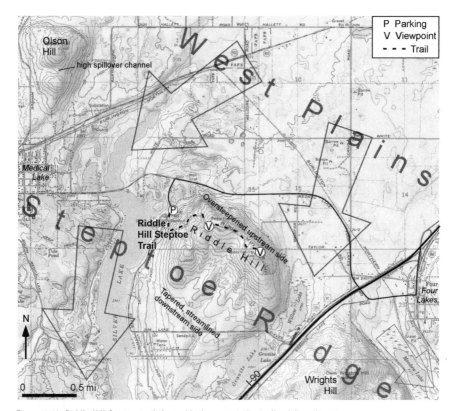

P Parking
V Viewpoint
- - - Trail

Figure 4-19. Riddle Hill Steptoe trail. Large block arrows indicate flood-flow direction.

Trail Log

0.0   Climb over metal gate.

0.1   A side road to the left leads to a wetland and pothole formed by a high-energy, hydraulic vortex that formed along the upstream side of Riddle Hill. Ascend the gravel road to the ridge above.

0.8   Arrive at first transmission tower. Great views of surrounding steptoe hills and flood-scoured lakes in the rock basins between hills. The steptoe hills align along an uneven ridge of older, pre-basalt rock (Figures 4-19, see Figures 3-21 and 3-22). Visible steptoes along the ridge, from east to west, are Needham Hill, Wrights Hill, Olson Hill, Booth Hill and Fancher Butte. Flood-scoured rock basins between steptoes are filled with Meadow, Willow, Granite, Silver, Medical and West Medical lakes – excavated as floodwaters eroded through the basalt into the deeply weathered granitic rock below. Also, due to the venturi effect, flood flow sped up through these narrow constrictions, causing the water to erode more deeply. On Olson Hill, to the north, a gap across the hill was eroded by cresting floodwaters (Figures 4-19 and 4-20). Steptoe Butte is visible in the distance, 40 miles to the southeast. Follow the road eastward along top of ridge toward another transmission tower.

Figure 4-20. Olson Hill steptoe is divided in two by an elevated spillover flood channel that hangs 100 feet above the surrounding plains. The core of Olson Hill is composed of 50 million-year-old granite rock. Only a thin layer of flat-lying Columbia River basalt (Priest Rapids Member) laps up against the base of Olson Hill as well as the other steptoes in the region. Looking northwest from the Riddle Hill steptoe.

1.0   View to the north looking over the West Plains toward the Spokane Airport. Beyond are the Selkirk Mountains and breakout area for the Missoula floods. The flatness of the West Plains reflects the underlying surface of the Columbia River basalt, which spread out in all directions here, lapping up against and completely surrounding the steptoes, including Riddle Hill, about 15 million years ago (see Figure 3-22).

1.3   Climb over a second locked gate. The top of Riddle Hill is covered with wheat fields, owing to a blanket of fertile windblown soil, preserved here because floods weren't deep or powerful enough to erode the very top of the ridge.

1.4   The core of Riddle Hill consists of extremely old (about 1.5 billion years) metasedimentary Belt rocks. Some blue-green quartzite is exposed in bedrock within the roadbed near the transmission tower.

1.5   Turn around at second transmission tower. Note Willow Lake scour basin immediately below where the floods eroded another spillover channel through the gap between the Riddle Hill and Wrights Hill steptoes (Figure 4-19). Granite Lake, located just downstream to the southwest, is an extension of the Willow Lake scour basin. These lakes are located at a drainage divide. Lake waters flow both south (as subsurface groundwater) into the Hog Canyon drainage, as well as to the north, eventually draining into the Spokane River.

Trail J. Medical Lake Loop   Flood Feature No. 12

Walk or bike completely around East Medical Lake, a flood-scoured rock basin midway along the Steptoe Ridge. En route witness the site of a former granite quarry and relax in the rural setting of quaint Medical Lake.

Geologic Highlights: Floodwaters squeezed between the high steptoes, accelerating and gouging out deep lake-filled basins. Erosion was greatest where a thin layer of basalt lies over deeply weathered granite.

Length: 3.1 miles round-trip

Elevation (Relief) Along Trail: 2,400 to 2,430 feet (30 feet)

Difficulty: Easy

Best Mode of Travel: Bike, hike

Best Observation Point: West, forested side of lake

Management/Ownership: City of Medical Lake

USGS 1:24,000 Scale Maps: Medical Lake, WA

Warnings: 10 mph bicycle speed limit

Directions: From Interstate 90 take exit 264 (from west) or exit 272 (from east) to the town of Medical Lake; proceed west on State Route 902 for 4.8 miles to Waterfront Park on south end of East Medical Lake. Other parking is available at Coney Island Park near city hall and on the north end of the lake. The trail description begins at Waterfront Park (N47.5626; W117.6942) and proceeds in a clockwise direction.

Trail Description: Entire loop trail is paved; section through town of Medical Lake on the east side follows a well-marked bicycle lane on paved road; informative kiosks provide a summary of local history. West side of trail follows quiet, serene trail through open forest; east side of trail follows a bicycle lane through sometimes-busy Medical Lake.

Trail Log

0.0   Begin at Waterfront Park (formerly Stanley Park). Proceed in clockwise direction along paved trail

0.5   Entire west side of lake is underlain by Eocene (34 million to 56 million year old) granitic rocks that comprise this steptoe.

0.6   A series of quarries here were excavated into relatively unweathered granite (Figure 4-21). Granite blocks were used to supply local building material to nearby Eastern State Hospital and the town of Medical Lake during the late 1800s and early 1900s.

Figure 4-21. Neatly cleaved granite slabs in former quarry along Medical Lake, date unknown. This rock is exposed in the steptoe that divides East and West Medical Lakes. The granite crystallized from a deeply buried magma chamber during the Eocene Epoch.

OTIS W. FREEMAN PHOTO, EASTERN WASHINGTON UNIVERSITY LIBRARY ARCHIVES AND SPECIAL COLLECTIONS

0.9   Steep, flood-scoured cliff of granite.

1.1   Northern parking lot (N47.5785; W117.6906), continue east and then south on roadway along designated bike route. The route here on the east side of the lake is located entirely on Columbia River basalt. Between here and the west side of the lake is the contact with the underlying granite, a very vulnerable area of intense chemical weathering where deep scouring by the floods occurred. Medical Lake, as well as the other rock basins across Steptoe Ridge, occupy depressions carved out along the basalt-granite contact.

1.9   Coney Island City Park. Site of former pavilion dance hall and steam-boat excursion boat docks in the late 1800s and early 1900s. Eleven hotels, many of which offered mud baths, once stood in the surrounding area in 1889. A 60-foot-deep, elongate, water-filled rock basin lies just south of this site, along the east edge of the lake.

2.5   Trail returns to an open, treeless area located in a butte-and-basin scabland. Note the several isolated scabland ponds occupying flood-scoured rock basins across the roadway,

3.1   Return to starting area at Waterfront Park.

Figure 4-22. Medical Lake has been transformed from its naturally alkaline, soap-like condition into a clean, fresh lake. Freshening of the lake is the result of runoff from surrounding development and the addition of an aeration system to reduce algal growth within the lake.

"In the Four Lakes country there are three small lakes, whose waters are strongly impregnated with carbonate of soda, and which have been dubbed the Medical Lakes. The water has a soapy feel and effect, and delightful to bathe in."

– Lieutenant Thomas Symons (1882)

Trail K. Cheney Overlook   Flood Feature Nos. 12, 17, 18

A short uphill walk to panoramic view atop a treeless island of Palouse loess toward the Steptoe Ridge spillover complex in one direction and the expansive, pine-covered head of the Cheney-Palouse scablands in the other.

Geologic Highlights: Erosional remnants of Palouse hills along the northern edge of the Cheney-Palouse Scabland Tract. To the north is a view of the Steptoe Ridge Spillover Complex (No. 12), which impeded flow of Missoula floodwaters from the north. The upstream end of the forested Cheney-Palouse scabland is visible to the south.

Length: A few hundred yards

Observation Point: Top of "Water Tower Hill" on Eastern Washington University (EWU) campus

Elevation (Relief) Along Trail: 2,540 to 2,590 feet (50 feet)

Difficulty: Easy

Best Mode of Travel: Walk

Management/Ownership: Eastern Washington University

USGS 1:24,000 Scale Maps: Cheney, WA

Warnings: The EWU parking lot below the water tower is a pay-lot during athletic events but free to the public the rest of the time.

Directions: From Interstate 90 take Exit 257 eastbound or Exit 270 westbound to Cheney. From Exit 257 follow signs to EWU campus via State Route 904 (Figure 4-23). After entering Cheney turn north onto Washington Street for one mile to a prominent water tower. Turn left (west) into parking lot P12 near the north edge of the campus and park at the base of the hill below the water tower. Climb a steep slope to the hilltop tower or find gently inclined, rough, dirt road that is accessed from both north and south of the water tower. The EWU campus lies directly east and southeast of the viewpoint.

Figure 4-23. Map of the Cheney Overlook viewpoint and vicinity. The main flow of floodwater occurred to the southwest, indicated by block arrow. Some flood flow also leaked through a secondary channel cut through the Palouse upland at upper left.

The Cheney Overlook lies along the edge of a flood-sculpted Palouse island that rises above a "sea" of scabland. The streamlined island of wind-blown loess is seven miles long by three miles wide and lies within the more protected downstream (south) side of the Wrights Hill steptoe (see Figure 3-21). Locally the island was partially dissected by high floodwaters that eroded along the sides of the Palouse island.

At this overlook it is easy to see the control geology plays on vegetation. For example, the mostly treeless rounded Palouse hills around the overlook are underlain by a few tens of feet of windblown loess. (In the heart of the Palouse, near Pullman, more than 200 feet of loess overlies bedrock). Loess soils at this latitude support primarily native grasses and dryland wheat but not trees. In sharp contrast, are the forested, low-relief basalt plains to the south, where all the Palouse soil was stripped away by Ice Age floods along the 30-mile-wide Cheney-Palouse Scabland Tract (Plate 10). Relatively thin scabland soils and a shallow water table support a totally different type of vegetation compared to the Palouse. Ponderosa pines, aspens and shrubs cover much of the surface here. Within the scabland to the south is the Turnbull National Wildlife Refuge (No. 13), where hundreds of flood-scoured rock basins lie filled with lush wet-lands and ponds – ideal for wildlife.

Figure 4-24. Telephoto view of Steptoe Butte, approximately 35 miles to the south. Beyond the rolling Palouse hills and forested scabland in the foreground, Steptoe Butte is composed of an extremely hard Belt rock called quartzite. Steptoe Butte along with the Steptoe Ridge Spillover Complex (No. 12) are eroded remnants of the nearby Bitterroot Mountains – later isolated by engulfing basalt flows.

Pyramid-shaped Steptoe Butte rises above the horizon to the south (Figure 4-24). Older rocks that protrude above the surrounding basalt plain are known as "steptoes" (Figure 3-22). This butte was tall enough to avoid burial by the massive lava flows of Columbia River basalt that erupted about 15 million years ago, burying most of eastern Washington under thousands of feet of lava. The string of hills to the north, referred to here as the Steptoe Ridge Spillover Complex (No. 12), comprise an ancient ridge of older, more resistant rocks, surrounded by basalt lava flows that flowed around the flanks of these ancient hills but not over the top. Many millions of years later, massive Ice Age floods, after spilling south from the West Plains, flowed through gaps in the steptoe ridge, locally removing the basalt along scour depressions, today occupied by numerous rock-rimmed lakes including Medical, Clear, Silver and Granite lakes (see Figure 3-21).

The largest floods were even deep enough to overtop some of the Palouse hills in this area. This is apparent from a channel eroded to the north and west, isolating the overlook hill from its once-connected neighbor to the northwest (Figure 4-23). During the largest flood(s) this overlook may have been a small, dry island or perhaps shallowly overrun by the largest Missoula floods. Either way, not a good place to be during an outburst flood!

Trail L. Turnbull Wildlife Refuge   Flood Feature Nos. 13, 17

Several short hikes through open pine forests and wetlands created by erosional scouring from the floods. Also located in the refuge is a peaceful 5.5-mile auto-tour loop.

Geologic Highlights: Low-relief scabland of the Cheney-Palouse Tract with numerous flood-scoured wetland basins

Best Mode of Travel: Walk, bicycle or drive the 5.5-mile Pine Creek Auto Tour route that winds through wetlands and scabland of the Turnbull Refuge. Walk several trails radiating off the auto tour loop (see descriptions below). Long Lake and Turnbull Slough along the Columbia Plateau State Park trail are found on the northwest side of the refuge (Trail M).

Elevation (Relief) Along Trail: 2,200 to 2,320 feet (120 feet)

Management/Ownership: U.S. Fish and Wildlife Service

USGS 1:24,000 Scale Maps: Cheney, WA

Warnings: Visitors must pay a user fee between March 1 and October 31. Bicycles and motorized vehicles not permitted on trails but allowed on the Pine Creek Auto Tour route. Visitors are required to stay on designated trails and roadways throughout the year in the Public Use Area and Columbia Plateau Trail. Elsewhere in the refuge, horseback riding, fishing, swimming, bathing, camping, fires and on-ice activities are prohibited. Dogs must be on leash at all times. Animals are wild; moose in particular should be viewed with caution.

Directions: From Interstate 90 take Exit 257 eastbound or Exit 270 westbound to Cheney. At Turnbull National Wildlife Refuge sign, go south on Cheney-Plaza Road. Access to the center of the refuge, the headquarters, and Pine Creek Auto Tour route is 4.2 miles south on Cheney-Plaza Road (Figure 4-25). Turn left (southeast) at refuge sign (see Figure 5-12) and pay user fee before continuing to the start of one-way, auto-tour road or proceed to the refuge headquarters at 1.7 miles. Trail and wildlife information is available at the refuge headquarters during regular working hours and on weekends during warmer months at the Friends of Turnbull Store located next to the refuge headquarters.

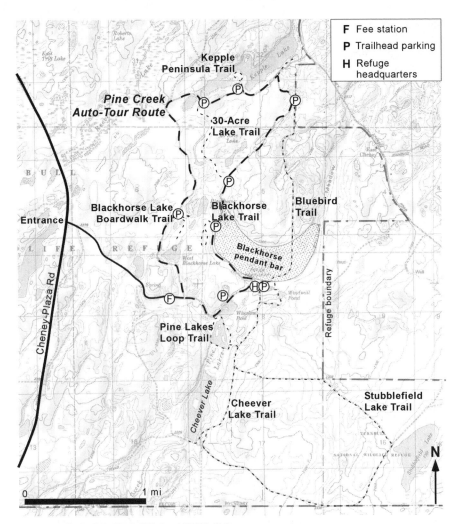

Figure 4-25. Trails of the Turnbull National Wildlife Refuge.

Flood deposits accumulated onto the Blackhorse pendant-shoulder bar (Figure 4-25), including many huge, rounded basalt boulders up to 6 feet in diameter. These are visible in a couple of abandoned gravel pits northwest of the refuge headquarters along the Pine Creek Auto Tour route. Some granite boulders are present as well, which required transport for many miles by flood currents to reach this location. The granite boulders are rounded, like the basalt, suggesting they were transported as bedload and rounded as they tumbled and rolled along the base of the flow. Keep in mind these rounded granitic boulders are different from "erratics" that rafted in on floating icebergs and are generally angular in shape.

Enigmatic, rounded mounds, called Mima mounds (see "Mysterious Mima Mounds" sidebar, page 83 in chapter 3), are ubiquitous within the refuge as well as most other scabland locations (see Figure 3-27). Those near Kepple and 30 Acre lakes (Figures 4-26 and 4-28) are easily observed because of the openness of the flat area near the roadway. The origin of Mima mounds is controversial, but one thing is known for certain: They must have formed since the last Missoula flood about 15,000 calendar years ago. For if they formed prior to or during the last floods, they would have been destroyed or at least molded into more streamlined shapes by the floods.

Figure 4-26. Post-flood features. Above: A fine-soil Mima mound buildup along the Pine Creek Auto Tour Route. Right: Stone net associated with a field of Mima mounds near the Kepple Lake Interpretive Trail. These jumbled zones of broken, angular basalt clasts encircle many of the Mima mounds. Like Mima mounds, their origin is also controversial; however, they are most likely related to freeze-thaw activity occurring at the ground surface.

Trail Network of the Turnbull National Wildlife Refuge

The many trails within the Turnbull Refuge provide wonderful opportunities to observe ponds, wetlands and wildlife as well as the rugged butte-and-basin scabland topography (Figure 4-25). The following trails of the Turnbull Refuge are described in the order that the trailheads appear along the Pine Creek Auto Tour Route, starting at the Refuge Headquarters.

Pine Creek Auto Tour Route. This narrow, unpaved loop winds through the scored scabland interspersed with lush wetlands. The road is designed for motor vehicles but also serves as a trail for those who want to walk or bike instead of drive the 5.5-mile tour route.

Pine Lakes Loop – Cheever Lake Trails. From Cheney-Plaza Road proceed southeast 1.4 miles to the Pine Lakes parking area. The shorter (about one mile) Pine Lake Loop Trail is paved and accessible by wheelchair. The Pine Lakes are flood-scoured, marshy depressions occupying an inner scabland channel. Low, man-made dams on the lower ends of the lakes help to maintain lake levels year-round. A cluster of basalt boulders lies along the west side of Pine Lake about 0.2 mile from the parking area. The boulders are somewhat rounded and therefore probably a flood-bedload deposit dropped onto the downstream side of a slight basalt rise.

The Pine Lakes Loop Trail can be extended by continuing south another 0.9 mile to Cheever Lake. The smooth, flood-scoured slope of the bedrock hill east of the Cheever Lake trail has abundant Mima mounds covering its surface. Some of the mounds are located in seasonally wet areas surrounded by basalt bedrock that may influence how the mounds formed. A few hundred yards eastward from the south end of Cheever Lake is an area where large, rounded to sub-rounded basalt boulders are plastered against the hillside, a product of Ice Age floods.

Stubblefield Lake Loop Trail. From the south side of the Refuge Headquarters parking lot the trail follows a gravel road south towards Cheever Lake. Total length of trail is 5.9 miles through mostly open prairie.

0.0   From the east end of the Refuge headquarters parking lot hike south along an unpaved service road through butte and basin scabland.

0.7   Intersection with the unmarked Stubblefield Lake Trail (double-track road) on the left (east). For those who wish to walk through a Mima mound paradise, this is the trail to take! Bear left at the intersection with the birdhouse atop a tall pole. Thousands of mounds are visible along the trail route.

1.2   Crest a flood-swept, Mima mound-studded upland (elevation 2,345 feet) where, during their maximum, floodwaters would have been up to 150 feet overhead. The hill slopes appear to be in the resistant entablature part of the exposed lava flow that resisted the onslaught of Ice Age floods. Soil is thin to absent except for that in the abundant Mima mound cover. Good views of dome-shaped Mica Peak (elevation 5,027 feet) visible about 25 miles to the northeast. Flood-streamlined loess hills to the south and east begin to appear from this vantage point.

1.5   At refuge boundary fence head southeast to cross over a small scabland wetland.

2.3   "T" intersection at Stubblefield Lake. Floodwaters sped up as they squeezed between two bedrock hills (venturi effect) gouging out the shallow depression now occupied by Stubblefield Lake. By late summer and fall the lake is usually dry. Turn right (southwest) and continue through Mima mound heaven.

2.7   Views of many streamlined and scarped loess hills along the scabland margin to the southeast. Numerous divide crossings up to 2,460 feet amongst the loess islands indicate that floodwaters were at least this high. The tallest, visible ridgetops were above maximum flood level. The closest, most prominent streamlined and scarped hill (2,440 feet) dominates the views in the near distance along this segment of the trail (Figure 4-27).

Figure 4-27. Elongate, flood-streamlined Palouse hill along the Stubblefield Lake Trail, looking south.

2.9   Bear right (west) where trail comes to a T.

3.3   Trail passes through a fence opening and heads northwest before rising over the lower end of a pendant bar developed beyond a bedrock obstruction. Mima mounds are absent or poorly developed on the gravel bar. Flood gravels appear in and along the trail, and the maximum clast size increases from pebble, to cobble, to boulder as the trail continues to the northwest into the ponderosa pine forest towards Cheever Lake.

4.3   Large basalt boulders are plastered on the edge of the inner canyon above Cheever Lake. Turn north to return to trailhead via the Cheever Lake trail (Figure 4-25).

5.2   End of the Stubblefield Lake Loop. Retrace route 0.7 mile back to starting point.

Bluebird Trail. Trail begins at a gate two miles along the auto-tour route. This 1.6-mile-long (one-way) double-track trail leads through some wonderful butte-and-basin topography containing numerous rock basins and potholes. The rugged topography helps one to imagine the chaotic turbulence of floodwaters that swirled through this area during outburst floods. The abundance of this type of topography was less attractive to early settlers who referred to the land as "Scabland." Stop along the trail in its northern section and try to imagine the confusing movement of high-energy currents that excavated this complex of rock basins and potholes. At the southern end of the trail, near the Refuge Headquarters, are a large group of Mima mounds with stone nets (Figure 4-26, right) exposed along their margins. The beginning south end of the trail also crosses the Blackhorse pendant flood bar (Figure 4-25). One can use the auto tour route as well as the 30-Acre Lake Trail to hike back to the point of origin, closing a loop back to refuge headquarters. Coauthor Bjornstad encountered a sizable moose and her calf partway along this trail; if this happens to you always give moose the right-of-way.

Blackhorse Lake Trail. This short 0.4-mile (round-trip) trail begins at the northwest end of the Blackhorse pendant bar (Figure 4-25). Large, rounded, flood-transported boulders in the parking area were excavated during road and parking area construction. The trail loops adjacent to a wetland area where there are views of Blackhorse Lake that fills the scour depression created by the Ice Age floods.

30-Acre Lake Trail. This 0.7-mile-long trail (one-way) is accessed from either end via the Pine Loop Auto Tour route. At the southeast trailhead is a large group of Mima mounds (Figure 4-28) near 30-Acre Lake. The trail winds its way across the wetland area starting near Blackhorse Lake on the south end and ending at Kepple Lake at the north. A low bedrock divide separates 30-Acre Lake from Kepple Lake. The trail enters another Mima mound area near the northwest end of the trail. This trail is a shortcut route that saves 2.5 miles for those walking the Pine Creek Auto Tour loop.

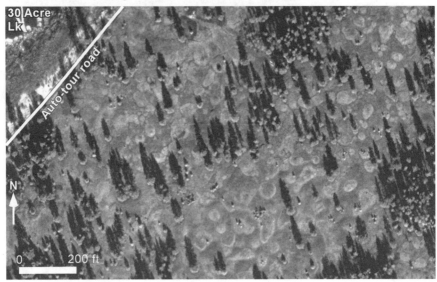

Figure 4-28. Field of evenly dispersed, circular Mima mounds southeast of 30-Acre Lake, within Turnbull National Wildlife Refuge. Larger mounds are several tens of feet in diameter.

Kepple Peninsula Trail. This short (0.5 mile round-trip), paved, nature trail provides scenic views of the wetland lake occupying the scour depression formed by Ice Age floods. Interpretive brochures are sometimes available at the trailhead during the summer season. Kepple Lake, like the other scabland lakes here, are oriented from the northeast to the southwest, the same direction as the Ice Age floodwaters. The basins here and most everywhere in the Channeled Scabland are located in the resistant entablature part of the basalt lava flow. The more vulnerable colonnade part of the flow is usually completely stripped off by floodwater, although some remnants of colonnade occasionally occur along the edges of some wetland depressions. A wildlife blind overlooking Kepple Lake conveniently lies at the end of the paved trail.

Blackhorse Lake Boardwalk. This short (0.4 mile round-trip) wheelchair-accessible trail allows one to traverse across a lush, marshy area on a sturdy, elevated boardwalk for engaging views of Blackhorse Lake, Swan Pond and the marsh below. At an elevation of 2,270 feet, the Blackhorse Lake area is the lowest elevation along the Cheney-Palouse Scabland Tract. Therefore, floodwaters were deepest here – towering up to 200 feet overhead. Because it lies in a low, poorly drained area, the Turnbull Wildlife Refuge collects lots of water, which is great for wetlands and wildlife.

Columbia Plateau Trail. A portion of one more trail, the Columbia Plateau Trail, passes through the northwestern part of the Turnbull Refuge for about five miles. This trail is described next.

Trail M. Columbia Plateau   Flood Feature Nos. 13, 14, 18

Follow the northern part of a rails-to-trails state park along the main thrust of ancient floodwaters through the Cheney-Palouse scablands.

Geologic Highlights: Recessional cataract canyons, butte-and-basin scabland, rock basin lakes, and flood bars of various shapes and sizes, as well as stream-lined and scarped Palouse hills

Length: 125 miles total one-way; however, only the first 23 miles at the northern end and 14 miles at the extreme southern end are improved for general use as of 2011. This guide covers only the first 23 miles of the Columbia Plateau Trail at its improved, upper end through a portion of the Cheney-Palouse Tract.

Elevation Along Trail: Trail slowly rises from 2,200 feet at Fish Lake to 2,300 feet at the Cheney Trailhead and 2,325 feet at Long Lake, before gently descending toward Martin Road (2,060 feet)

Difficulty: Easy, longer distances more difficult

Best Mode of Travel: Mountain bike or hike. Southwest of the Cheney Trailhead (Figure 4-29) the surface is crushed gravel and also suitable for horses.

Best Observation Points: Fish and Amber lakes

Management/Ownership: Washington State Parks

USGS 1:24,000 Scale Maps: Fishtrap Lake, Amber, Lance Hills, Cheney, Four Lakes, WA

Warnings: Potable water only at water station at Cheney entrance during the summer season. Do not trespass onto Turnbull Wildlife Refuge or private lands across the fenced trail right-of-way, no fires permitted. First 3.8 miles of trail from Fish Lake to Cheney trailheads are paved. Washington Discover Pass required.

Directions: Four trailheads are currently available (Figure 4-29):

1. Fish Lake – three miles northeast of Cheney along Cheney-Spokane Road

2. Cheney Trailhead – 0.9 mile southeast of Cheney along Cheney-Spangle Road

3. Amber Lake Trailhead – one mile west on Cheney-Tyler Road (State Route 904), left (south) on Mullinix Road for 10 miles, west on Pine Springs Road for 1.5 miles

4. Martin Road – Take Exit 245 off Interstate 90 into Sprague. Follow signs for the Columbia Plateau Trail, which lead 2.5 miles east on Sprague Highway, then southeast on Williams Lake Road for four miles to trailhead. The Martin Lake Trailhead can also be accessed from Cheney via Mullinix Road.

This former railroad bed is paved for the first 3.8 miles between the Fish Lake and Cheney trailheads. The remaining part of the improved 23 miles is surfaced with fine, crushed gravel. Mountain bike or horse recommended for long distances. Mileposts along the old Spokane Portland & Seattle (SP&S, later the Burlington Northern) Railway help to locate points of interest. Completion of the remaining 88 miles of right-of-way to the Snake River to the south, connection with the Centennial Trail in the Spokane River Valley to the north, and connection with the yet-to-be-built cross-state trail planned by Washington State Parks is planned but dependant on adequate future funding.

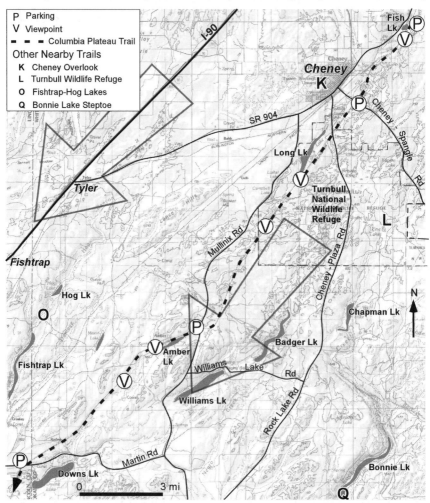

Figure 4-29. Map of the 23-mile, improved portion of the Columbia Plateau Trail (CPT) State Park. Bold letters identify other nearby trails featured in this chapter. Four public entrances to the CPT are identified with parking symbols.

Trail Log

(Parentheses indicate railroad mile from Portland, Oregon – marked with mileposts along trail)

0.0 (365)   The Fish Lake Trailhead (N47.5220, W117.5157) is located in a flood-scoured depression adjacent to the Prosser Hill steptoe, composed of extremely old (about 1.5 billion years) metasedimentary Belt rock. Follow the trail southwest through a railroad cut that exposes Columbia River basalt, one-thousandth the age of the Belt rocks! For it was a mere 15 million years ago the basaltic lava flows lapped onto the edge of Prosser Hill here.

0.25 (364.75)   The trail opens up into the Fish Lake rock basin rimmed by basalt and the old metasedimentary rocks. The lake bottom is separated into two sub-basins by a narrow rock blade that is barely exposed during low water. During the wet spring and early summer seasons, the blade lies submerged but marked by aquatic plants growing on the shallower lake surface. Missoula floodwaters, more than 400 feet deep, slowed and piled up behind the resistant Steptoe Ridge (see Figure 3-21) before shooting southward through this and other low gaps along the ridge. High-velocity megafloods enlarged and deepened the gap and lake.

1.4 (363.6)   Just southwest of the Anderson Road bridge the trail passes through a deep vertical cut that exposes a contact between two lava flows. A thin soil layer of sediment and red-weathered rock lies sandwiched between the flows. The weak zone created at the flow contact contributes to the unstable walls and rockfalls here in "rockfall alley." Weathered contact zones like this one were more prone to flood erosion and account for many of the broad basins and channels encountered along this trail and elsewhere within the Channeled Scabland.

Figure 4-30. A stockpile of rounded, light-colored, foreign (mostly non-basalt) boulders along the Columbia Plateau Trail next to the Cheney-Plaza Road overpass. Stockpiled here by road crews, these were probably once transported as bedload along the base of a flood. Looking east.

1.9 (363.1)   Anderson Meadow is one of the many flood-scoured basins concentrated along the contact zone between lava flows. A shallow lake and marsh occupying this closed depression was later drained during railroad construction that occurred from 1906 to 1910. Note the fine sediment layers and the prominent layer of post-flood volcanic ash from the eruption of Mount

Mazama (Crater Lake, Oregon) about 7,700 years ago. Here and elsewhere along the trail watch for occasional flood-transported rocks such as granite and quartzite that were transported many miles from their sources.

4.0 (361)   Cheney trailhead (with rest rooms). Continue southwest through another flood-eroded basin, into the Turnbull National Wildlife Refuge, and through a series of railroad cuts to Long Lake (Figure 4-29).

5.5 (359.5)   Next to the Cheney-Plaza Road overpass that crosses the CPT is a man-made grouping of rounded boulders originally transported by the floods (Figure 4-30). While some of the boulders are of local basalt origin, many are composed of granitic and Belt rocks. The rounded nature of the boulders suggests they were transported as bedload along the base of the flood and not rafted in on icebergs. Technically, these are just boulders – not erratics – a term reserved for foreign boulders transported by glacial ice.

7.0 (358)   Long Lake lies in another, broad, flood-excavated basin scoured out along the weak zone between basalt flows and between the basalt and underlying granite. Here the floods eroded a "window" through the basalt exposing the granitic "Turnbull steptoe" present just below the surface. Watch for the exhumed steptoe, which is exposed along the south side of the trail near milepost 358. Light-colored patches of crystalline granite are visible through the lichens covering these rocks.

The trail continues through butte-and-basin scabland for another 8.5 miles to the Amber Lake Trailhead and 16 miles to Martin Road Trailhead where the improved section of the trail (as of 2011) ends (Figure 4-29). Beyond the Martin Road Trailhead, the trail surface is covered with rough railroad ballast, up to the size of baseballs, which makes traveling much more difficult. Long Lake is a reasonable place to turn around for those looking for a moderate-length trip. Alternatives are to explore in either direction of any of the other trailheads.

Figure 4-31. Columbia Plateau Trail State Park. An elongate, flood-scoured rock basin, located along the Columbia Plateau Trail. Looking southwest.

Trail N. Audubon Lake   Flood Feature Nos. 12, 18, 20, 22

Hike to a water-filled rock basin at the confluence of three Ice Age flood channels. Along the way rise over a set of giant current ripples before coming to the bird blind that allows for hidden viewing of wildlife around the lake.

Geologic Highlights: Water-filled, flood-scoured rock basin along the strongly weathered basalt/granite contact zone, potholes, giant current ripples and grooves eroded in basalt. Excellent views of the distant Steptoe Ridge to the south.

Length: 0.6 mile round-trip

Elevation (Relief) Along Trail: 2,460 to 2,500 feet (40 feet)

Difficulty: Easy

Best Mode of Travel: Hike, wheelchair accessible

Best Observation Point: From or around the bird blind

Management/Ownership: Washington Department of Fish and Wildlife

USGS 1:24,000 Scale Maps: Reardan East; Reardan West

Directions: From U.S. Highway 2 at Reardan turn north on State Route 231, proceed one mile, turn east (right) on Euclid Road. At 0.3 mile turn right into Audubon Lake parking area (Figure 4-32). Washington Discover Pass required.

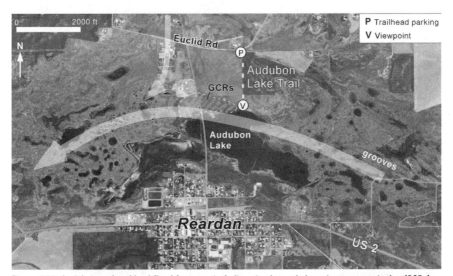

Figure 4-32. Aerial view of scabland flood features, including circular potholes, giant current ripples (GCRs) and grooves carved into a thin cover of Priest Rapids Member basalt near Reardan. Audubon Lake lies at the junction between three drainage divides, Spring Creek from the north, Deep Creek to the east, and Crab Creek to the west. Reardan lies along a potholed flood coulee that carried floodwaters spilling over from the east via the West Plains and Deep Creek, and from the north via Spring Creek Canyon. These two channels merged to flow down Crab Creek on the left. A bird blind is located at the viewpoint (V).

Trail Log

0.0   Megafloods swept across the area at a maximum elevation of 2,600 feet (about 140 feet above Audubon Lake) but below the tops of the high steptoes visible to the south. Grays Butte, directly to the north, was another steptoe of quartzite Belt rock that lay 250 feet above the maximum flood level. Basalt cliffs north of Euclid Road are also near the contact with the underlying pre-basalt rocks. Proceed across flood sand and gravel overlain by a thin cover of post-flood loess.

0.15   From the crest of the flood bar, the Steptoe Ridge (No. 12) is visible to the south, including the double-peaked Fancher Butte. Proceed across the flood bar mantled with low-relief giant ripples disturbed by farming (undisturbed ripples lie just southwest of here, Figure 4-32). Just west of here floodwaters from the West Plains joined those coming south via a spillover from Spring Creek Canyon. From here the megaflood flow continued west into the Crab Creek.

0.3   Bird blind with view across Audubon Lake at end of trail. Retrace route to trailhead.

Trail O. Fishtrap and Hog Lakes   Flood Feature No. 18

Here, at the edge of the prairie, lie miles of trails and roads featuring two, scenic rock-basin lakes flanked by flood-dissected Palouse hills of the Cheney-Palouse scabland.

Geologic Highlights: Seasonal waterfall at head of Hog Lake, abandoned cataracts, water-filled recessional cataract canyons, buttes, potholes, rock benches, Mima mounds as well as streamlined and scarped Palouse hills

Trails: Two trails are featured; one trail loops 5.7 miles past the west side of Hog Lake; the other loops 9.3 miles past the west side of Fishtrap Lake (Figure 4-33). Other trails crisscross the area and public boat launches at both lakes offer opportunities for kayakers, canoes and power boaters.

Elevation Along Trails: 1,975 feet at Fishtrap Lake to 2,250 feet along bases of streamlined Palouse hills. The higher hills rise to 2,375 feet, however, no publicly accessible trails go to hilltops.

Difficulty: Moderate, longer trails more difficult

Best Modes of Travel: Hike, bike or horseback

Best Observation Points: Hog Canyon Falls overlook (N47.3805, W117.8016), Fishtrap Lake overlook (N47.3436, W117.8373)

Management/Ownership: U.S. Bureau of Land Management

USGS 1:24,000 Scale Map: Fishtrap Lake, WA

Warnings: No potable water along trails. Steep cliffs around lakes, beware of hunters in fall. Numerous barbed wire fences pass through the area; most are safely crossed at conveniently placed BLM swing gates along route.

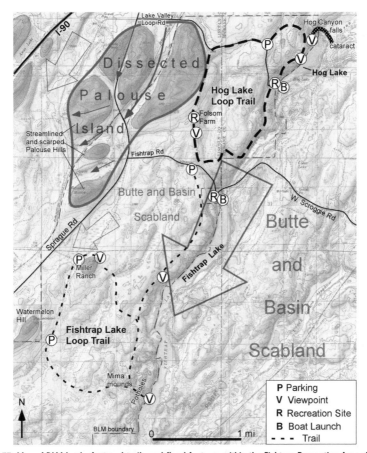

Figure 4-33. Map of BLM lands, featured trails and flood features within the Fishtrap Recreation Area. Arrows indicate flow directions during Ice Age floods.

Figure 4-34. The smoothed surface of a Palouse loess island (No. 18) lies in stark contrast to the flat-lying layers of jagged basalt exposed along a scabland channel below. A continuous blanket of windblown Palouse loess, many tens of feet thick, once covered basalt in this region before the onslaught of Ice Age floods. Looking southwest.

Hog Lake Loop Trail (01)

"The roughness of the channel floors, due to the gashed basalt, is in striking contrast with the smooth flowing contours of the inclosing hills."

– J Harlen Bretz (1923)

Directions: Exit 254 from Interstate 90 and proceed south 0.75 mile on the Sprague Highway. Turn left after 0.9 mile onto unpaved Lake Valley Loop Road. At 0.4 mile farther cross railroad tracks and continue straight on Lake Valley Loop Road onto Bureau of Land Management property. After 0.5 mile road passes through a gate on the left. Trailhead is another 0.7 mile at gate and small parking area among pine trees on the left.

Trail Log

0.0   Park by gate (N47.3803, W117.8126) where road bends south. Go through gate and follow double-track trail going northeast.

0.1   Pass by aspen-lined rock basin and through another gate after 0.2 mile.

0.5   Rise over rock bench, begin descent toward Hog Lake. Notice rounded granitic boulder in middle of the road. This boulder was probably transported here along the base of the flood flow during one or more Ice Age floods.

Figure 4-35. Hog Canyon Creek descends over Hog Canyon Falls, spectacular during the spring when snowmelt and runoff cascade over a cataract cliff into Hog Lake. The falls are dry most of the rest of the year. Looking northeast.

0.6   Viewpoint from rock bench above Hog Lake (Figure 4-35, above). To the northeast is Hog Canyon Falls (Figures 4-35, right), which seasonally flows over a cataract at the head of the lake. Here also is a goat island – an isolated butte of basalt eroded out during cataract recession. From here one can descend to the base of the waterfall, continue south along the double-track road, or travel cross-country along the rim above the lower end of the lake.

1.0   The double-track trail passes another aspen-lined scour depression along the rock bench high above Hog Lake. At 1.2 miles the trail changes from double-track to single-track.

1.6   Trail makes steep descent towards the Hog Lake shoreline.

1.8   A man-made earthen dam near the boat ramp and parking lot raises the level of Hog Lake. Ascend gravel road to the west.

2.0   A huge basalt column lies along the south (left) side of the road (Figure 4-36). At the BLM sign and where the road bends to the right, leave the road by bearing left (south). Hike along the rock bench that parallels the west side of Hog Canyon. (Another option is to cut the loop short by heading back to starting point, which is only 0.4 mile to the north, along this road.) From here the longer loop trail may be difficult to follow at first but can be found by hugging the west side of the rock bench above Hog Canyon.

Figure 4-36. A broken, polygonal basalt column 3 feet in diameter sits atop a dissimilar rock bench near the Hog Lake boat ramp. No outcrops of columnar basalt are nearby; thus, the massive column must have been transported here intact by rushing floodwaters.

2.7   Trail ascends onto a higher rock bench (i.e., flood-scoured surface of a younger basalt flow).

3.2   Arrive at barbed wire fence. Without crossing fence turn right (west) up moderately steep slope that rises out of the canyon.

3.3   Trail flattens out onto plateau above canyon where it joins another double-track trail. Head west toward Fishtrap Road visible in the distance.

3.8   Pass through gate and turn right onto unnamed gravel road toward the Folsom Farm Historical Site.

4.3   At Folsom Farm, continue north on road along the base of the dissected, streamlined Palouse hill (No. 18). Pass through another gate after another 0.4 mile.

5.1   Intersection with entrance road. Follow road right (east) 0.6 mile back to the start of the loop.

Fishtrap Lake Loop Trail (02)

*"The hill groups are elongated northeast-southwest, in harmony with the elonga-
tion of the channels on the basalt surface and with the scabland tract as a whole."*

— *J Harlen Bretz (1923)*

Directions: Leave Interstate 90 at Exit 254 and proceed south 2.4 miles on the
Sprague Highway passing through the heart of a flood-dissected loess island
(Figure 4-33). Turn left (east) onto Fishtrap Road and proceed 0.6 mile to the
trailhead at a gate and small parking area on the right.

Figure 4-37. Fishtrap Lake scabland, looking south. Note the many distinct Mima mounds at lower left.

Trail Log

0.0   From parking area at south side of Fishtrap Road (N47.3606,
W117.8307), pass through the swing gate and head south along double-track
trail, well-marked with signs like the one in Figure 4-3. Well-developed Mima
mounds cover the surface of the rock bench here (Figure 4-37). Continue south
across flood-swept plateau above Fishtrap Lake, a southwesterly extension of
Hog Canyon.

0.3   Pass through the gate with "Welcome – Trespassing OK" sign to cross
a few hundred yards of private property, before reentering BLM land.

1.4   Trail skirts west edge of Fishtrap Lake canyon. Take a short detour
to the rimrock overlooking Fishtrap Lake. Nice viewpoint at N47.3436,
W117.8373.

Figure 4-38. Watermelon Hill, an elongated flood-streamlined Palouse Loess Island (No. 18) west of Fishtrap Lake. Looking south.

2.1   Intersection with trail to Miller Ranch. Continue straight (south). Pass through gate after another 0.1 mile.

2.6   A large water-filled, flood-scoured depression lies to the right (west).

2.9   Many classic, well-developed Mima mounds (see "Mysterious Mima Mounds" sidebar, page 83 in chapter 3) along trail here.

3.1   Swarm of deep pothole depressions along west side of Fishtrap Lake.

3.2   Trail comes to a T. Turn left (east) and descend to the west shore of Fishtrap Lake.

3.5   Peaceful oasis of meadows and trees with lovely views up and down the Fishtrap Lake shoreline. To continue, retrace route uphill.

3.8   At trail intersection continue west across butte-and-basin scabland towards Watermelon Hill (Figure 4-38). Double-track trail slowly bends to the right (north).

5.1   Pass through gate (N47.3335, W117.8636) at base of Watermelon Hill and follow dirt road northeast toward Miller Ranch.

6.0   Just northeast of Miller Ranch pass through a couple of gates, the first one located at N47.3467, W117.8559, and follow trail around north side of flood-sculpted streamlined Palouse hill (Figure 4-33).

6.5   Heading southeast descend into shallow, flood-scoured coulee.

7.2   Junction with original trail at N47.3367, W117.8427. Turn left to return to starting point.

9.3   End of loop.

Trail P. North Rock Lake

Flood Feature Nos. 15, 16, 17, 18

Iron Horse State Park/John Wayne Pioneer Trail

Follow an abandoned railroad along a portion of the state-owned John Wayne Pioneer Trail through two basalt tunnels and along the eastern embankment of the deepest of all scabland lakes.

Geologic Highlights: Water-filled, deep recessional cataract canyon; buttes, mesas, rock benches, trenched spurs, streamlined and scarped Palouse hills, long and straight flood-etched tectonic fractures.

Length: 10.6 miles round-trip

Elevation (Relief) Along Trail: 1,900 to 1,940 feet (40 feet)

Difficulty: Easy on mountain bike, moderate for hikers because of length

Best Observation Point: High overlook over Rock Lake at 2.9 miles from trailhead (N47.2156, W117.6346)

Best Modes of Travel: Hike, mountain bike, horse

Management/Ownership: Washington State Parks

USGS 1:24,000 Scale Maps: Pine City, Rock Lake, WA

Warnings: Trail is not officially open and is mostly unmaintained. As of 2011 day permits are required to use the trail; these can be obtained from the park manager of the Columbia Plateau Trail State Park at 509-646-9218 (e-mail: eacolt@parks.wa.gov). Little shade exists during midday; no potable water. Steep cliffs along trail, unimproved trestle crossing requires caution, flashlights in curved tunnels are recommended (walking bikes strongly recommended). Respect all private land adjacent to the public trail. The trail ends at private-land boundary, marked with cross barriers, at 5.3 miles from trailhead. Exercise care in crossing areas of rockslides. Isolated boulders and large cobbles on trail can be hazardous for bicyclists. Be aware of rockfall hazards. No hunting permitted on state park land, but be aware of hunters in adjacent lands during hunting season.

Directions: Proceed south on the Cheney-Plaza Road from Cheney (follow signs in Cheney toward Turnbull National Wildlife Refuge). At 9.8 miles Cheney-Plaza Road turns abruptly east (left) toward Chapman Lake; continue straight south onto Rock Lake Road. About 17 miles south of Cheney turn left (east) onto unpaved Belsby Road. Descend and cross the deep recessional Rock Creek Coulee (Hole-In-The-Ground Canyon) (Figure 4-39, see Figure 3-28, Plate 13). The road climbs out of the canyon on the other side. Bear right at the Belsby/Hole-In-The-Ground Road (unsigned) intersection. After one mile (23.6 miles from Cheney) turn right at the state park trail sign onto the Old Milwaukee Railroad corridor. Park at gated trailhead (do not block gate) or in a wide area a short distance down Hole-in-the-Ground Road by the highway bridge over Pine Creek.

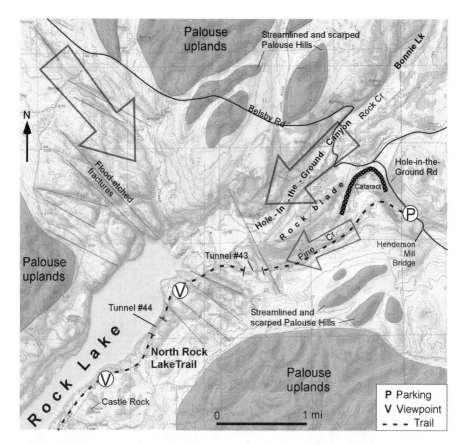

Figure 4-39. North Rock Lake trail. Block arrows indicate floodwater from multiple directions converged at the head of Rock Lake. Note the many subparallel, tectonic fractures preferentially eroded by megafloods at the northeast end of Rock Lake. See aerial photo in Figure 3-29.

The North Rock Lake Trail follows the former Chicago, Milwaukee, St. Paul and Pacific Railroad, also known as the Milwaukee Railroad. The railroad began abandoning its western lines due to financial troubles in the 1970s. Washington State Parks acquired the right-of-way along most of the railroad bed and began to open segments in western Washington as early as 1984. The formal opening of the trail through the east part of the state is anticipated for 2013 – the centennial for Washington State Parks. The trail, also known as the John Wayne Pioneer Trail, is part of Washington State's Iron Horse State Park.

The Rock Lake area abounds in interesting history and legends. Chief Kamiakin, leader of the Yakama Tribe and an important figure in conflicts between American Indians and white settlers, lived to be an old man along the southeast shore of the Rock Lake with his family; he died here in 1877 at 77 years of age. Years later the lake was temporarily a tourist destination when a large tour boat operated on the lake and a hotel was built at Lavista also at the southeast end of Rock Lake. As is true of many large lakes, Rock Lake has its share of monsters, some capable of capsizing canoes. The dead were never found, suggesting that they may have been consumed! A train wreck that sent boxcars full of brand-new Ford Model T's to the lake bottom has never been verified. The lake is an amazing 400 feet deep at its head and 200 to 300 feet in a number of places.

Trail Log

0.0   Park in wide area just before Henderson Mill Bridge and Pine Creek along Hole-in-the-Ground Road (Figure 4-39). Pine Creek Coulee (No. 16) carried outburst floodwaters southwestward after spilling out of Hangman (Latah) Creek. The broken boxcars strewn about along the west end of the trestle hint at the problems of maintaining a railroad through this rugged terrain.

0.5   A rugged, flat-topped basalt ridge (rock blade) separates the flood-deepened Pine Creek Coulee from Rock Creek Coulee (Hole-In-The-Ground Canyon) on the west side of the ridge (Figure 4-39, Plate 13). The canyon complex here was cut by recessional cataracts incised by high-energy flood-waters locally over 800 feet deep and moving at freeway speeds!

Figure 4-40. Rock Lake scabland. View looking south across Rock Lake from the North Rock Lake Trail (N47.2156, W117.6346).

1.8   A short side canyon on the left (southeast) follows one of a number of major parallel northwest-southeast trending tectonic fractures in the basalt (part of the Cheney Fracture Zone) that were preferentially enlarged by flood erosion (Figure 4-39; see also Figures 1-7 and 3-29). The weakened rock along the fracture zones is more susceptible to erosion and accounts for the location of side canyons here, the abrupt northwestward turn of Pine Creek into Hole-In-The-Ground Canyon (Rock Creek channel), and the continuation of the fracture visible across the valley of Hole-In-The-Ground Canyon. The basalt rocks are relatively thin here as indicated by outcroppings of old, pre-basalt Belt rock exposed across the coulee along the valley bottom. The older rocks were later buried by massive flows of Columbia River basalt and lastly exhumed by mega-flood erosion.

1.9   Tunnel No. 43. Construction of the tunnel produced steep rock slopes, particularly above the tunnel ends. Watch out for rockfall.

2.1   Good views of the flood-etched fracture zone across Rock Creek discussed above. Flood-streamlined Palouse hills (No. 18) visible above the canyon rim to the north.

2.8   The recessional cataract that excavated the Rock Lake basin ends here at the northeast end of the lake (see Figure 3-29). The trail enters flood-enlarged side canyons along northwest-southeast trending fractures at the head of Rock Lake. The recessional cataract rim was extensively dissected and eroded when floodwaters ate away at the fracture complex. Rock Lake is a spectacular body of water with vertical basalt cliffs plunging directly into its deep waters along most of its length. The deepest part of the lake (400 feet) lies at the northeast end. Strong southwest winds can quickly turn the lake into a wind tunnel and a fury of whitecaps. A number of small boats and their occupants have been lost to Rock Lake's unpredictable waters.

2.9   Note the two major fractures in the basalt on the west wall of Rock Lake and the flood-sculpted Palouse hills on the canyon rim above. Distant views to the southwest of a prominent isolated scabland butte (one of several Castle Rocks in the Channeled Scabland – see "Scabland Homonyms" sidebar, page 27 in chapter 2) located on the east side of Rock Lake above the trail.

3.2   Cross wooden trestle. Use caution as there are some broken planks and no side rails. The trestle is relatively safe but can be a psychological challenge! The trestle crosses a short but deep minor side canyon.

3.3   Tunnel No. 44. Good views at either end of the tunnel of the Columbia River basalt and pillow-palagonite zones (see Figure 1-4) of weakness between lava flows. Rock weaknesses reduce support for the rock above and promote rockfall activity. A rock slide on the south end of the tunnel requires bicyclists to carry their bikes across the large boulder field. The easiest path is along the east side of the rockfall debris.

3.4   Note the railroad milepost sign on the abandoned electric pole along the farm road at left (east). On the old Milwaukee Railroad this location was 1,894 miles from Chicago! The streamlined loess hills on the canyon rim on the west side of Rock Lake display an asymmetrical longitudinal profile caused by flood erosion. The steep upstream side or "steamboat prow" faces north towards the oncoming rush of floodwater with a gentler, tapered slope on the downstream side (see examples in Figures 2-22).

5.3   Farm equipment placed across the trail marks the end of the public trail. Retrace route back to trailhead.

Trail Q. Bonnie Lake Steptoe

Flood Feature Nos. 15, 17

Paddle to a solitary steptoe island within Bonnie Lake composed of ancient, meta-morphosed, marine sediments exhumed during Ice Age flooding. Along the way witness an extremely rare natural bridge in the flood-scoured basalt that looms above Rock Creek Coulee canyon.

Geologic Highlights: Bonnie Lake is another deep rock basin scoured out by the Ice Age floods (see Figures 3-30, 6-3). An isolated, steptoe island, composed of extremely old, Belt-type rock, protrudes out from the middle of the lake. Rare natural bridge exists along west wall of the canyon.

Length: 2.8 miles one-way to the steptoe island. The far upper end of the lake is another three miles (5.8 miles total one-way).

Difficulty: Moderate to difficult depending on wind, weather and type of watercraft

Best Observation Point: Bonnie Lake steptoe island

Best Modes of Travel: Portable watercraft (i.e., canoe or kayak). Rock Creek is very narrow and not suitable for larger boats, especially during fall and winter when stream flows are low.

Management/Ownership: Both Rock Creek and Bonnie Lake are public water-ways. The Bonnie Lake steptoe island is public land owned by the U.S. Bureau of Land Management. All the lands surrounding Bonnie Lake are private – respect landowners' wishes and do not trespass.

USGS 1:24,000 Scale Maps: Pine City and Chapman Lake, WA

Warnings: Avoid paddling on Bonnie Lake during high winds, especially those coming from the southwest, which can create dangerous, capsizing swells. Many boats (and boaters) have been lost in these conditions. Morning is generally a calmer and safer time to explore the lake.

Directions: From Cheney drive south on Cheney-Plaza Road that changes to Rock Lake Road after approximately 11 miles. Proceed another six miles before turning left (east) onto Belsby Road. Belsby Road crosses Rock Creek along Hole-in-the-Ground Canyon at 4.9 miles (Figures 4-39 and 4-41). Pull off and safely park along one of the few wide spots available here, being careful not to block the paths into any of the gated side roads.

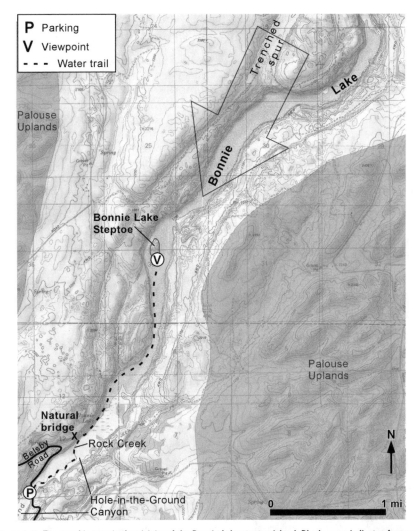

Figure 4-41. Topographic map in the vicinity of the Bonnie Lake steptoe island. Block arrow indicates former flood flow down Rock Creek Coulee, which was funneled through Palouse uplands on either side. Note that the only areas open to the public on this map are Belsby Road, Rock Creek, Bonnie Lake and the Bonnie Lake steptoe. See Figure 2-20 for an aerial view of the flood-scoured trenched spur at the north end of the lake.

Trail Log

0.0   Enter Rock Creek via portable watercraft at Belsby Road heading northeast (Figure 4-41). Follow Rock Creek to the northeast as it meanders up the floor of Hole-in-the-Ground Canyon toward Bonnie Lake. Keep in mind that only the waterway is open to public, lands on either side are private. Hole-in-the-Ground Canyon is named for a large, 6-foot diameter void in a basalt flow (on private land) that is purported to be a weathered-out tree cast in basalt.

1.3   Pass by natural bridge (see Figure 2-14) in basalt cliff along the west wall of Rock Creek Coulee.

1.8   Rock Creek transitions into marsh where it merges with Bonnie Lake.

2.0   Waterway opens up into Bonnie Lake.

2.8   Arrive at south end of the Bonnie Lake steptoe island (Figure 4-41, see aerial view in Figure 3-30). The rocks here consist of a rock known as schist (Figure 4-42), very different than the Columbia River basalt that line the canyon walls. The schist, part of the Belt Supergroup, was deposited in an ancient sea about 1.5 billion years ago. Many eons later (only 15 million years ago), the steptoe was enveloped and buried beneath a thin cover of Columbia River basalt lava flows. Only relatively recently did Ice Age floods erode through the basalt cover, exhuming the older Belt rocks of the island. Feel free to explore the publicly owned island and the rest of Bonnie Lake, but lands surrounding the lake are privately owned and off-limits to the public.

6.0   North end of Bonnie Lake at Rock Creek. Return to trailhead.

Figure 4-42. View from the Bonnie Lake steptoe island, looking south. The island is composed entirely of a pre-basalt rock called schist (i.e., metamorphosed ancient marine sediments) belonging to the Precambrian Belt Supergroup. Notice how these ancient strata are tilted almost vertical – in sharp contrast to the layers of horizontally bedded, black Columbia River basalt in the background. This is a classic example of what geologists call an "angular unconformity" and demonstrates the large gap of geologic time missing between the deposition of these two extremely different rock units. In fact, the schist is a mind-boggling one-thousand times older than the basalt!

Trail R. Escure Ranch to Towell Falls   Flood Feature Nos. 17, 18

Pleasant trek through a remote scabland canyon (Rock Creek Coulee), ending where Rock Creek drops over a rocky bench, creating Towell Falls.

Geologic Highlights: Flood bars, trenched spurs, mesas, buttes, rock benches and basins, waterfalls, Mima mounds

Length: 6.6 miles round-trip

Elevation (Relief) Along Trail: 1,400 to 1,560 feet (160 feet)

Difficulty: Moderate

Best Observation Point: Rock bench above east side of Rock Creek about 1.7 miles from trailhead (Plate 16).

Best Mode (other modes) of Travel: Hike (mountain bike, horse)

Management/Ownership: U.S. Bureau of Land Management

USGS 1:24,000 Scale Map: Honn Lakes, WA

Warnings: No potable water or midday shade

Directions: From Interstate 90 at Sprague (Exit 245) drive 17 miles south on State Route 23 along the Cow Creek Scabland Complex. At Lamont cross up and over a huge island of Palouse loess (No. 18) before descending into the Rock Creek Scabland Complex. Turn right (south) onto Wagner Road and continue 5.6 miles to intersection with Davis Road. Bear left (west) onto Revere Road for three miles. Beyond Revere turn left (south) again onto Jordan Knott Road. After 2.2 miles bear right at entrance to the BLM's Rock Creek Management Area. Continue south 2.5 miles to road's end and park at gate adjacent to the old, abandoned Escure Ranch (Figure 4-43).

Trail Log

0.0   At trailhead (N47.0143, W117.9435) pass through swinging gate and head south along double-track trail that parallels the east side of Rock Creek. Based on the heights of eroded scarps and spillover channels in nearby Palouse hills (No. 18), the largest floods towered up to 500 feet overhead here and elsewhere along the bottom of the canyon!

0.5   Trail passes below flat–topped mesa and trenched spur shown in Plate 16. Long flood bar along opposite side of Rock Creek extends northward all the way back to trailhead. Continue south and east along the canyon. Near here an American Indian hearth used as recently as 500 years ago was unearthed from beneath a Mima mound (see "Mysterious Mima Mounds" sidebar, page 83 in chapter 3).

1.6   Trail leaves Rock Creek floodplain and rises onto rock bench. Nice views from the top of the bench (Plate 16).

2.0   Trail descends into narrow, trenched-spur canyon with a maze of basalt buttes located along east side of a large, flood-swept mesa. One-half mile farther the trail flattens out atop a huge pendant-expansion flood bar at the south (downstream) end of the mesa.

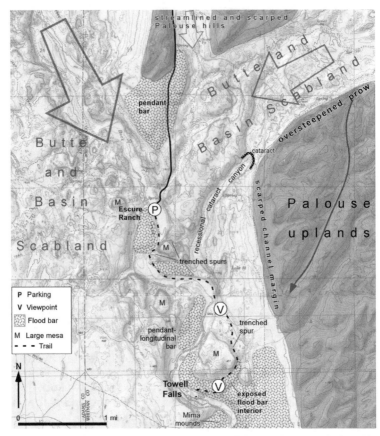

Figure 4-43. Flood features near the Escure Ranch to Towell Falls Trail. Block arrows signify the primary flood-flow directions. Some floodwaters also spilled over the Palouse uplands along east side of Rock Creek valley.

Figure 4-44. Exposed interior of a pendant-expansion flood bar (foreground) along Rock Creek. Note large size of some of the basalt boulders within the bar deposits. Hiker (circled) for scale. In the background is a pendant-crescent-type flood bar, dimpled with post-flood Mima mounds. Looking south.

2.8   Panoramic view across Rock Creek canyon toward a Mima mound studded flood bar, aspen groves and Towell Falls. From here you can take a short detour a few hundred yards to the south where a side stream has cut down through the pendant-expansion flood bar, exposing its interior (Figure 4-44), or continue descending west to Towell Falls.

3.3   Towell Falls drops over a rock ledge (top of eroded basalt flow) along Rock Creek (Figure 4-45). Retrace route to trailhead.

Figure 4-45. One of the two Towell Falls drops about 10 feet over a flood-eroded rock bench of more resistant basalt entablature. Looking northwest. See also Figure 6-5 for an aerial view of the falls.

Trails in the Vicinity of the Telford-Crab Creek Scabland Tract

Trail S. Crab Creek Meanders   Flood Feature Nos. 18, 22

Crab Creek passes through the desolate heartland of the Channeled Scabland. Follow Crab Creek Coulee to a set of unusual, broad, curving meanders incised into the floor of the coulee. The meanders, created by the normal, lazy flow of Crab Creek, were quickly overwhelmed and overrun during massive Ice Age torrents.

Geologic Highlights: Ice Age floods cut straight across two tight meanders within the Crab Creek Coulee. Huge crescent flood bars formed along the inside of the meanders. Nearby, as The Crab Creek Coulee overfilled, mega-floods spilled south into an adjacent coulee and carved several classic streamlined and scarped Palouse hills.

Length: 6.2 miles round-trip

Elevation (Relief) Along Trail: 1,800 to 1,940 feet (140 feet)

Difficulty: Moderate

Best Mode (other modes) of Travel: Mountain bike (hike, horse)

Best Observation Point: End of trail at overlook onto the flood-swept, western meander (N47.3018, W118.3175)

Management/Ownership: U.S. Bureau of Land Management

USGS 1:24,000 Scale Maps: Harrington SE, WA

Warnings: Only picnic tables at trailhead campground. No potable water, restrooms or shade here or anywhere else along trail.

Directions: From Interstate 90, take Tokio exit (No. 231). Go north, then west along Danekas Road for 1.6 miles, before turning right (north) onto Hills Road. At 4.3 miles cross bottom of coulee (south fork of Crab Creek) that extends east from Sprague Lake. Continue north on Hills Road, which changes to Harrington-Tokio Road as it rises up onto a line of Palouse hills. At 6.2 miles pass through one of a series of parallel, high, flat-bottomed, scarped spillover channels that were cut when the main Crab Creek Coulee was overfilled by floodwaters (Figure 4-46). From here descend north into Crab Creek Coulee. Continue another 1.2 miles before coming to trailhead at primitive BLM campground on the left (west).

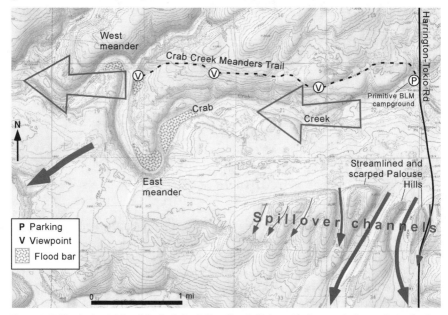

Figure 4-46. Map in the vicinity of the Crab Creek Meanders Trail. Large block arrows indicate primary flood-flow direction down Crab Creek Coulee. Excess floodwater also escaped to the south via a series of parallel spillover channels carved into the Palouse upland.

Trail Log

0.0   Park at northeast end of primitive campground (N47.3027, W118.2528). Pass through swinging gate and up double-track trail to the northwest. After 0.25 mile trail flattens out onto rock bench heading west. Continue past several small eroded buttes along the rock bench.

0.7   Notches in the ridge of Palouse loess across the valley are hanging spillover channels that developed after floodwaters overfilled the valley and escaped south into an adjacent coulee (Figure 4-46). The maximum height of megafloods in this area was about 2,100 feet, several tens of feet above the highest of these streamlined hills.

1.2   Where a side road veers off to the left is the first viewpoint into Crab Creek Coulee. Continue west along rock bench.

2.5   View into the central Crab Creek Coulee and the east meander.

3.1   Double-track trail leads to scenic overlook onto the west meander of Crab Creek Coulee (Figures 4-46 and 4-47). The meanders were originally formed by normal drainage of perennial Crab Creek in between Ice Age floods. Megafloods, on the other hand, took a totally different course, which was straight up and over the meander spurs, completely stripping away all topsoil and eroding a complex maze of channels, basins, buttes and mesas across the spurs. Viewpoint is from a pendant flood bar, which formed immediately downstream of the rock bench behind. A wonderful example of a crescent flood bar formed at the nose of the west meander spur (Figure 4-47). Retrace route back to trailhead.

Figure 4-47. View across the tight west meander of Crab Creek Coulee (N47.3018, W118.3175). Spur of Roza Member basalt along inside of meander was totally stripped off by megafloods. Crescent flood bar was deposited on the right as the last of the receding floodwaters resumed flowing the long way around the outside of the meander. Looking west.

Belching Volcanoes

It was late on the night of May 18, 1980, when I (Bjornstad) found myself on a school bus heading home to Cheney via U.S. Highway 2. We were deep in the heart of the Channeled Scabland in the midst of a choking ash cloud – a far-reaching cloud that buried all of eastern Washington under a blanket of gritty, volcanic ash. Mount St. Helens (Figure 4-48) had erupted early that morning, and we had spent the rest of the day attempting to get over the Cascade Mountains back to the Eastern Washington University campus. The previous three days were spent on a geology field trip to the Washington coast. It was a glorious weekend and Sunday, beginning as a warm, bluebird-spring morning, promised to be more of the same. Driving east past Chehalis we were still more than 30 miles west of White Pass on our way over the Cascade Mountains when we saw flashing lights and a roadblock – the police were turning vehicles away. Ahead in the mountains was an unexpected gray cloud. Our first thoughts were, *Mount St. Helens has erupted while we're on a geologic field trip – how cool (and coincidental) is that!*

Figure 4-48. Mount St. Helens volcano in Washington's Cascade Mountains. Left: Cone reflected in Spirit Lake circa 1925. Its beautiful volcanic symmetry was destroyed in seconds when the upper 1,300 feet of the volcano slid into Spirit Lake in a massive rock-debris avalanche on the morning of May 18, 1980. PHOTOGRAPH BY ASAHEL CURTIS COURTESY OF THE UNIVERSITY OF WASHINGTON LIBRARIES, SPECIAL COLLECTIONS, NEGATIVE NUMBER UW1666. Right: U.S. Geological Survey photo taken during the May 18 eruption. PHOTOGRAPH BY AUSTIN POST

We had all seen the images of Mount St. Helens sending up small puffs of ash for months, but little did we know that this eruption was different from all the others. Our bus full of stoked college students returned to Interstate 5 before heading north to the next Cascade pass. Surely, we thought, we can get over Snoqualmie Pass – far from the inconvenience of an awakening volcano. Wrong! Again we were turned back. More concerned now and growing weary of hours of fruitless wandering that wasn't getting us any closer to home, our enthusiasm for this historic geologic event was starting to wane. We had one more chance to get over the Cascades via Stevens Pass and on to Cheney where many of us needed to finish papers and prepare for final exams. We were relieved that no roadblocks greeted us at Stevens Pass; however, a little unsettling was one hastily posted sign that read: "U.S. Highway 2 closed beyond Wenatchee." Arriving in Wenatchee after dark we were welcomed by a most surreal experience.

A snowstorm in May? Fine flakes floated down and glistened in the headlights. Only problem: It was a stifling 80 degrees, and the tiny particles permeated every space within the bus, including our lungs. We had entered the ash cloud raining down from the eruption of the mountain that blew its top only a half-day earlier. Anxious to get back to Cheney, we foolishly ignored the warning signs and continued our trek eastward. Soon each oncoming car sent a billowing, blinding cloud of dusty powder that hung in the air, blocking our view of the road and intensifying the blackness of the still-warm, sultry night. (The unusual warmth came from the heat carried with the ash that only hours earlier had solidified from liquid magma deep within the bowels of the earth. The insulating cloud of ash kept the heat of the day and the ash from radiating away.) For the next several hours, while we traveled at a snail's pace across U.S. Highway 2 to Cheney, I breathed through a water-soaked T-shirt to keep the suffocating ash out of my lungs and contemplated what would come from this unbelievable historic event.

Exhausted after the long night without sleep, we arrived in Cheney just before daybreak, nearly a full day after starting our 400-mile journey home. The bus did not fare well – its engine, as many others in the region, succumbed to the severe damage caused by the abrasive ash and would need replacement. Awakening the next day was like waking up to fresh snowfall in New Hampshire where I grew up. And like my childhood, after a heavy snowfall, school was canceled. Only this time it was for the entire rest of the semester.

Meanwhile in Cheney the morning of May 18, coauthor Kiver received a phone call from his neighbor who had been working in his garden and heard a distant, muffled roar at 9 a.m. from the exploding volcano. (It took a full half hour for the sound of the 8:32 a.m. blast to travel the 300 miles to Cheney!) Kiver spent the rest of the day "battening down the hatches" on his small farm before the ominous cloud arrived about 3 p.m. By 5 p.m. it had deposited a three-quarter-inch-carpet of gray ash over everything (Figure 4-49). Checking on his livestock the following morning, Kiver followed bovine tracks through a broken fence to discover that one of his cows had given birth to a calf. The calf was quickly named "Ashley" – also a popular name for babies born in nearby hospitals that day.

Figure 4-49. Volcanic ash from the 1980 eruption of Mount St. Helens spread east as far as the Great Lakes states. Like a blanket of snow, ashfall on coauthor Kiver's back porch in Cheney, the morning after the May 18 eruption, measured 0.75 inch thick in the Kiver rain gauge.

All of the Channeled Scabland received a coating of ash that day; the ash plume over Ritzville, dropped the greatest amount of ash (2 to 3 inches). It was many months before northeast Washington dug itself out and recovered from the pervasive, annoying ashfall. In the dozens of years since the 1980 eruption, the ash has been reworked by wind, rainfall and melting snow. Much of the ash has gathered and compacted into depressions; elsewhere only a thin, discontinuous surface layer of light-gray, powdery ash is the only reminder of this unforgettable, once-in-a-lifetime geologic event.

When preserved in the sedimentary record, an ash layer marks a short instant of geologic time and is extremely useful in dating geological and archaeological events. Mount St. Helens has erupted a number of times in the past few tens of thousands of years, indicated by other ash layers in the sediment record. One particular eruption 15,400 years ago occurred between two of the last Ice Age floods and is preserved as the distinctive double ash layer (known as the "set S" couplet) that often lies near the top of slackwater flood deposits in southeastern Washington (Figure 4-50). Because volcanic ash layers are widespread and occur within a geologic instant, they represent distinctive "marker" beds; thus the Mount St. Helens "set S" couplet is extremely useful for correlating late-glacial Ice Age flood deposits from one isolated locality to another. Other Cascade volcanoes have also erupted since the last Ice Age floods including Glacier Peak (13,100 calendar years ago) and Mount Mazama (today's Crater Lake) about 7,700 years ago; these are all preserved locally within the sediment record of the Channeled Scabland and surrounding areas.

Figure 4-50. A thin, double layer of white Mount St. Helens "set S" volcanic ash (at tip of trowel) lies between two slackwater beds from cataclysmic, outburst floods laid down toward the end of the Ice Age about 15,400 years ago. This exposure is at the Lake Sacajawea Flood Bar locality along the Snake River of southeastern Washington.

Trail T. Twin Lakes Loop   Flood Feature Nos. 18, 23

Loop through pastoral, low-relief scabland along Lake Creek Coulee on abandoned, double-track jeep trails in the heart of the Channeled Scabland.

Geologic Highlights: Elongate, water-filled rock basins, abandoned cataract, recessional canyon, buttes, mesas, rock benches, as well as streamlined and scarped Palouse hills

Length: 9.5 miles

Elevation (Relief) Along Trail: 1,880 to 2,250 feet (370 feet)

Difficulty: Entire loop is difficult due to its length and exposure as well as a shortage of trail markers, creating several route-finding challenges along the way.

Best Observation Point: Above head of recessional cataract canyon (Figure 4-51) 3.6 miles counterclockwise from trailhead (N47.5420, W118.4715)

Best Mode of Travel: Mountain bike or horse due to extreme length and exposure

Management/Ownership: U.S. Bureau of Land Management

USGS 1:24,000 Scale Map: Swanson Lakes, Rocklyn SW, WA

Warnings: No potable water. Lots of gates, fences and crisscrossing trails; route finding can be a challenge so carry a good topographic map and compass (or GPS).

Directions: On State Route 21 drive either 30 miles south of Wilbur, or six miles north of Odessa before turning northeast onto Coffeepot Road. After 0.6 mile pass trailhead for the Wild Garden Crater of the Odessa Ring Craters (Trail U2). At 6.1 miles follow Coffeepot Road as it turns 90 degrees to the right (east). Continue east another 6.4 miles, past the north end of Coffeepot Lake before turning left (north) onto Highline Road (Figure 4-52). Drive 1.3 miles farther and turn right (east) onto unpaved road to the Twin Lakes Recreation Site. Trailhead is 2 miles farther at road's end where a recreation site is located (Figure 4-52).

Figure 4-51. Twin Lakes scabland incises into basalt of the Roza Member. Lake Creek winds through the canyon below a recessional cataract cliff. Looking west.

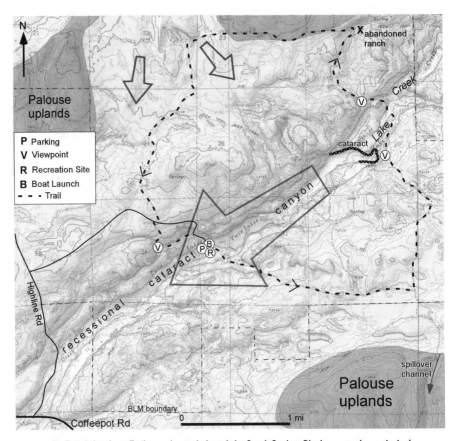

Figure 4-52. Twin Lakes Loop Trail map, located along Lake Creek Coulee. Block arrows show principal flood-flow directions.

Trail Log

0.0 Trailhead starts at end of road in recreation site between the Twin Lakes (Figure 4-52). Directions lead in a counterclockwise direction around the 9.5-mile loop. Cross footbridge and follow double-track to gate and trail that heads uphill (east) out of the canyon. Follow brown BLM trail posts (see Figure 4-3 for example)

1.0 Rise up onto basalt plateau. Sloped farmlands ahead are Palouse uplands, scarped and smoothed by the floodwaters racing down Lake Creek Coulee.

2.1 Double-track trail turns sharply to the left (north). After 0.75 mile pass by a water-filled, pothole oasis teeming with birdlife.

3.6 Viewpoint over head of cataract. N47.5420, W118.4715

4.3   Cross Lake Creek and head west up other side of the pine-studded canyon.

5.3   At abandoned ranch, trail turns left (west) onto 7 Springs Dairy Road. For the next 1.3 miles the road crosses the gentle, south-sloping margin of a streamlined Palouse hill (Figure 4-52).

6.6   A side flood channel comes in from the right (north). A pond-filled rock basin lies 0.4 mile farther below a 40-foot tall cataract. Turn left (south) here onto another double-tracked jeep trail.

8.9   Intersect with access road to the Twin Lakes Recreation Area. Follow this road a few hundred feet west to another double-track that descends toward lower Twin Lake.

9.5   Reconnect with access road, which leads back to the trailhead, 0.2 mile farther.

Trail U. Odessa Craters   Flood Feature Nos. 23, 24

Hike through a swarm of unusual and unique ringed craters, plucked out by repeated Ice Age floods. Two nearby trails are featured. See chapter 2 for a more thorough discussion on the origin of the unusual ringed craters.

Geologic Highlights: Swarm of Odessa Ring Craters (No. 24) within weakened areas of Roza basalt flow, plucked out during flooding; disappearing lakes

Length: Cache Crater Trail is 0.4 mile round-trip; Odessa Craters Trail is one to two miles round-trip

Elevation (Relief) Along Trails: 1,640 to 1,770 feet (130 feet)

Difficulty: Easy (Cache Crater) to moderate (Odessa Ring Craters)

Best Observation Points: Cache Crater Trail, overlook at end of trail (N47.4209, 118.6968). Odessa Craters Trail, atop Amphitheater Crater (N47.4228, W118.6846) – the most impressive and accessible crater in this particular swarm.

Best Mode of Travel: Hike

Management/Ownership: U.S. Bureau of Land Management

USGS 1:24,000 Scale Map: Pacific Lake, WA

Warnings: The Odessa Craters Trail is overgrown with vegetation and difficult to follow in places. Look for brown and white BLM posts that mark the trail (see Figure 4-3). No potable water or midday shade.

Directions: Trailheads are six to seven miles north of Odessa via State Route 21. Three trailheads exist for the two trails shown in Figures 4-53 and 4-54. The west end of the Odessa Craters Trail is 6.3 miles north of Odessa; the Cache Crater trailhead is 0.7 mile farther. The east end of the Odessa Craters Trail starts along Coffeepot Road, 0.75 mile north of the intersection with State Route 21.

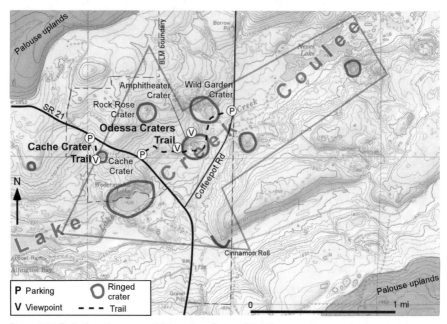

Figure 4-53. Trails through a swarm of Odessa Ring Craters (No. 24), exposed by megaflood erosion along Lake Creek Coulee (No. 23).

Cache Crater Trail (U1)

Trail Log

0.0   Trailhead (N47.4229, W118.6981) leads south from State Route 21, seven miles north of Odessa or 29 miles south of Wilbur. Follow easy, level, well-defined trail.

0.2   Overlook at sitting bench into Cache Crater (N47.4209, 118.6968). Retrace route to trailhead.

Odessa Craters Trail (U2)

Trail Log

0.0   Trailhead parking is provided at either end of the Odessa Craters Trail (Figure 4-53). The following mileages are from the east trailhead off Coffeepot Road. Head west from swinging gate at Coffeepot Road pullout (N47.4254, W118.6775).

0.2   Arrive at marsh, which lies inside the Wild Garden Crater. Many of the craters once contained sizable lakes, but many of the lakes in the region have gone dry due a recent drastic lowering of groundwater levels in this area (see "Disappearing Lakes and Aquifers" sidebar, page 99 in chapter 3). Trail turns south.

0.4   Entrance to 700-foot wide Amphitheater Crater (Figure 4-55). This

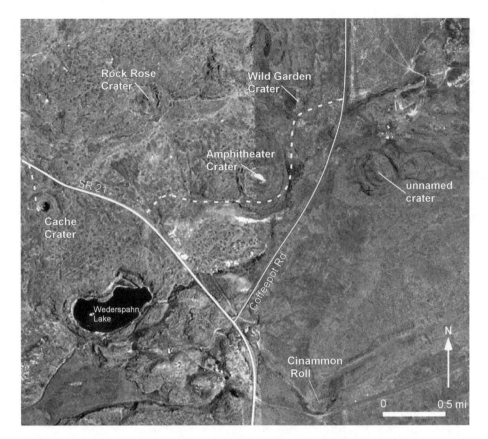

Figure 4-54. Aerial photo of several Odessa Ring Craters. Dashed lines are two established U.S. Bureau of Land Management trails. The Cinnamon Roll to the south is an only partially formed crater. Note: Unnamed crater in upper right is on private land, as is Wederspahn Lake.

crater is clearly defined by several concentric basalt dikes that dip steeply toward the outside of the crater. Large, rectangular-shaped, light-colored mineral grains dispersed within the basalt, identify this lava flow, which produced the ringed craters as the Roza Member (Figure 4-56).

0.5   Trail rises up over the west side of crater with panoramic view of the concentric ring dikes (Figure 4-55). Continue west another 0.4 mile to western trailhead at junction with State Route 21, or retrace route to Coffeepot Road.

Figure 4-55. View looking southeast across 700-foot-wide Amphitheater Crater. Notice multiple concentric basalt dikes that encircle the crater. The lowest part of the crater lies in the center where a dried-up, playa lakebed exists today.

Figure 4-56. Light-colored, rectangular feldspar crystals (circled) dispersed through the dark basalt characterize this as the 15 million-year-old Roza Member (see Figure 1-1).

Trail V. Lake Creek Coulee   Flood Feature Nos. 23, 24

Explore another lonely and remote, desolate landscape along Lake Creek Coulee, which once held several large lakes (Bobs Lakes). The lakes are mostly gone now but the impressive scabland remains.

Geologic Highlights: Abandoned cataract and recessional canyon, buttes, mesas, hanging coulees, potholes, scarped Palouse hills, ice-rafted erratics, ringed craters and disappearing lakes

Length: 13 miles one-way. In this guide, we divide this long challenging trail into two, more manageable segments (north and south), each about six miles long one-way.

Elevation (Relief) Along Trail: 1,450 to 1,830 feet (380 feet)

Difficulty: Difficult due to long distance and exposure. Route-finding challenges exist in several places where the trail is overgrown or poorly marked.

Best Observation Points: South segment, east side Lake Creek Coulee, at overlook (N47.3625, W118.7538) about 4.9 miles from south trailhead. North segment, west side of Lake Creek Coulee at overlook (N47.3773, W118.7667) about six miles from north trailhead (Figure 4-57 and Plate 18b).

Best Modes of Travel: Mountain bike or horse. Due to long distances and exposure, hiking is not recommended except with a shuttle and/or in cooler-weather conditions.

Management/Ownership: U.S. Bureau of Land Management, except for a short section of open-access private land along the bottom of Lake Creek canyon that links the north and south trail segments.

USGS 1:24,000 Scale Map: Odessa, Irby, Sullivan Lake, WA

Warnings: No potable water or midday shade. Long, desolate approach required to get into the more remote and scenic areas at the heart of Lake Creek Coulee. Carry lots of water and artificial shade (in summer), especially if on foot. Route finding is sometimes a challenge – carry a good topographic map and compass (or GPS). Brown and white BLM trail markers are posted along the trail but not always visible (see Figure 4-3). If doing the entire 13-mile (one way) trail, a car shuttle is recommended to get back to starting point.

Figure 4-57. Tiered rock benches of the Frenchman Springs Member (lower Wanapum Basalt) lie along the flood-swept walls of Lake Creek Coulee. Looking southeast.

North Lake Creek Coulee Trail (V1)

Directions: Drive 8.5 miles north of Odessa on State Route 21. Turn left (west) onto Lakeview Ranch Loop Road. Follow road as it bends south after 0.8 mile. Trailhead is at turnout on right side after another mile, just before main road descends into Lake Creek Coulee (Figure 4-58).

Trail Log

0.0   Park along Lakeview Ranch Loop Road at N47.4213, W118.7419. Nice view here looking south down the throat of Lake Creek Coulee. Travel west on double-track trail along edge of Palouse upland that bounds the north side of coulee. Odessa Towers (Plate 18a) are visible in the distance to the south.

1.3   Trail bends south. After rushing down Lake Creek Coulee from the east, floodwaters divided here where the valley takes a sharp turn to the south. Most of the floodwater flowed around this bend, but the tremendous force and momentum behind the floodwaters caused some of the water to continue straight ahead, up and over the divide into Marlin Hollow (No. 25), the next flood coulee to the west.

3.0   Turn left (east) onto another double-track trail that jogs over to an impressive view of cataracts and hanging coulees at the head of Bobs Lakes (Figure 4-59).

3.6   Connect with double-track trail coming in from the north. Turn right (south) near head of the cataract.

3.9   Lush vegetation suddenly appears at a fenced-in oasis at Waukesha Spring. Trail continues uphill to the west. For another panoramic view of Lake Creek Coulee, consider a short detour to the rock promontory just south of the split-rail fence that surrounds the spring.

4.1   Intersection with double-track – continue west and south.

4.3   An erratic granodiorite boulder protrudes out of trailbed at N47.3947, W118.7737, elevation 1,700 feet. At 0.2 mile farther pass through gate and continue along rock bench to the south.

4.8   A cluster of ice-rafted erratics lie just downslope of the trail. Trail continues south, up and over a flood-smoothed and scarped Palouse hill of windblown loess.

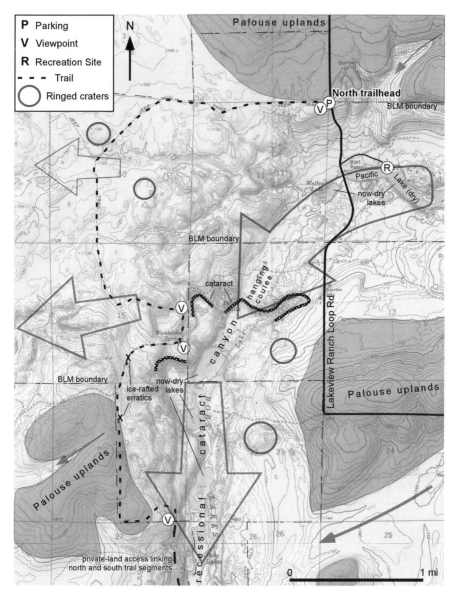

Figure 4-58. Trail map for the north segment of the Lake Creek Coulee Trail. Arrows indicate flow directions for Ice Age floods; size of the arrows is roughly proportional to amount of floodwater moving through the various channels. Another flood coulee, Marlin Hollow, is off the map at upper left.

Figure 4-59. Small, isolated, remnant lake of the once, much-larger Bobs Lakes system. Exposed are eroded basalt flows of the Roza Member. Looking southwest.

5.5   Trail turns 90 degrees to left (east), toward the west rim of Lake Creek Coulee.

6.0   Trail descends to the coulee edge below. Wonderful panoramic viewpoint (N47.3773, W118.7667) from the dramatically eroded coulee rim (Figure 4-57, Plate 18b). This is a good place to turn around if only wanting to do the north segment of the trail. Or continue another mile on posted, single-track trail to connect up with the south segment of the Lake Creek Coulee Trail that continues for another seven miles to Odessa (Figure 4-60).

South Lake Creek Coulee Trail (V2)

Directions: Turn north at west end of Odessa onto State Route 21 following signs to the Odessa – Lake Creek Trail. At 0.1 mile turn left at Cenex station onto the gravel road heading west. Trailhead is another 0.3 mile at road's end.

Trail Log

0.0   Trailhead starts at parking lot and kiosk at road's end (N47.3345, W118.7011, elevation 1,565 feet). Pass through access gate and ascend single-track trail leading northwest (Figures 4-60 and 4-61).

0.4   Intersect with double-track road that runs beneath an overhead power line. A shallow ringed crater (No. 24), partially covered with flood deposits, lies a few hundred feet north of this intersection. Turn left heading west beneath the power line. Over the next mile the trail follows a rock bench along the north side of Crab Creek Coulee, partially covered with flood sediment molded into a long series of giant current ripples (Figure 4-61). The shape of the asymmetric ripples (steeper on west side) indicates that the floodwater flowed from east to west down Crab Creek.

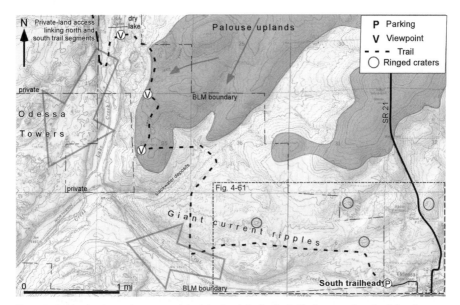

Figure 4-60. Map for the south segment of the Lake Creek Coulee Trail. Block arrows show flood flow from Lake Creek Coulee joined that of Crab Creek Coulee just west of Odessa. An aerial photo of giant current ripples and ringed craters located in lower right corner is shown in next figure.

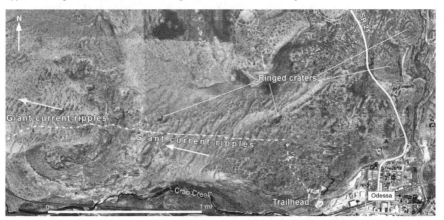

Figure 4-61. Aerial view showing giant current ripples along a portion of the South Lake Creek Coulee Trail (dashed). Note how ringed craters in basalt bedrock locally poke through the thin cover of flood deposits and megaripples.

1.2   Pass through fence via gate at N47.3404, W118.7225.

1.9   Gently rise and fall over more low, giant current ripples before descending off rock bench toward Crab Creek.

2.2   Come to a fence trending north and south. N47.3393, W118.7441. Do not cross fence. Instead, turn right following the fence uphill to the north.

2.5   Trail flattens off on top of rock bench covered with more well-developed giant current ripples.

2.9   Near the crest of the hill pass through another barbed wire fence via a swinging gate. In the distance, to the northwest, is the first sight of scabland of the Odessa Towers (Plate 18a, see Figure 2-16). In the foreground is a minor spillover channel that carried floodwater leaking over from the Palouse uplands to the north (Figure 4-60). Exposed in the valley bottom, about a quarter mile below, some slack-water flood deposits are visible in a stream bank; these were probably laid down by later, smaller floods that back-flooded this valley from the south. Descend north towards valley bottom.

3.7   After a long descent the trail begins gradual ascent up loess-covered slope to the west.

4.2   Just beyond the hillcrest is a great viewpoint where trail passes through another barbed wire fence and gate. N47.3546, W118.7547. Beyond the gate the trail continues on double-track to the north along hill crest.

4.9   Another good view (N47.3625, W118.7538) looking west across lower Lake Creek Coulee toward the Odessa Towers (Plate 18a).

5.1   Bear left (northwest) onto single-track trail that descends toward Lake Creek Coulee.

5.7   Another good view of Odessa Towers from a different perspective.

5.8   Trail passes by large, spring-fed, water basin (N47.3706, W118.7617), just above the dry lakebed of former Bobs Lakes.

6.1   Turn around at footbridge (N47.3667, W118.7635) at the south end of Bobs Lake flat (Figure 4-62). Elevation 1,450 feet. Or continue on trail that turns north up the other side of the valley, which connects up with the north Lake Creek Coulee Trail segment (see Figure 4-58).

Figure 4-62. A seemingly out-of-place footbridge (circled) is a reminder of the once extensive Bobs Lakes system that used to exist in this valley. Most of the Bobs Lakes have dried up due to agricultural overpumping of groundwater, which has dramatically lowered water levels in the region (see "Disappearing Lakes and Aquifers" sidebar on page 99 in chapter 3). Looking southwest.

Trails in the Vicinity of Upper Grand Coulee

"Grand Coulee is ... the simplest but grandest case of canyon cutting by glacial streams on the plateau."

– J Harlen Bretz (1923)

Figure 4-63. The Upper Grand Coulee during a survey by Lieutenant Thomas Symons (1882) to determine the navigability and adaptability of the Columbia River for steamboat transportation. Alfred Downing, with the Symons expedition, produced this image in 1881. FROM THE WASHINGTON STATE UNIVERSITY LIBRARIES DIGITAL COLLECTION

Trail W. Candy Point   Flood Feature Nos. 29, 30, 63

Hike the west wall of the Columbia Valley below Grand Coulee Dam, an area that once sat under thousands of feet of glacial ice of the Okanogan Lobe. Just south of here the ice-blocked Columbia River became Glacial Lake Columbia, backing up all the way to Idaho. The trail culminates with a spectacular view of the Columbia Valley, Grand Coulee Dam, and the breached head of Grand Coulee. The trail passes over 50 million- to 60 million-year-old granitic basement rocks the entire way.

Geologic Highlights: Glacial Lake Columbia sediment terraces and a hanging coulee as well as glacial erratics, grooves and striations (Plate 23)

Length: Candy Point can be accessed via two trailheads (Figure 4-64): one mile round-trip from the Crown Point Trailhead, or 1.5 miles round-trip from the Candy Canyon Trailhead

Elevation (Relief) Along Trail: 1,575 to 1,725 feet (150 feet) from Crown Point Trailhead, or 1,075 to 1,725 feet (650 feet) from Candy Canyon Trailhead

Difficulty: Moderate from Crown Point Trailhead; moderately strenuous from Candy Canyon Trailhead due to steeper, rougher trail

Best Observation Points: Candy and Crown Point vistas

Best Mode of Travel: Hike

Management/Ownership: U.S. Bureau of Reclamation and Washington State Parks

USGS 1:24,000 Scale Map: Grand Coulee Dam, WA

Warning: Candy Canyon is a dry, exposed canyon with summer temperatures that sometimes exceed 100 degrees. Washington Discover Pass required to park at Crown Point.

Directions:

For Candy Canyon Trailhead: From Grand Coulee take State Route 155 north to the town of Coulee Dam (the community immediately below the dam). Continue straight on North Columbia Avenue (unsigned) just before the State Route 155 bridge crosses the Columbia River. If approaching from the north on SR155 turn right onto North Columbia Avenue at the west end of the bridge. Proceed 0.2 mile to Candy Point trail sign (small, difficult to read) and park along the residential street, near house numbers 428 and 430. Cross the lawn (OK with landowner) at sign for the Candy Point Trail.

For Crown Point Trailhead: From the town of Grand Coulee head north on State Route 174 for 1.9 miles to turnoff for Crown Point State Park. Trailhead is 1.3 miles farther on right at restroom/kiosk along south side of the Crown Point Vista parking area.

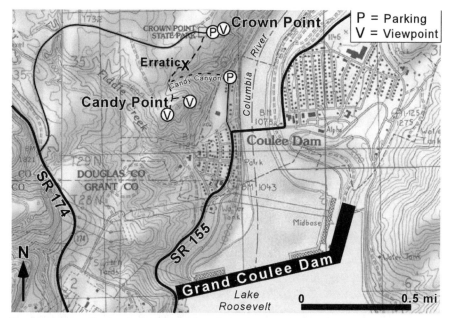

| P | = Parking |
| V | = Viewpoint |

Figure 4-64. Two trailheads exist for the Candy Point Trail, one at Crown Point and the other at the base of Candy Canyon. Photo of unusual basalt erratic is shown in next figure (Figure 4-65). Candy Point has two viewpoints, separated by a deep saddle.

Trail Log *(from Crown Point Trailhead)*

0.0   Park at trailhead next to the Crown Point State Park bathroom and kiosk. Before (or after) your hike take in the view from Crown Point, which include great views of the Columbia Valley and Grand Coulee Dam. Head southwest toward upper Candy Canyon (Figure 4-64). Along the way notice how some of the bedrock exposed along the edge of the canyon was smoothed and polished by the long-absent glacier. Linear striations, scratched into the bedrock by gravel dragged along the base of the glacier, are also sometimes visible (Plate 23).

0.2   After following the upper lip of the canyon come to a basalt boulder resting on the glacially smoothed granite outcrop (Figure 4-65). This is a glacial erratic. Normally in the Channeled Scabland we see granite erratics resting on top of basalt bedrock; here is an opposite example, where a basalt is the foreign rock that rests on granite bedrock.

0.3   Unmarked trail intersection at base of slope. Turn right to go to either of two Candy Point viewpoints (Figure 4-64), which are 0.2 mile farther. From the Candy Point summit are spectacular views of the Columbia Valley, Grand Coulee Dam, Lake Roosevelt, and the spillover-breach channel (No. 29) and hanging valley at the head of Grand Coulee (Plate 22). Trail to the left descends 0.5 mile along a series of stair-step switchbacks into Candy Canyon; trail ends at Columbia Avenue in Coulee Dam.

Figure 4-65. Along the trail to Candy Point lies an erratic boulder of basalt on top of glacially smoothed granite bedrock at elevation 1,600 feet. The boulder was deposited here at the end of the last Ice Age after melting out of the Okanogan Lobe, which once towered over a thousand feet thick in this area. Note glacial-age terrace in the background. The huge pile of sand across the river is a spoils pile remaining after construction of Grand Coulee Dam from 1933 to 1941. Looking northeast.

Trail Log *(from Candy Canyon Trailhead)*

0.0   In Coulee Dam park at sign for Candy Point Trail along Columbia Avenue, 0.2 mile north of bridge over the Columbia River. The trail starts climbing the hillside only a few dozen yards away across the lawn of a private residence (resident gives permission to cross). The U.S. Civilian Conservation Corps, President Franklin D. Roosevelt's Depression-era, public-works program, constructed this rarely used little gem of a trail in 1937.

0.1   Enter the lower end of Candy Canyon. Meltwater from the retreating Okanogan Lobe cut this steep notch in the canyon wall. Note the exposures of Eocene-age, granitic basement rock similar to that used for the abutments to anchor the massive concrete structure of Grand Coulee Dam.

0.5   Unmarked trail intersection near head of Candy Canyon. At intersection bear left to go to either of two Candy Point viewpoints (Figure 4-64), which are 0.2 mile farther. From the Candy Point summit are spectacular views of the Columbia Valley, Grand Coulee Dam, Lake Roosevelt, and the spillover-breach channel and hanging valley at the head of Grand Coulee (Plate 22). Trail to the right goes 0.3 mile northeast to Crown Point State Park, where there exists another excellent viewpoint and beautifully preserved glacial striations scratched into bedrock by the Okanogan Lobe (Plate 23).

"Again and again the writer has asked others and himself 'Where is the dangerously weak point in the flood hypothesis?' One can stand on the brink of Northrup Canyon and aver with confidence that it can never be satisfactorily explained except as an extinct Niagara (Falls). He can look across to the scabland summit of Steamboat, or down the trenched gravel bar in the mouth of Northrup, or back at the summit scabland that margins the coulee. The ensemble in every detail supports the cataract hypothesis."

— J Harlen Bretz (1932)

Trail X. Northrup Canyon Flood Feature Nos. 30, 31, 32, 33, 35

Explore an open-forested canyon where Ice Age floods scoured through the layered basalts into granitic basement rock underneath as they spilled over a side canyon into Grand Coulee via Northrup Creek. Northrup Canyon (No. 32) is a side canyon at the northeast end of the Upper Grand Coulee and part of the Washington State Park system. Two wonderful trails are featured here (Figure 4-68). A northern trail follows the deep, narrow canyon to a plunge pool (Northrup Lake) at the head of the canyon. Another trail follows an old wagon road to the Summit Plateau Scabland (No. 35) along the south rim of Northrup Canyon. From the elevated plateau are great views up and down Northrup Canyon, Upper Grand Coulee, Steamboat Rock (No. 31), and the Castle Rock Cataracts (No. 33).

Geologic Highlights: Eroded contact between ancient 50 million- to 100 million-year-old granite beneath 15 million-year-old basalt, spillover channels, abandoned cataracts and recessional canyons, plunge pools, a rock blade, giant grooves, flood bars, mesas, buttes and ancient dry lake beds

Management/Ownership: Washington State Parks

USGS 1:24,000 Topographic Maps: Electric City, Steamboat Rock SE, WA

Directions: From State Route 155, directly across from Steamboat Rock, turn east onto Northrup Road. Pass eddy flood bar at mouth of canyon (Figure 4-66) and ascend 0.6 mile, past granitic Gibraltar Rock, to parking area and restroom at end of gravel road.

Figure 4-66. Close up of high-energy flood sediments exposed in eddy bar at the mouth of Northrup Canyon. The huge size of flood-deposited boulders and poorly sorted debris layers are stark testimony to the speed and power of the floods. This pile of flood debris was probably laid down by the last floods that came down Grand Coulee but not Northrup Canyon. Looking east.

Figure 4-67. The abandoned Northrup homestead on the way to the Northrup Lake plunge pool. Looking northeast.

Northrup Lake Trail (X1)

Geologic Highlights: Steep-walled canyon follows the contact between granitic basement and overlying basalt rock, plunge-pool lake, flood bars, now-dry ancient lakes, Northrup Homestead.

Length: 7.2 miles round-trip

Difficulty: Moderate

Elevation (Relief) Along Trail: 1,790 to 2,270 feet (480 feet)

Best Mode of Travel (other modes): Hike, horse. Bike travel not approved by Washington State Parks

Best Observation Point: From Earthcache at cataract rim above the Northrup Lake plunge pool (N47.8879, W119.0407)

Earthcache: Northrup Canyon Plungepool (Identification code GC2CH5Q at www.geocaching.com)

Warnings: No potable water; trail closed during eagle-nesting season (November 15 to March 15)

Trail Log

0.0   Park next to gate and vault toilet at end of Northrup Road. N47.8660, W119.0824, elevation 1,750 feet.

0.1   Trail junction. Trail to the right goes up the Wagon Road Grade Trail (Trail X2). Bear left to continue up the double-track Northrup Lake Trail. Upvalley the vegetation transitions from dry shrub-steppe to a wetter, aspen and ponderosa pine forest.

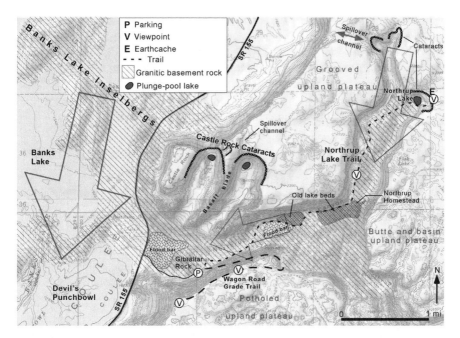

Figure 4-68. Northrup Canyon area map. A tall ridge of granite runs down the middle of the canyon. At one time the granite was completely buried under basaltic lava flows but later exhumed by Ice Age floods.

1.0 Trail rises over a low, rounded pendant-crescent flood bar that extends across the valley bottom (Figures 4-68 and 4-69). At the northeast end of the flood bar, the trail flattens out onto an old, dried-out lake bed that probably developed behind the flood bar. Notice the significant relief along the contact between basalt and granite here. On the left (north) side of the valley, layered dark basalt flows go all the way down to the valley bottom. In contrast, to the right, light-colored granite basement rock rises 100 to 200 feet above the valley floor. This indicates a ridge of granite rock existed here before being buried beneath a cover of basalt lava.

Figure 4-69. A pendant-crescent flood bar in Northrup Canyon temporarily blocked Northrup Creek, causing a lake to form behind the blockage. The lake has since drained away but the table-flat lake bed remains.

1.3 Cross stream over wooden bridge onto another higher, dried-out, flat lake bed that extends up to the old Northrup homestead (Figures 4-67 and 4-68).

1.7   Where Northrup Canyon splits is the abandoned homestead of John Warden Northrup, who settled here in 1889 (Figure 4-67). The Northrup family continued living here until 1927. Please leave this site as it is for others to appreciate. Continue on single-track trail that ascends up the north branch of the canyon.

1.9   Trail rises through a maze of granite outcroppings before coming to a scenic overlook back down the canyon toward the Northrup homestead.

2.3   Contact between light-colored granite and dark basalt. Consider for a moment the many tens of millions of years that passed between the time the granite crystallized from a magma chamber deep underground, before it was unroofed and covered with basalt lava flows.

3.2   Arrive at Northrup Lake plunge pool (Figure 4-70). Trail continues along south side of lake and links up with an old jeep trail that traverses diagonally up the east side of the cataract wall ahead.

3.6   Walk north along the rim of west-facing cataract cliff. This is the location for Northrup Canyon Plungepool Earthcache (www.geocaching.com, GC code: GC2CH5Q). To the right is the flood-swept upland plateau that surrounds all of Northrup Canyon (see Figure 3-60, Plate 22). To the southwest is a spectacular view back down the canyon (Figure 4-70).

Figure 4-70. Northrup Lake plunge pool from cataract cliff at head of Northrup Canyon. A ridge of more flood-resistant granite (arrow) runs up the middle of Northrup Canyon, dividing it into two subcanyons. View from the featured Earthcache. N47.8879, W119.0407, 2,270 feet elevation.

Wagon Road (Scheibner) Grade Trail (X2)

Geologic Highlights: Spectacular views of the narrow, steep-walled Northrup Canyon, Gibraltar Rock, Castle Rock Cataracts (No. 33), Steamboat Rock (No. 32), Summit Plateau Scabland (No. 35) and the granitic Banks Lake Inselbergs (No. 30).

Length: 3.8 miles round-trip

Elevation (Relief) Along Trail: 1,790 to 2,320 feet (530 feet)

Difficulty: Moderate

Best Mode of Travel: Hike

Best Observation Point: Southwest rim of Northrup Canyon where it hangs over the Upper Grand Coulee across from Steamboat Rock

Warnings: No potable water, cliff drop-offs; trail closed from November 15 to March 15 to avoid disruption of eagle-nesting activity

Trail Log

0.0   Park next to gate and outhouse at end of Northrup Road. N47.8660, W119.0824, elevation 1,750 feet.

0.1   Trail junction. Double-track trail to the left goes to Northrup Lake. Bear right onto the Wagon Road Trail that ascends diagonally across a long basalt scree slope along the south side of Northrup Canyon. The Scheibner Brothers built this wagon road, which was part of the Almira-Brewster Stage Route used in the late 1890s and early 1900s.

0.6   At the end of the long scree slope the trail bends south into a side canyon of lower-relief, weathered granitic rock.

0.7   Notice the light-colored coarse sand covering the trail here. Normally, a sorted sand like this implies movement by running water. This sand, however, comes from the exposure of weathered granite immediately above the trail. Freezing and thawing of the granite over a long period of time as well as chemical weathering are decomposing and slowly breaking apart the granite reducing it to sand-sized mineral grains of mostly quartz and feldspar (known as grus) that make up the granite.

1.0   Trail bends to the west as it gains the top of the high, flood-swept, Summit Plateau Scabland (No. 35) south of Northrup Canyon (Figure 4-68). So much floodwater was coming down Northrup Canyon that it spilled up and over the sides, sweeping across this plateau. Follow rock cairns (sometimes difficult to see) westward along the south rim of the canyon.

1.2   Spectacular views (Figure 4-71) from canyon rim at N47.8666, W119.0752, elevation 2,310 feet, of Northrup Canyon, Gibraltar Rock, Castle Rock Cataracts (No. 31), the Upper Grand Coulee and Steamboat Rock (No. 32). For more phenomenal views continue southwest along canyon rim.

Figure 4-71. View from the south rim of Northrup Canyon. Only a couple of eroded, flat-lying basalt flows cap the summit of Castle Rock mesa. Under the basalt is an east-west trending ridge of irregularly weathered granitic rock exhumed by the Ice Age floods. Looking northeast.

1.9   Along the canyon rim at the mouth of Northrup Canyon lies an even more expansive overview of Upper Grand Coulee. Retrace steps back to trailhead.

Trail Y. Banks Lake Archipelago   Flood Feature Nos. 29, 30, 31, 33, 34, 38

— — — — — — — — — — — —

Float and wander through an exotic group of granite-inselberg islands and peninsulas within Banks Lake, within spitting distance to majestic Steamboat Rock.

Geologic Highlights: Granite inselbergs in Banks Lake exhumed by Ice Age floods; basalt-covered Steamboat Rock Monolith and Castle Rock Mesa loom above; Big Cave Arch Rock Shelter and delta bars of Glacial Lake Columbia are present near Barker Canyon at the west end of the archipelago; numerous interesting exposures of Glacial Lake Columbia silt exposed along the Banks Lake shoreline.

Length: 0.5 to 12 miles or more

Difficulty: Easy to difficult depending on distance and mode of travel

Best Observation Point: Base of Eagle Rock

Best Mode of Travel: Watercraft. Kayak or canoe is best for exploring the often narrow and shallow passageways between the islands.

Management/Ownership: U.S. Bureau of Reclamation, Washington State Parks and Washington Department of Fish and Wildlife (Banks Lake Unit)

USGS 1:24,000 Scale Map: Electric City and Barker Canyon, WA

Warnings: Beware of rough water due to heavy boat traffic and/or high winds that are common to Banks Lake. No potable water except at Northrup Point launch site. Washington Discover Pass required to park.

Directions: The closest and most convenient access to the island archipelago is via the Northrup Point boat launch site located 0.4 mile west of State Route 155 (Figure 4-72). Turnoff to Northrup Point is five miles southwest of Electric City or 3.4 miles northeast of the turnoff to Steamboat Rock State Park.

Trail Log

0.0   Launch from Northrup Point and head north.

0.3   Arrive at closest of tiny inselberg islands.

0.5   Arrive at first of the larger islands. Flat-topped Castle Rock looms above to the east. Continuing northward, hug the east shore of the island straight south of Eagle Rock (Figure 4-72).

— —

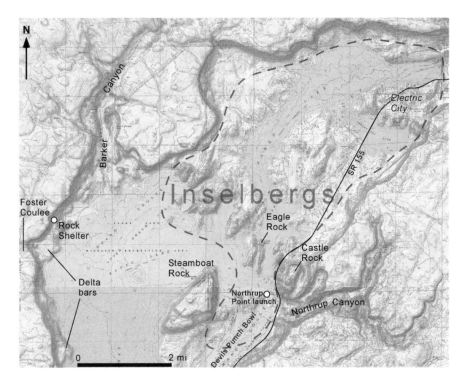

Figure 4-72. Map in the vicinity of the Banks Lake archipelago. Dashed line shows the area of granitic inselbergs.

1.0   Circle around Eagle Rock at the north end of the island exploring the many inlets and bays around this granite monolith. Many options for further exploration of Banks Lake and the inselbergs exist from here. For example, continue north toward Electric City and the upper end of Banks Lake (another 6.5 miles), or head back towards Steamboat Rock before heading northwest toward Barker Canyon (about four miles distance). Another two miles places one in close proximity to the Big Cave Arch Rock Shelter (see Figure 2-11) and the lobate delta bar (Glacial Lake Columbia feature) at the base of hanging Foster Coulee (see Figure 4-81). Another option is to return south for the calmer waters of Devils Punch Bowl located along the shores of Steamboat Rock State Park.

Figure 4-73. Banks Lake Archipelago. Inselberg islands in foreground with the Castle Rock mesa in background. Arrow points to one of many outcroppings of Glacial Lake Columbia silt (No. 38) exposed along the Banks Lake shoreline.

Trail Z. Steamboat Rock

Flood Feature Nos. 29, 30, 31, 32, 33, 34, 35, 38, 62

A challenging ascent to the summit plateau is rewarded with a primitive trail that circles the entire monolith with breathtaking, panoramic views of the Upper Grand Coulee including Northrup and Barker canyons.

Geologic Highlights: Rock blade remnant of recessional cataract canyon (see Steamboat Falls in Figure 3-54, Stage 4), geologic contact between basalt lava and much-older granitic basement rock; huge glacial erratics and glacial till from former ice sheet that once covered the summit plateau; pendant flood bar; post-flood Lake Columbia silt deposits along Banks Lake; spillover breach at the head of the Upper Grand Coulee

Length: 3.8 to 5.5 miles round-trip with shorter options

Elevation (Relief) Along Trail: 1,580 to 2,300 feet (720 feet)

Difficulty: Moderate to difficult. Trail to summit requires some scrambling up steep, scree-covered slopes. Although primitive and unmarked, the trail around the perimeter of Steamboat Rock is relatively easy.

Best Observation Point: Many excellent views in all directions from a trail that circles the top of the summit plateau (Figure 4-75, Plate 24)

Best Mode of Travel: Hike

Management/Ownership: Washington State Parks

USGS 1:24,000 Scale Maps: Steamboat Rock SE, Steamboat Rock SW, Barker Canyon, Electric City, WA

Earthcache: Steamboat Rock Glacial Moraine (Identification code GC2EN2R at www.geocaching.com)

Figure 4-74. Steamboat Rock monolith (No. 31) rises above Steamboat Rock State Park. Devils Punch Bowl, an embayment of Banks Lake, is in the foreground. Looking northwest.

Warnings: No potable water or shade. Use care on steep, loose scree slope, which can shift underfoot, during ascent and descent. Beware of extremely steep, 800-foot drop-offs around the rim of Steamboat Rock. Not recommended for young children or those prone to vertigo. Washington Discover Pass required.

Directions: Access road to Steamboat Rock State Park is via State Route 155, either 18 miles north of Coulee City, or eight miles south of Electric City. Access road bends northeast toward the State Park facilities, located on the southeast side of Steamboat Rock (Figure 4-75). The first trailhead starts across from the picnic/campground 2.6 miles from SR 155; a second trailhead starts 0.4 mile farther near the end of the public road, across from the day-use area.

Trail Log

0.0   Start at the more distal trailhead (N47.8640, W119.1218) across from day-use area. Trail heads west toward the base of Steamboat Rock (Figure 4-75).

0.2   Fifty million to 100-million-year old granitic basement rock forms the low, rounded slope on the right. Ahead is the contact between granite and basalt lava that flowed over the granite multiple times about 15 million years ago (Figure 4-76). That means the record of tens of millions of years of geologic time is missing due to extensive erosion of the granite by ancient rivers and streams prior to burial by the basalt lava. On the left (south) is a large pile of sand and gravel, laid down onto a pendant flood bar during Ice Age floods.

0.5   Trail junction. Trail bends to the right (north) and begins a steep ascent toward the top of Steamboat Rock.

0.7   A number of large granitic erratic boulders lie along the trail where it levels off temporarily.

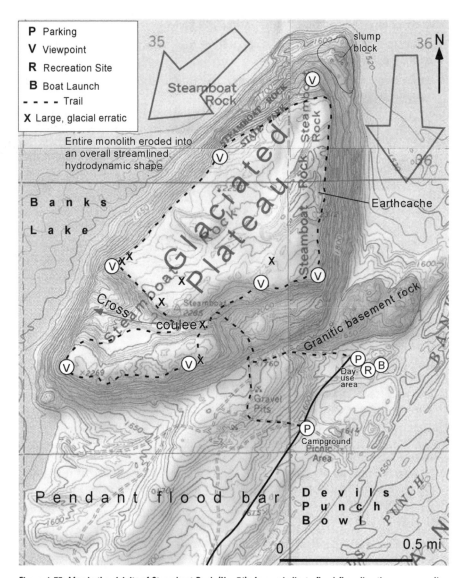

Figure 4-75. Map in the vicinity of Steamboat Rock (No. 31). Arrows indicate flood-flow direction; some earlier floods also went over the top of the monolith. The Steamboat Rock Moraine Earthcache is perched high above the northeast wall.

0.9   Near the top of Steamboat Rock, the trail terminates onto a trail that circles the monolith. To follow directions in this guide, go left (southwest), to encircle Steamboat Rock in a clockwise direction from the trail junction.

Figure 4-76. Contact between granite and basalt along northeast side of Steamboat Rock.

1.0　　　Trail traverses head of cross coulee (Figure 4-75, see Figure 3-59). This shallow, hanging coulee may be part of the old channel of Foster Creek (No. 62) that only partially cut into the Waterville Plateau before cataract recession later gouged out much-deeper Grand Coulee (see Figure 3-54, stage 1). Since cataract recession and the formation of Steamboat Rock, Ice Age floods may have modified the cross channel somewhat, but its orientation, which is across the main flood flow, suggests the cross coulee likely started out as a non-flood feature.

To hike the entire perimeter of Steamboat Rock, continue up steep slope to the south. By bearing right and heading diagonally up the north side of the cross coulee, you can cut off the southern end of the trail and shorten the distance by about 1.5 miles. This trail log follows the extended route to the south.

1.1　　　Trail passes an erratic, an 8-foot diameter boulder of granodiorite. N47.8653, W119.1336. Elevation 2,180 feet.

1.2　　　Continue across south summit to scenic cluster of granitic erratic boulders at cliff's edge (N47.8636, W119.1334). Awesome view south down the throat of Upper Grand Coulee. Head west along the southern edge of the Steamboat Rock summit plateau.

1.8　　　At the westernmost point atop Steamboat Rock, turn right (north and then east). Looking over the cross coulee ahead, notice enormous erratic boulders and hummocky surface (i.e., remnants of ancient glacial till) atop the plateau surface to the north.

2.3　　　Pass bottom of the cross coulee a second time and continue up north side. Near the top bear left (northwest) before rejoining the plateau above.

2.4　　　Pass a prominent, 15-foot-wide, cleaved, erratic boulder (N47.8667, W119.1366, elevation 2,230 feet). Unlike earlier Ice Age floods, the last floods weren't large enough to overtop Steamboat Rock. This is indicated by the preservation of glacial features like moraines and erratics atop the plateau, which would have been obliterated if the last Ice Age floods had passed over the summit.

Figure 4-77. Two large glacial erratics precariously perched high above the western wall of Steamboat Rock; another pair of granitic erratics rest in background (arrows). Note: Unlike most other erratics within the Channeled Scabland, these boulders were deposited by the ice sheet itself and not rafted into place by floating icebergs. Looking southwest.

2.5   Pass by the largest glacial erratic (30 feet wide) observed on Steamboat Rock. N47.8679, W119.1350. Head west again to cliff edge.

2.8   Two groupings of large glacial erratics are perched precariously atop the 600-foot cliff that drops precipitously into Banks Lake (Figure 4-77). Trail continues north along west rim of Steamboat Rock with spectacular views of western and northern Upper Grand Coulee, including Barker Canyon (No. 34).

3.7   North "prow" of Steamboat Rock. Like a giant ship the steep, pointed prow of Steamboat Rock points upstream into the direction of maximum flood flow. In nature this is the most hydrodynamically stable shape that creates the least amount of drag during passage of the floodwaters (Figure 4-75). Notice spillover channel that breached the head of Upper Grand Coulee (No. 29), eight miles northeast of here (see Figure 3-55, Plates 22 and 25). This spillover channel formed after the dual cataract that left behind Steamboat Rock, had receded all the way upcoulee to the Columbia River. Trail turns sharply to the south to follow the east edge of the summit plateau.

4.1   Ten feet or more of glacial till (Earthcache ID GC2EN2R, www. geocaching.com) are exposed in a small slump face at the cliff's edge (Figure 4-78). The till, lying within a hummocky glacial moraine, is characterized by its wide range of grain size with angular cobbles and boulders floating in a matrix of fine silt and clay. This hodgepodge of debris was deposited by glacial ice of the Okanogan Lobe that crept over the top of this plateau during the last

Ice Age. It is unclear if the glacier that covered Steamboat Rock was in place before or after this part of Grand Coulee was carved out by the floods. One thing we know for sure is that more Ice Age floods came afterward but weren't high or deep enough to completely erode all the evidence for glaciation atop Steamboat Rock.

Figure 4-78. Steamboat Rock Glacial Moraine Earthcache site. Remnant of glacial till in a moraine is exposed along the east edge of Steamboat Rock. The till formed along the edge of a thick sheet of glacial ice that once covered the monolith toward the end of the Ice Age. Looking north.

4.2   Highest point along the trail (elevation 2,300 feet). Great views to the east including Steamboat Rock State Park, Devils Punch Bowl, Banks Lake Inselbergs (No. 30), Castle Rock (No. 33) and the mouth of Northrup Canyon (No. 32) (see Plates 22 and 26).

4.4   Trail continues southwest along the cliff edge. In another 0.3 mile trail begins its descent toward the original point of diversion.

4.9   Complete loop around Steamboat Rock summit. Turn left (southeast) and descend the same steep access trail used to gain the summit.

5.5   End of trail loop.

Trail AA. Giant Cave Arch Rock Shelter Flood Feature Nos. 30, 31, 34, 38, 62

The largest natural rock shelter of the Channeled Scabland is accessible from Barker Canyon along the west side of the Upper Grand Coulee. A couple of giant delta bars are also here, reminders of a persistent Glacial Lake Columbia that occupied the upper coulee for centuries after the last Missoula flood.

Geologic Highlights: Natural rock shelter eroded into west wall of Upper Grand Coulee. Nearby are Barker Canyon scabland complex (No. 34) and Foster Coulee (No. 62) with post-Missoula flood delta bars that protruded out into former Glacial Lake Columbia (No. 38). Visible to the east are the Banks Lake Inselbergs

(No. 30) and Steamboat Rock (No. 31) toward the middle of the coulee.

Length: One to two miles one-way

Elevation (Relief) Along Trail: 1,600 to 1,900 feet (300 feet)

Difficulty: Moderate

Best Mode of Travel: Hike

Best Observation Point: Rock knob just below and east of the rock shelter (N47.8951, W119.1947)

Management/Ownership: Washington Department of Fish and Wildlife

USGS 1:24,000 Scale Maps: Barker Canyon

Warnings: No potable water. Steep slopes below the rock shelter require some scrambling across loose scree. A Washington Discover Pass is required to park at this state-owned and operated site.

Directions: From the town of Grand Coulee drive north, then west, on State Route 174. Turn left onto unpaved Barker Canyon Road between MP 11 and 12. Continue six miles with long descent to the mouth of Barker Canyon (Figure 4-79). Turn right just before reaching Banks Lake and park in or near grove of shade trees about 0.2 mile to the west (N47.9024, W119.1733).

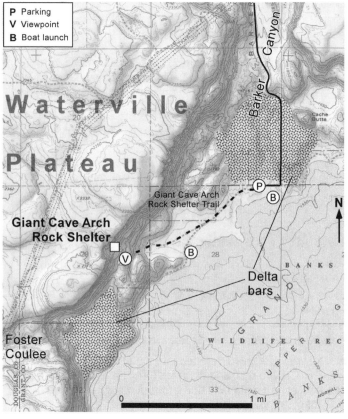

Figure 4-79. Giant Cave Arch Rock Shelter Trail. Delta bars formed where glacial meltwater from the melting Okanogan Lobe drained off the Waterville Plateau and into ancient Glacial Lake Columbia at the close of the Ice Age.

Trail Log

0.0   Hike along unpaved road that continues to the southwest.

0.5   Bear right at fork in the road. Giant Cave Arch is visible in the basalt cliff ahead (see Figure 2-11).

0.9   Road ends at base of bluff below rock shelter. Scramble across slope to the southwest toward rock shelter. Nice views to the northeast of Upper Grand Coulee open up along the climb (Figure 4-80).

Figure 4-80. View looking north across mouth of Barker Canyon (No. 34) toward the Banks Lake Inselbergs (No. 30).

1.1   Arrive at rock bench just below rock shelter. If feeling adventurous continue up the steep scree slope to the rock shelter opening. The overhang is the result of megafloods eroding out a weaker rock zone where a number of thin basalt flows are concentrated (see Figure 2-11). The overhang for the cave consists of the stronger basalt entablature (see Figure 1-2). Retrace route to beginning or continue 0.2 mile farther southwest to a saddle with a view above the delta bar that formed below the mouth of Foster Coulee (Figure 4-81, see Figure 3-74).

Figure 4-81. Looking southwest onto a 70-foot-tall delta bar (arrow) that developed as a glacial-meltwater stream descended over a tall waterfall from hanging Foster Coulee into Glacial Lake Columbia, spreading its sedimentary load outward into a lobate form. The base of the delta lies another 70 feet below Banks Lake. Pristine deltas like this that jut out into the coulee channel, in combination with a thick blanket of silt deposits, signify a 300-foot-deep, long-lived lake (i.e., Glacial Lake Columbia) persisted here for centuries after the last Missoula floods.

Trail BB. Salishan Mesa   Flood Feature Nos. 31, 35, 38

A short climb follows the route used by American Indians to a high butte with a commanding view of the Upper Grand Coulee.

Geologic Highlights: Climb across eroded basalt flows to a flat-topped butte that drops precipitously 400 feet into Banks Lake on one side (Plate 28, see Figure 3-66); pillow basalt structure containing microcrystalline quartz that was quarried by American Indians for tool making, enigmatic rock walls along the approach to the butte, views north and south along Grand Coulee including Steamboat Rock and undulating surface atop the Paynes Gulch flood bar, which appear to represent silt-draped giant current ripples.

Length: One to 1.3 miles depending on route choice

Elevation (Relief) Along Trail: 1,860 to 1,970 feet (110 feet)

Difficulty: Moderate, due to short scramble up steep, scree-covered slope

Best Mode of Travel: Hike

Best Observation Point: Salishan Mesa summit plateau

Management/Ownership: U.S. Bureau of Reclamation

USGS 1:24,000 Scale Maps: Hartline NW

Warnings: Faint trail may be difficult to follow in places; steep drop-off on west side of the mesa. If parked on east side of highway, use care crossing over to the west side of State Route 155.

Directions: From Coulee City proceed north on State Route 155 to 0.4 mile north of MP 7 and park in the wide area by an obscure dirt road on east side of the highway. If arriving from the north, there is also a wide area along the west side of SR 155 for parking. The Salishan Mesa hike starts here on the west side of SR 155 (N47.7367, W119.2375) (Figure 4-82).

Trail Description: Two routes are possible: around the south edge of the lower elevation butte, or between the lower butte and the higher northern butte (Salishan Mesa). The description here is of the southern route around the lower butte (Figure 4-82).

Trail Log

0.0   From the small pullout area on the west side of SR 155, follow an abandoned road towards the coulee edge.

0.2   At the coulee edge are excellent views of the Upper Grand Coulee, Banks Lake, the surrounding scabland and the tall Salishan Mesa immediately to the north. Note the pillow lava layer above the prominent scree slope on the side of the mesa. Proceed north towards the saddle between the buttes.

0.4   Rock walls in the saddle were constructed by American Indians for some unknown purpose. A nearby pit house was used as early as 2,300 years ago. Scramble up the side of Salishan Mesa to its slightly tilted, plateau summit (Figure 4-83).

0.7   Top of Salishan Mesa (Plates 17b and 28). Spectacular views of Steamboat Rock (No. 31) to the north, the edge of the Waterville Plateau

Figure 4-82. Aerial view onto the Salishan Mesa Trail. Looking northeast. Banks Lake is on the left.

along the west wall of the coulee, and vertical coulee walls, some of which are more than 800 feet high! Large basalt boulders (Haystack Rocks – No. 59), transported by the Okanogan Lobe, are silhouetted along the edge of the Waterville Plateau across the coulee. The mesa top is at an elevation of 1,967 feet, and the highest flood level here was about 2,400 feet; that translates to a maximum water depth of more than 400 feet over this spot! Retrace route to trailhead.

Figure 4-83. Salishan Mesa and Steamboat Rock of Upper Grand Coulee. Looking north.

Trails in the Vicinity of Lower Grand Coulee

"Catastrophic flooding of glacial water ... remade preglacial valleys into an anastomosing complex of great river channels with huge cataracts, deep rock basins, and bars attaining magnitudes unknown elsewhere on earth."

– J Harlen Bretz et al (1956)

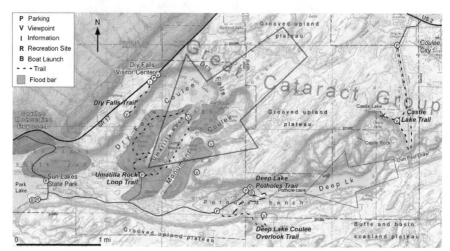

Figure 4-84. Features and trails along the Great Cataract Group in the vicinity of Sun Lakes-Dry Falls State Park.

Trail CC. Dry Falls   Flood Feature Nos. 36, 37, 41, 42, 43, 45

After soaking in the incredible views from the Sun Lakes-Dry Falls Visitor Center, head south a short ways on an unimproved path for more eye-popping views in a more secluded setting.

Geologic Highlights: Dual recessional cataract canyons (Dry Falls and Monument Coulees) with plunge pools, Umatilla Rock blade (No. 43), flood bars at the west end of the four-mile wide Great Cataract Group (Figure 4-84, Plate 31)

Length: Up to 0.6 mile one-way

Elevation (Relief) Along Trail: 1,550 to 1,560 feet (10 feet)

Difficulty: Easy

Best Mode of Travel: Hike

Best Observation Point: Impressive views starting at the visitor center and all along the 0.6 mile trail to the south

Management/Ownership: Washington State Parks

USGS 1:24,000 Scale Maps: Coulee City, Park Lake, WA

Warnings: Mostly cross-country travel along unmarked trail south of the visitor center. No established trail exists here yet, but one could be built if and when a planned upgrade to the visitor center is completed. High cliffs with precipitous drops-offs and no guardrails or other protection from cliff edge. Not recommended for young children. Washington Discover Pass required.

Directions: Trail starts at the Dry Falls Visitor Center along State Route 17, four miles southwest of Coulee City and 18 miles north of Soap Lake.

Trail Log

0.0   Start at visitor center parking area where there are great views into the head of Dry Falls and Monument coulees beyond Umatilla Rock Blade (see Figure 3-80, Plate 29). For more breathtaking views in a more natural setting, head south from the existing visitor center along an unimproved path that parallels the lofty precipice of the coulee.

0.6   A side canyon cuts across the coulee margin here, which inhibits hiking farther to the south (Figure 4-84). Retrace route back to the visitor center.

Trail DD. Umatilla Rock Loop   Flood Feature Nos. 41, 42, 43, 56

Hike along and over Umatilla Rock, perhaps the most famous rock blade or isolated "goat island" left behind during cataract retreat of looming Dry Falls.

Geologic Highlights: Umatilla Rock Blade (No. 43), a rib of basalt below Dry Falls Cataract (No. 41) recessional canyon (Plate 31), plunge pools, monument-like slump-blocks, flood bars

Length: 2.6 miles round-trip

Elevation (Relief) Along Trail: 1,220 to 1,360 feet (140 feet)

Difficulty: Moderate

Best Observation Point: Umatilla Rock Blade saddle (N47.6003, W119.3561) with combined, unobstructed view of both Dry Falls and Monument coulees

Best Mode of Travel: Hike. Horses and mountain bikes prohibited on this state park trail.

Management/Ownership: Washington State Parks

USGS 1:24,000 Scale Map: Coulee City, Park Lake, WA

Warnings: Use caution navigating a short, steep, scree-covered slope to get up and down from saddle across Umatilla Rock. No potable water or midday shade. Access via Deep Lake Road is closed in the winter. Washington Discover Pass required.

Directions: At MP 92.5 on State Route 17, turn east into Sun Lakes State Park. Proceed across flood bars for 1.2 miles before turning left onto state park road toward Deep Lake. Head east up Deep Lake Coulee and after 0.9 mile take another left onto unpaved road toward Perch/Dry Falls Lake. Umatilla Rock trailhead kiosk and parking is 0.4 mile farther.

south

Deep Lake Coulee

Umatilla Rock

saddle

Dry Falls Coulee

Monument Coulee

Figure 4-85. View looking south toward Umatilla Rock Blade (No. 43) from Dry Falls cataract. The Umatilla Rock Loop Trail passes through a low saddle in the basalt rib plucked out by megafloods.

Trail Log

0.0   Park at trailhead kiosk. Following the loop trail in a counterclockwise direction, head northeast up the east side of Umatilla Rock via Monument Coulee (No. 42). Follow red trail markers.

0.5   Basalt pinnacles tilting at various angles (Figure 4-86) are part of a large topple block that slumped away from the edge of Umatilla Rock during or soon after the last Ice Age flood about 14,000 years ago. Path crosses remnants of an old stone wall purportedly built by American Indians. Continue northeast through the slump blocks toward the head of Umatilla Rock.

Figure 4-86. Umatilla Rock Loop Trail's monument-like pinnacles.

1.0   Trail turns northwest to go up and over a distinct saddle in Umatilla Rock (Figure 4-85), above and to the left. Trail up and down saddle on the other side is moderately steep and covered with loose scree – use care climbing up and down this slope. (This steep section over the saddle can be circumvented by hiking another 0.3 mile north, to go around the nose of Umatilla Rock with much less elevation gain. If going this route the trail hooks up with gravel road back to trailhead after going around the north end of Umatilla Rock.)

1.1   Arrive at saddle in Umatilla Rock (N47.6001, W119.3561). Behind, notice Green and Red Alkali lakes in Monument Coulee (Plate 35). Ahead, to the west, lies the Dry Falls Visitor Center across Dry Falls Coulee.

1.4   After reaching saddle descend west into Dry Falls Coulee. At the base of the coulee bear left (southwest) and follow trail markers (or gravel road) back.

2.1   Overlook into Perch Lake fills a large hollow in a giant flood bar that covers much of the bottom of Dry Falls Coulee (Figure 4-84).

2.6   Arrive back at trailhead. End of loop.

Trail EE. Deep Lake Potholes   Flood Feature No. 46

From the side of Deep Lake Coulee crawl through a short cave into the bottom of a deep pothole. Via another exit out of the pothole above, explore a swarm of deep potholes nearby, drilled into a flood-ravaged rock bench above Deep Lake.

Geologic Highlights: Pothole swarm atop flood-scoured rock bench of Grande Ronde Basalt. Preferential erosion during Ice Age flooding along a zone of weakness (i.e., base of colonnade in rubbly basalt flow bottom, see Figure 1-2) created a unique and unusual cave opening into the side of a pothole.

Length: 1.5 miles round-trip

Elevation (Relief) Along Trail: 1,240 to 1,300 feet (60 feet)

Difficulty: Moderate, except may be difficult for some through cave opening

Best Observation Point: Rock bench above Deep Lake (N47.5876, W119.3355)

Best Mode of Travel: Hike

Management/Ownership: Washington State Parks

USGS 1:24,000 Scale Map: Coulee City, WA

Warnings: Short cave opening drops about 8 feet into bottom of the pothole. Therefore, not recommended for young children or the timid. Use the many good hand and footholds in the basalt rock to assure a safe descent. Beware of steep drop-offs around many of the potholes. Beware of poison oak while climbing out of pothole. Access via Deep Lake Road is closed in the winter. Washington Discover Pass required.

Directions: At MP 92.5 on State Route 17, turn east into Sun Lakes-Dry Falls State Park. Proceed across flood bars for 1.2 miles before turning left onto state park road toward Deep Lake. Continue 2.5 miles to end of the road at Deep Lake.

Trail Log

0.0   Park at the Deep Lake Recreation Site at road's end. Follow trail east along south (right) side of 120-foot Deep Lake. Note a dark hole in south coulee wall visible ahead about one-quarter mile away (Figure 4-87). This is the cave entrance to a pothole that lies (out of sight) immediately on other side of the basalt cliff wall.

0.2   Primary trail continues east along Deep Lake. Bear right (southeast) onto secondary trail toward coulee wall and what appears to be a dark, dead-end cave, located several tens of feet above the valley floor.

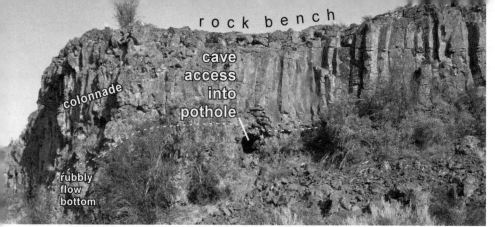

Figure 4-87. Cave entrance into Deep Lake pothole. Cave formed when Ice Age floods eroded through a weaker, rubbly zone at the base of the colonnade within a lava flow. Looking southeast.

0.25   Scramble up to cave entrance at coulee wall (N47.5875, W119.3358). At the entrance one can see the cave angles downward into a large void – the bottom of a deep pothole! Climb through the several-foot-wide cave opening, which rapidly opens up into the base of a large (100 feet wide by 50 feet deep) pothole. Bottom of pothole is about 8 feet below cave entrance. Use some of the many solid hand and footholds to safely descend to bottom.

0.3   After climbing out of the gentler east side of the pothole, rise up onto top of rock bench (Plate 17a) and head west along ledge that separates this pothole from Deep Lake Coulee. Continue west (cross-country – no established trails here) along rock bench peering into the many other cavernous potholes that are congregated here (Figures 4-88).

0.5   Several well-developed, especially deep and circular potholes lie in the vicinity of N47.5868, W119.3422 (Figure 4-89, Plate 34, see Figure 3-85).

0.8   Hike south to connect up with double-track trail that leads northwest to Deep Lake Road.

1.0   Intersection with Deep Lake Road at the Washington State Park's Caribou Trailhead. Turn right (northeast) and follow paved road 0.5 mile back to the Deep Lake Potholes trailhead.

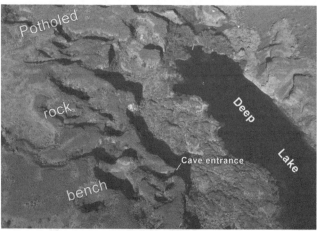

Figure 4-88. A dense swarm of potholes (No. 46) eroded into a rock bench of Grande Ronde Basalt above Deep Lake. Potholed rock bench can be accessed by crawling through a short cave in the south wall of Deep Lake Coulee (Figure 4-87). Looking west.

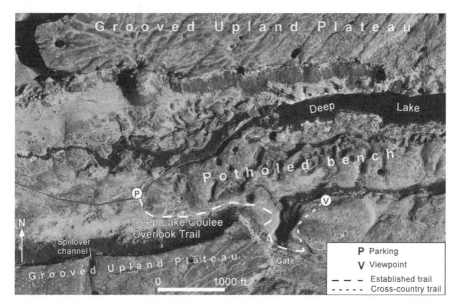

Figure 4-89. Aerial photo in the vicinity of the Deep Lake Coulee Overlook Trail. A spectacular view down onto the Deep Lake Pothole Swarm (No. 46) lies at the end of the trail.

Trail FF. Deep Lake Coulee Overlook Flood Feature Nos. 42, 43, 44, 46

Ascend out of Deep Lake Coulee for a commanding view onto Deep Lake and its pothole swarm. Flood-faceted Castle Rock butte, within the Castle Lake basin, is also visible in the distance.

Geologic Highlights: Recessional cataract canyons, butte-and-basin scabland, potholes and rock basins, faceted basalt escarpment (Castle Rock)

Length: 1.6 miles round-trip

Elevation (Relief) Along Trail: 1,240 to 1,530 feet (290 feet)

Difficulty: Moderate

Best Observation Point: Edge of Deep Lake Coulee above Deep Lake

Best Mode of Travel: Hike

Management/Ownership: Washington State Parks

USGS 1:24,000 Scale Map: Coulee City, Park Lake, WA

Warnings: No potable water or midday shade. Access via Deep Lake Road is closed in the winter. Washington Discover Pass required.

Directions: At MP 92.5 on State Route 17, turn east into Sun Lakes-Dry Falls State Park. Proceed across flood bars for 1.2 miles before turning left onto state park road toward Deep Lake. Continue 2.1 miles and park at kiosk for Washington State Park's Caribou Trailhead.

Trail Log

0.0   At Caribou Trailhead (N47.5850, W119.3486) cross road and pass through gate following the double-track trail that ascends to the southeast.

0.3   Enormous pothole on the left, one of many within the Deep Lake Pothole Swarm (No. 46; Figure 4-89). Double-track trail begins to ascend side canyon to the south.

0.6   Pass through barbed wire gate at N47.5828, W119.3384. From here bear left (north) and bushwhack about 0.1 mile to gain the top of the upland plateau. Continue another 0.2 mile to the edge of Deep Lake Coulee.

0.8   Arrive at overlook onto Deep Lake and a dense swarm of potholes on rock bench above the lake. Notice Castle Rock butte (see Figure 3-83, Plate 43) in the distance to the right (east). Retrace route back to trailhead.

Trail GG. Castle Lake   Flood Feature Nos. 44, 45, 46

Hike across grooved scabland to the Castle Lake cataract precipice and an expansive view across the Castle Lake plunge pool and a pothole-cratered bench above Deep Lake. Also visible is "the Castle," a prominent, flood-truncated basalt butte. Make an exciting descent to Castle Lake via a pair of ladders permanently affixed to the cataract wall. During the return, take a short side trip to the edge of Don Paul Draw past the head of the Bacon Siphons and Tunnels, key engineered structures in the workings of the Columbia Basin Project.

Geologic Highlights: Grooved upland plateau, abandoned cataract, plunge pool, mesas, rock bench, faceted-butte escarpment (Castle Rock), potholed bench

Length: 3.5 miles round-trip

Elevation (Relief) Along Trail: 1,370 to 1,570 feet (200 feet)

Difficulty: Moderate to difficult. Most of the route is cross-country (i.e., no established trail). The short scramble up and over a berm may be somewhat challenging. Be careful on the two, short, secured metal ladders and steep trail descending to the Castle Lake plunge pool and basin.

Best Observation Points: A number of eye-popping views occur along the edge of the cataract above the Castle Lake plunge pool and beyond toward Deep Lake cataract canyon.

Best Mode of Travel: Hike

Management/Ownership: U.S. Bureau of Reclamation, Washington Department of Fish and Wildlife, Washington State Department of Natural Resources, Washington State Parks

USGS 1:24,000 Scale Map: Coulee City, WA

Warnings: No potable water or midday shade, cliff drop-offs; large basalt boulders on berm may shift while climbing over and around.

Directions: From U.S. Highway 2 at east end of Dry Falls Dam, just west of Coulee City, turn south onto Road I NE (N 8th Street). Drive about 100 yards past the Dry Falls Dam power plant and turn right. Cross bridge over the Main

Canal and immediately turn left onto the U.S. Bureau of Reclamation (USBR) service road that parallels the west side of the canal. After one-quarter mile, park at pullout at end of road (Figure 4-90) next to canal at the head of a tall, man-made berm of basalt boulders.

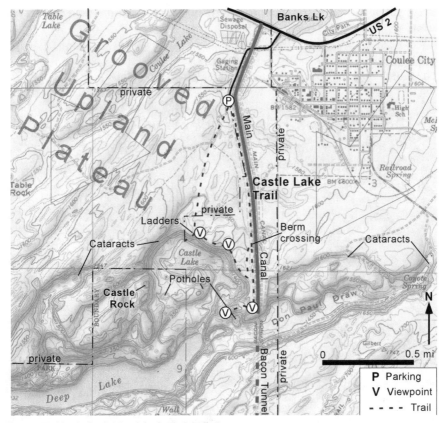

Figure 4-90. Map in the vicinity of the Castle Lake Trail.

Trail Log

0.0 Park at pullout just short of the gated end of road next to the Main Canal (N47.6116, W119.3039). Pass through an opening in the fence that heads west and proceed south (Figure 4-90). The massive berm was derived from the blasting and removal of basalt bedrock from the Main Canal constructed between 1946 and 1951 as part of the Columbia Basin Project.

0.5 After passing through a series of flood-gouged, giant, longitudinal grooves in the basalt bedrock, arrive at the edge of the upper (shorter) cataract for the Castle Lake basin. After descending the cataract continue south across a rock bench towards the main cataract.

0.8 Arrive at Castle Lake Cataract precipice (Plate 43) and top of ladders that descend to Castle Lake (N47.6010, W119.3072). Great views of the Castle Lake plunge pool and rugged butte-and-basin scabland beyond. This is near the east end of what J Harlen Bretz referred to as the Great Cataract Group, a long series of eroded cliffs, altogether almost four miles wide (see Plate 31). Beyond Castle Lake, notice several enormous, deep potholes and channels on rock bench above Deep Lake. The prominent butte off the right is Castle Rock (see Figure 3-83). Imagine, during the largest Ice Age floods, water was already up to 300 feet deep before going over the precipice and more than 500 feet deep over Castle Lake.

If feeling adventurous descend the first ladder (Figure 4-91) before traversing west a short distance to catch the second ladder that drops to near the lakeshore. Retrace route to the top of cataract via the ladders.

Figure 4-91. Castle Lake basin. One of a pair of metal ladders descending to Castle Lake.

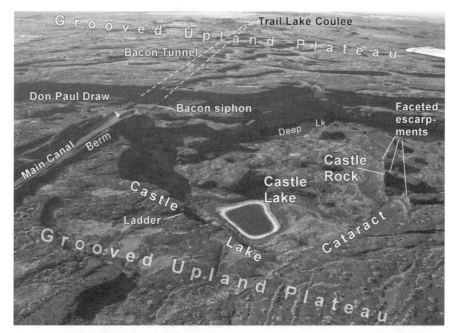

Figure 4-92. Aerial view of the Castle Lake Basin, looking southeast. The Columbia Basin Project's Main Canal delivers irrigation water from Banks Lake to the Bacon Siphon. From there the water travels underground through the Bacon Siphons and Tunnels for two miles before discharging into Trail Lake Coulee (top center).

0.9   From the top of the ladders, continue southeast along the lip of the cataract to where the berm intersects the cataract cliff.

1.3   Leave the edge of the cataract to head north along the base of the berm (Figure 4-90).

1.5   Ascend more gently sloping portion of berm and through a saddle at N47.60015, W119.30163. Beware of shifting blocks of loose basalt while crossing the berm. Hike south along crest of berm to the edge of Don Paul Draw.

2.0   At the south end of the berm, along Don Paul Draw, the Main Canal divides and disappears into the two Bacon Siphons (Figure 4-93). The siphons lead to the head of Bacon Tunnel on the opposite side of the draw before running underground for two miles all the way to the head of Trail Lake Coulee. From here return to the trailhead by following the access road north between the canal and berm. Head west along top of rock blade of basalt for a great view onto Deep Lake.

2.2   After passing above a cavernous pothole (Figure 4-90), reach far west end of rock blade overlooking Deep Lake. Retrace route to the berm.

2.4   Follow service road (Figure 4-93) north along east side of the berm to the trailhead.

3.5   Arrive at trailhead – end of trail loop.

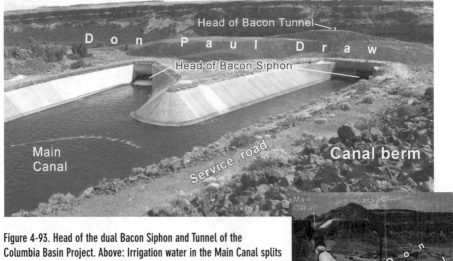

Figure 4-93. Head of the dual Bacon Siphon and Tunnel of the Columbia Basin Project. Above: Irrigation water in the Main Canal splits into two conduits before disappearing into the Bacon Siphons. Looking south. Right: Construction of the 1,000-foot-long siphon (now buried) spans Don Paul Draw, circa 1946, looking north. PHOTO COURTESY OF CENTRAL WASHINGTON UNIVERSITY ARCHIVES, RUFUS WOODS PHOTOGRAPHIC COLLECTION. A second buried siphon leading to a parallel tunnel was completed in 1980.

Trail HH. East Park Lake
Flood Feature Nos. 36, 53, 56

An easy trip, mostly on a barricaded, paved road, along the east side of Park Lake with great views of the Coulee Monocline and associated hogbacks. A side trip crosses two flood bars and a rare cluster of ice-rafted erratics located within the deep throat of Lower Grand Coulee.

Geologic Highlights: Coulee Monocline (No. 36), Hogback Islands (No. 53), Hanging Valleys (No. 56), flood bars, ice-rafted erratics, basalt pinnacle and Mount St. Helens ash fall of 1980

Length: 2.6 to four miles round-trip

Elevation (Relief) Along Trail: 1,100 to 1,300 feet (200 feet)

Difficulty: Easy, except for optional, short, steep hike up onto flood bar

Best Observation Point: From atop flood bar 0.4 mile southeast of Park Lake

Best Mode of Travel: Hike or bike

Management/Ownership: Washington State Parks

USGS 1:24,000 Scale Map: Park Lake, WA

Directions: At MP 92.5 on State Route 17, turn east into Sun Lakes State Park. Proceed another 1.5 miles through the state park to recreation site at the end of road (Figure 4-94). Washington Discover Pass required.

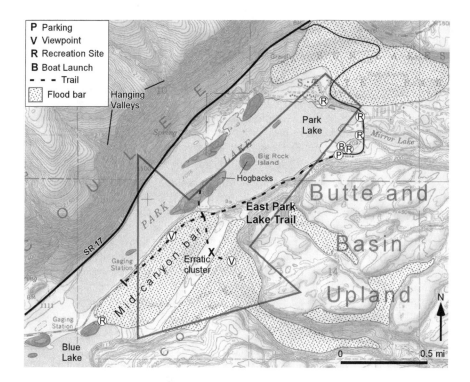

P Parking
V Viewpoint
R Recreation Site
B Boat Launch
- - - Trail
Flood bar

Figure 4-94. East Park Lake Trail within Sun Lakes State Park, Lower Grand Coulee.

Trail Log

0.0   Park at end of road (N47.5869, W119.3934) at Sun Lakes State Park recreation site (Figure 4-94, Plate 33). Continue southwest on paved road along east side of Park Lake.

0.7   Steep cliff on left side of road and islands protruding out of Park Lake on the right are hogbacks (No. 53) – remnants of basalt flows tilted along the Coulee Monocline (No. 36) and later eroded by high-velocity floodwaters flowing down Grand Coulee. Behind, to the northeast, is a great view of inclined basalt flows of the Coulee Monocline (Figure 4-95).

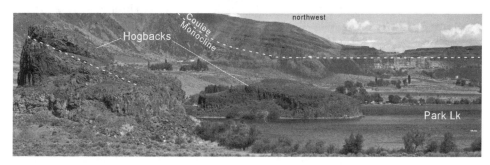

Figure 4-95. Hogbacks are eroded remnants of dipping basalt, tilted along the Coulee Monocline. Note how tilted hogback at left reflects the dip of the Coulee Monocline in background.

0.9 Trail junction. A double-track trail crosses the road here. Trail to the right goes about 0.2 mile down to the hogback peninsula that extends out into Park Lake. The log description provided here is for the trail that goes up and over the giant, domed mid-canyon flood bar to the left (southeast).

1.0 On the east side of the mid-canyon bar lies a pocket of white volcanic ash filling a surface depression (Plate 37). This is an accumulation of ash from the 1980 eruption of Mount St. Helens, located in the Cascade Mountains, nearly 200 miles southwest of here (see "Belching Volcanoes" sidebar, page 252 in chapter 3). Airfall tephra from past volcanic eruptions often collects and gets preserved in topographic depressions like this one.

1.1 Erratic cluster. A grouping of angular granitic boulders (Figure 4-96) are scattered about on the south side of the trail between the mid-canyon bar and taller pendant bar to the east (Plate 37). Some of the boulders are composed of a special type of granitic rock with especially large mineral grains, referred to by geologists as "pegmatite." Similar pegmatite rocks can be traced back to the vicinity of the ice dam for Glacial Lake Missoula. Another source for granitic rocks lies at the head of Grand Coulee (e.g., Banks Lake Inselbergs, No. 30), and the floods did indeed rip up and carry boulders, free of ice, along with the floodwaters. These types of boulders, however, were generally rounded and smoothed during transport as they bounced and tumbled along the base of the flood flow.

The very angular nature of the boulders preserved here at Park Lake, however, indicates they were not carried along the base of the flow as flood bedload, but instead were transported well above the bottom of the flood, encased in floating icebergs. For ice-rafted erratics to be preserved in this extremely high-energy, low-elevation (1,125 feet) location requires grounding of the iceberg during the waning stage of the last megaflood down Grand Coulee. If another flood had come later, these boulders would have likely been dispersed downstream and not preserved in a tight cluster. Furthermore, the fresh, unweathered surfaces of these boulders is consistent with a last-flood origin. In contrast, boulders from older floods normally display a weathered, lichen-encrusted surface. Interestingly, both types of boulders, bedload (rounded) and ice-rafted (angular), are present here (see Figure 2-38).

Continue up the steep double-track trail that climbs to top of pendant flood bar (Plate 37) to the southeast.

1.2 At barbed wire fence on top of flood bar, bear left onto another double-track trail that ends after another 0.1 mile for a high view across Park Lake to hanging valleys, hogbacks and a basalt pinnacle (see Figure 2-18). Retrace route to paved trail.

1.7 At paved trail turn left to continue to end of state park trail (another 0.6 mile), cross road to the hogback peninsula below, or go right to return 0.9 mile to trailhead.

Figure 4-96. Cluster of angular, unweathered, ice-rafted, erratic boulders along East Park Lake Trail. Looking north.

II. Lake Lenore Caves to The Great Blade and East Lenore Coulee Flood Feature Nos. 51, 52, 53, 54, 55, 56

After hiking to popular Lake Lenore Caves, continue up and over Bretz's Great Blade into the wild scablands of hidden and remote East Lenore Coulee. Or, via an alternate route, explore a cratered rock bench leading to a gigantic pothole within lower East Lenore Coulee.

Geologic Highlights: Overhanging rock shelters (Lake Lenore Caves, No. 52), Hanging Valleys (No. 56), Hogback Islands (No. 53), East Lenore Coulee Cataract Canyon (No. 55) lie hidden behind The Great Blade (No. 54) with dozens of potholes and giant crisscrossing longitudinal grooves; ice-rafted erratics.

Length: Up to four miles or more round-trip; one mile one-way to The Great Blade notch (Figure 4-97).

Elevation (Relief) Along Trails: 1,140 to 1,600 feet (460 feet)

Difficulty: Moderate; difficult into East Lenore Coulee

Best Observation Point: Overlook into East Lenore Coulee from notch (Figure 4-97) in The Great Blade. N47.5130, W119.4929

Figure 4-97. A giant rib of eroded basalt, The Great Blade (No. 54), separates Lake Lenore and Lower Grand Coulee on the right from East Lenore Coulee on the left. Trail from Lake Lenore Caves to East Lenore Coulee passes through a narrow notch in The Great Blade, visible in the foreground.

Best Mode of Travel: Hike

Management/Ownership: Washington State Parks and Washington Department of Fish and Wildlife

USGS 1:24,000 Scale Maps: Soap Lake, Little Soap Lake, Park Lake, WA

Earthcache: Great Blade Notch (Identification code GC2BX9T at www. geocaching.com)

Warnings: No potable water or midday shade. Use caution up short, steep, scree-covered slopes below notch in The Great Blade. No established trails exist in East Lenore Coulee; map and compass (or GPS) recommended. While much of East Lenore Coulee is within public lands, there are large, unmarked and unfenced tracts of private land that should be avoided, out of respect for landowner(s). Washington Discover Pass required.

Directions: On State Route 17, nine miles north of Soap Lake or 10 miles south of Dry Falls Visitor Center, turn east onto short access road to Lake Lenore Caves within the Lake Lenore State Wildlife Management Area. Well-marked trailhead to Lake Lenore Caves is 0.4 mile ahead at road's end. A second unmarked trail is located about two miles south of here in a small pullout at MP 83 off the east side of SR 17 (Plate 40).

Trail Log

0.0   Start at well-marked and well-used trailhead for the Lake Lenore Caves (N47.5175, W119.4939). Heading southwest, ascend across bluffs of 16 million-year-old Grande Ronde Basalt ahead.

0.4   Arrive at first of the Lake Lenore Caves (see Figure 3-93) rock shelters. Several more caves lie along trail to the south. To the west are good views of hogback islands (Plate 38, see Figure 2-21) and hanging valleys (see Figure 2-23, right).

0.7   Trail rises to top of the flood-scoured rock bench above the Lake Lenore

Caves. Here is a pothole eroded into the rock bench with an overhang at the downstream (south) end (Figure 4-98). At the pothole the trail turns sharply northeast, continuing along a rock bench above the Lake Lenore Caves before climbing toward a notch in The Great Blade above (Plate 39, see Figure 3-93).

Figure 4-98. Pothole along Lake Lenore Caves Trail. Overhanging rock shelter at downstream end of the pothole lies at the same flow boundary within the Grande Ronde Basalt as nearby Lake Lenore Caves. Looking south.

0.9   Just below the notch, the trail steepens across a scree slope.

1.0   Arrive at notch in The Great Blade (No. 54) with breathtaking views on either side (Plate 39). The Great Blade Notch Earthcache is located at this spectacular overlook (Figure 4-99). In full view the expansive and desolate East Lenore Coulee dramatically spreads out to the east. This is near the end of the distinguishable trail, but those wishing to explore farther can wander cross-country either north or south along The Great Blade, where there are an unlimited number of other great viewpoints, or descend into the wilds of East Lenore Coulee (No. 55) with its impressive potholed rock bench and giant, crisscrossing, longitudinal and curvilinear grooves (Plate 41, Figure 4-99).

The grooves were scoured in multiple directions on top of the Grande Ronde Basalt by the Ice Age floods. One direction generally aligns with the flood-flow direction; grooves going in other directions appear to reflect erosion along curvilinear fractures within the basalt. These curving fractures may be from large-scale cooling fractures that formed as the basalt solidified from molten lava or perhaps are related to more regional tectonic forces applied to the basalt after it cooled. A deep notch eroded into The Great Blade (Figure 4-99, Plate 39), through which the trail passes, appears to have been lowered along weakened rock in one of the many parallel, curvilinear grooves.

East of the crisscrossing set of grooves is a well-developed, flood-channel escarpment marking the edge of the paleoflood channel. The highest floods rose even higher, however, all the way to the edge of High Hill (No. 51) where several ice-rafted erratics were grounded up to 300 feet above the valley floor (Figures 4-99 and 4-100).

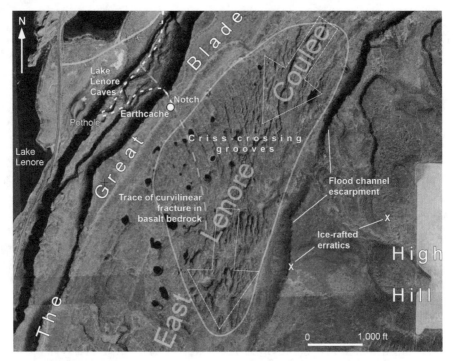

Figure 4-99. Aerial photo showing crisscrossing, giant grooves and potholes of East Lenore Coulee (No. 55). The grooves and potholes were eroded into the top of the Grande Ronde Basalt by powerful flood currents moving through this area.

Figure 4-100. An angular, ice-rafted granitic boulder (erratic) lies within a protected side valley along the east side of East Lenore Coulee. N47.5066, W119.4782, elevation 1,730 feet.

An alternate trail into East Lenore Coulee (Plate 40) is via a small pullout along State Route 17 at MP 83 (N47.4896, W119.5126). This unmarked trail follows a double-track uphill to the south end of The Great Blade, located about 0.2 mile to the northeast. Along the way, a dark cave recess in the cliff to the south lies at the same level as Lake Lenore Caves, two miles to the north. At the top of a broad rock bench, the trail levels off and rapidly loses definition; from here one can travel cross-country to the north on the elevated rock bench that lies between The Great Blade and Lake Lenore, or head south across the rock bench, cratered with potholes, to an enormous, 800-foot wide pothole at N47.4774, W119.5065 (see Figure 3-98, Plate 42).

Trail JJ. Spring Coulee (Billy Clapp Lake) Flood Feature Nos. 40, 47, 51

Discover a rich diversity of scabland features where floods squeezed through two uplands east of Lower Grand Coulee. A mostly primitive trail follows the west side of Billy Clapp Lake (Plate 44).

Geologic Highlights: Coulees, buttes, mesas, potholes, grooves, abandoned cataracts, giant current ripples and spillover channels

Best Mode of Travel: Hike or watercraft

Management/Ownership: Washington Department of Fish and Wildlife (WDFW)

USGS 1:24,000 Scale Maps: Stratford, Wilson Creek NW, WA

Warnings: No potable water or midday shade. Travel is mostly cross-country (i.e., no established trails), except at the southwest end of the coulee, where an established trail heads north from the Pinto Dam recreation site but gradually disappears after about one-half mile (Figure 4-101). Carry a good topographic map and compass (or GPS) to assist in navigation. Because of the long distance of cross-country travel over some difficult terrain, a car shuttle is recommended to get back to starting point. A Washington Discover Pass is required to park at the Pinto Dam recreation site.

Directions: Recommend dropping off a shuttle vehicle at Summer Falls Park, which is off Pinto Ridge Road, 6.6 miles north of State Route 28. To get to opposite end of the route at the south end of Billy Clapp Lake, return 1.3 miles to Pinto Ridge Road, turn left (south), and drive up and over Pinto Ridge (No. 46). At six miles along Pinto Ridge Road, turn left (east) onto State Route 28 for two miles. At Stratford turn left (north) toward Pinto Dam and Billy Clapp Lake. Road ends at recreation site and boat launch at trailhead 2.3 miles farther.

Length: Five to six miles one-way

Elevation (Relief) Along Trail: 1,350 to 1,600 feet (250 feet)

Best Observation Point: Top of long mesa on west side of Billy Clapp Lake (Figure 4-101)

Difficulty: Easy along 0.5 mile beginning trail; difficult for next five, cross-country miles to Summer Falls. Some steep ascents and descents required with many route-finding challenges along the way.

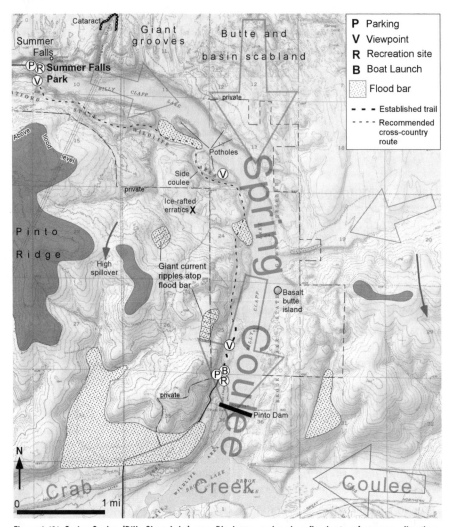

Figure 4-101. Spring Coulee (Billy Clapp Lake) map. Block arrows show how floodwaters from many directions converged onto Spring Coulee. Dark areas lie above maximum flood level

Trail Log

0.0   Trailhead starts at a boat-launch parking area (N42.4530, W119.2529), just north of Pinto Dam. Washington Discover Pass required. Head north on well-used trail that ascends a small rise behind the restroom.

0.2   Small lake embayment with inviting, protected beach.

0.3   Great example of scabland topography, including a prominent monolith (isolated basalt butte) across the valley (Figure 4-102).

0.5   Trail loses definition and eventually disappears. Turn around or begin cross-country travel uphill across moderately steep slope ahead. Giant current ripples blanket a giant flood bar that lies directly upslope from here (Figure 4-101).

Figure 4-102. Spring Coulee (No. 40) scabland. View to the northeast through eroded Frenchman Springs Member (lower Wanapum Basalt) from west shore of Billy Clapp Lake. Note tall, basalt-butte island in distance.

1.5 Side coulee comes in from the left (northwest). Cross a pendant flood bar that blankets the slope ahead.

2.3 Turn left into another, narrower side coulee that comes in from the left. A prominent, resistant butte stands out a short distance up the side coulee at N47.4831, W119.2523. Follow this coulee west as it wraps around a one-mile-long mesa (Figure 4-103). For a wonderful panoramic view, take a short detour to the top of the mesa. Along the way check out an almost perfectly circular pothole on top (N47.4852, W119.2547).

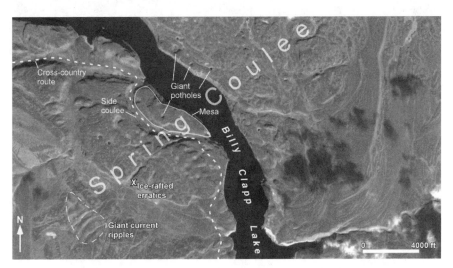

Figure 4-103. Aerial image showing flood features along a portion of the Spring Coulee Trail. Dashed line shows the recommended cross-country route.

2.8 Come to the head of the side coulee where it rejoins Spring Coulee. Turn northwest up another side coulee and across more flood bars.

3.7 Continuing west, climb over barbed wire fence.

4.0 Small water-filled rock basin lies at base of a side coulee. Beyond the pond begin ascent up a rock bench, about 100 feet above, on the left.

Continue northwest atop the rimrock wall.

4.5   View of Summer Falls and the Main Canal of the Columbia Basin Project; Trail Lake Coulee (No. 47) lies beyond (Figure 4-104).

4.7   Begin descent down moderately steep slope into Summer Falls Park.

Figure 4-104. Man-made Summer Falls drops 165 feet into Billy Clapp Lake. The falls are created by diverting water from the Main Canal of the Columbia Basin Project, after flowing out of Trail Lake Coulee. Hydroelectric power is generated as water from the Main Canal drops into Billy Clapp Lake. Looking north.

5.0   End of route at Summer Falls Park (includes restroom, grass, shade and picnic facilities).

Trails in the Vicinity of Moses Coulee

"A great ragged, dry cataract, 400 feet high and 1 mile wide, crosses the coulee about 20 miles above its mouth"

– J Harlen Bretz (1930)

Trail KK. Three Devils Scabland Complex   Flood Feature No. 61

Explore the Three Devils region in some of the most spectacular scabland, which lies midway along Moses Coulee (see Figure 3-109), an outlier channel system, used by only a few of the earlier Ice Age floods.

Geologic Highlights: Abandoned cataracts and recessional canyons, plunge pools, buttes, mesas, potholes, hanging coulees, rock benches and spillover channels

USGS 1:24,000 Scale Map: Rattlesnake Springs, WA

Warnings: No potable water or midday shade

Directions: The Three Devils area is accessed from Palisades Road, located 19 miles northeast of its intersection with State Route 28; this intersection is located 16 miles southeast of Wenatchee. Alternate access is from the northeast: From Coulee City head west on U.S. Highway 2 for 20 miles. Turn south onto Coulee Meadows Road for 11.3 miles, driving past the faltering resort community of Rimrock Meadows. Turn right (west) onto 12 Road SE, which follows the long, straight border between Douglas and Grant counties. The Three Devils area is about three miles farther.

Figure 4-105. Aerial view of the Three Devils scabland complex. Looking northeast.

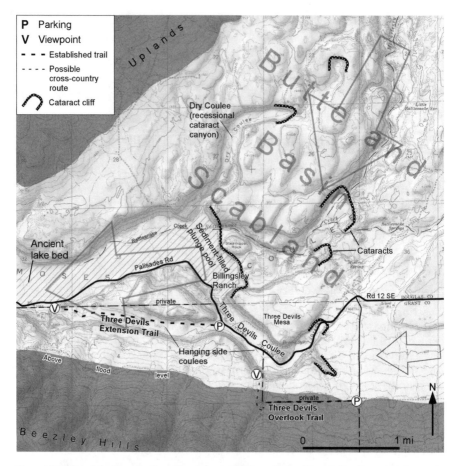

Figure 4-106. Map of the Three Devils scabland complex of Moses Coulee (No. 61). See Figure 2-19 for aerial view of Dry Coulee at top center of this map.

"Two great castellated buttresses face down the coulee, with lesser walls connecting them. This notched cliff clearly was a waterfall, and before the deep notching it was comparable in height to Grand (Dry) Falls at Coulee City."

– J Harlen Bretz (1923)

Three Devils Extension Trail (KK1)

Length: 3.2 miles round-trip

Elevation (Relief) Along Trail: 1,200 to 1,280 feet (80 feet)

Difficulty: Easy

Best Observation Point: At mouth of side coulee that hangs high above lower Moses Coulee, (N47.4378, W119.8330)

Best Mode of Travel: Hike, bike or horse

Management/Ownership: U.S. Bureau of Land Management

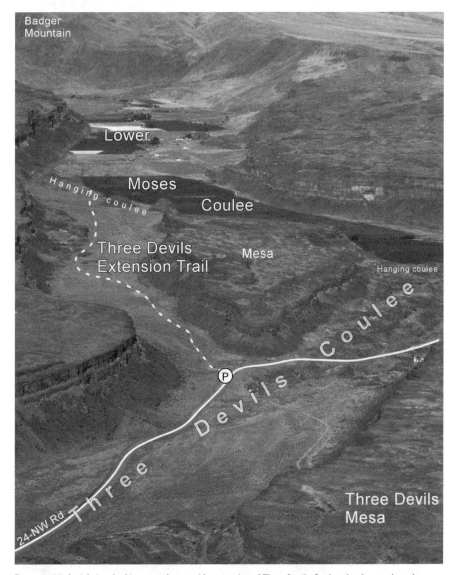

Figure 4-107. Aerial view looking west down a side extension of Three Devils Coulee that hangs above lower Moses Coulee.

Trail Log

0.0   Trailhead (N47.4353, W119.7995) is in small pullout at west end of Three Devils Grade, 0.4 mile southeast of the Billingsley Ranch. After parking pass through gate and head west along double-track trail that runs down the deep side coulee (Figure 4-107).

0.4   Double-track trail turns to a single cow path after passing through fence.

1.6   Viewpoint (N47.4378, W119.8330) at mouth of side coulee that hangs 200 feet above lower Moses Coulee. Retrace route to trailhead.

Three Devils Overlook Trail (KK2)

Length: 2.8 miles round-trip

Elevation (Relief) Along Trail: 1,600 to 1,720 feet (120 feet)

Difficulty: Moderate

Best Observation Point: Overlook into Three Devils coulee and cataract (N47.4277, W119.7905)

Best Mode of Travel: Hike

Management/Ownership: U.S. Bureau of Land Management (BLM)

Directions: At cattle guard along Road 24 NW (N47.4390, W119.7691) drive south for one mile and park at the BLM boundary (Figure 4-106).

Trail Log

0.0   At trailhead (N47.4245, W119.7688) pass through gate and head west along old double-track jeep trail.

0.5   Another double-track trail heads south up into the Beezley Hills. Continue straight (west).

1.0   Road bends uphill. Just above an old dilapidated bridge, leave the double-track and head cross-country across the dry creek bed to the west. On other side of the creek, turn north and hike about 0.4 mile to an impressive overlook into Three Devils coulee and cataract (Figure 4-108). Retrace route back to trailhead.

Figure 4-108. View from the Three Devils Overlook Trail. N47.4277, W119.7905

Trails in the Vicinity of Former
Glacial Lake Columbia

Lake Roosevelt (Plate 50), the reservoir behind Grand Coulee Dam, extends 150 miles – nearly all the way to the Canadian border. Lake Roosevelt today is a much-smaller version of the water body that existed here during the Ice Age (Plate 1). Damming of the Columbia River by the Okanogan Lobe, near the present-day Grand Coulee Dam, formed a much-deeper and extensive lake, Glacial Lake Columbia. At one time Glacial Lake Columbia was almost 1,500 feet deep and backflooded all the way to the Idaho panhandle – almost to the ice dam for Glacial Lake Missoula (today occupied by Lake Pend Oreille, Plate 3)!

Flood features visible from Lake Roosevelt today include strandlines, as well as rhythmites and terraces deposited within the much-deeper Glacial Lake Columbia. The size and extent of Lake Columbia varied due to the whims of advancing and retreating glaciers and heights of the spillover channels into the Channeled Scabland that controlled the lake level and the paths of escaping outburst floods (Plate 11). Numerous flood-faceted slopes line the valley margins of the Columbia from its confluence with the Spokane River. Floodwaters careened off the outside bends, severely eroding and oversteepening the valley slopes.

Perhaps the best way to view these Ice Age flood and glacial features is via boat from Lake Roosevelt. This is especially true for witnessing flood rhythmites, which are very well exposed along the shore of the Sanpoil arm and elsewhere along Lake Roosevelt (see Figures 2-36 and 3-116). In contrast to other areas of eastern Washington, relatively few established hiking trails exist along Lake Roosevelt. This is in part due to the extreme fluctuations in man-controlled lake levels that occur throughout the year within the reservoir. The combination of changing lake levels and steep slopes produce unstable slopes, leading to extensive landsliding along the lakeshore. The two trails included in this chapter, Fort Spokane and Hawk Bay, are both located near the confluence of the Columbia and Spokane rivers (Figure 4-109). The best times to visit these trails, especially Hawk Bay, is during spring drawdown in April and May when lake levels are lower and the shoreline is more accessible. Low reservoir levels also provide an excellent opportunity to observe modern standlines – a great analog for those that formed during the Ice Age.

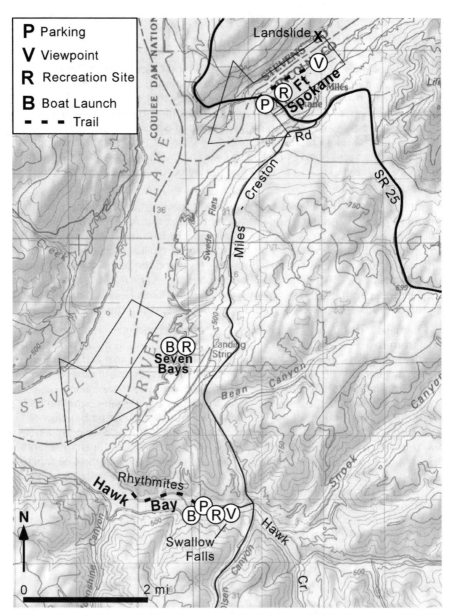

Figure 4-109. Map in the vicinity of the Fort Spokane and Hawk Bay trails. Outburst megafloods invaded this area from the upper right (block arrows). Because of its marginal position with respect to outburst floods, water flow backflooded (reversed) into Hawk Bay.

Trail LL. Fort Spokane

Flood Feature Nos. 63, 64

Follow along the top of some tall Glacial Lake Columbia terraces that line the Spokane River valley to view other ancient-lake features and the recent Jackson Springs landslide.

Geologic Highlights: A well-developed trail follows a high terrace along the south rim of Lake Roosevelt just above the confluence between the Spokane and Columbia rivers. Much of the trail parallels the upper edge of landslide scarps with steep drop-offs immediately below. Enjoy excellent views of the opposite bank, the surrounding bedrock hills and bluffs, and the largest landslide to occur in the upper Columbia River drainage in modern times.

Length: 1.5 miles one-way

Elevation (Relief) Along Trail: 1,320 to 1,440 feet (120 feet)

Difficulty: Easy

Best Mode of Travel: Hike or boat

Management/Ownership: National Park Service/U.S. Bureau of Reclamation

USGS 1:24,000 Scale Map: Lincoln, WA

Warnings: Stay clear of steep, unstable cliffs; a few fallen trees lie across the trail, which is more obscured at far end and requires a short climb and some bushwhacking to access the final viewpoint

Directions: From U.S. Highway 2 at Davenport, proceed north on State Route 25 for 22.8 miles to historic Fort Spokane. Park in the Fort Spokane picnic area just east of bridge that spans the Spokane River.

Trail Log

0.0   From the park picnic area, walk beneath the tall highway bridge and continue northeast through the park campground along the Spokane Arm of Lake Roosevelt. Continue on trail past the northeast end of campground.

0.5   Across the river, on the Spokane Indian Reservation, are prominent outcrops of 50 million-year-old granite near river level with layers of flat-lying Columbia River basalt high above. Sediments deposited in Glacial Lake Columbia partially bury the granite beneath a prominent sediment terrace. Another lower terrace lies below the trail on the Fort Spokane side. Notice the horizontal rows of brush growing in the slope below the terrace across the river (Figure 4-110). These slopes expose a profile of the sediment layers that underlie the terrace. The rows in the slope mark the boundaries between individual rhythmites where fine-grained, glacial-lake sediments are interrupted by coarser flood deposits. Greener and more lush vegetation grows in the finer sediments once laid down in Glacial Lake Columbia; the intervening coarse flood sediments, on the other hand, dry out more quickly and thus don't support as much plant growth.

Figure 4-110. View looking north across the Spokane River arm of Lake Roosevelt towards an ancient, Glacial Lake Columbia, flat-topped terrace. Subtle color and vegetation changes in the slope below the terrace mark the boundaries between Ice-Age-flood rhythmites and inter-flood lake deposition within Glacial Lake Columbia. Sandy flood sediments allow percolating rain and snowmelt to move more rapidly through them. Fine-grained Lake Columbia sediments impede the downward movement of the water, forcing the moisture to move laterally to the exposed face of the terrace. Greener and more abundant vegetation mark these seep lines. On the right is west end of the massive Jackson Springs Landslide, which sent debris completely across the river, temporarily blocking the Spokane Arm of Lake Roosevelt on March 26, 1969. Exceptionally low reservoir levels in conjunction with expansion at Grand Coulee Dam and a large spring snowmelt contributed to the massive slide. Remnants of the debris that initially stretched completely across the Spokane River can still be seen today during low water conditions. Views of the huge Jackson Springs Landslide improve farther along the trail.

1.0   Trail gradually disappears and bushwhacking is required to climb the last 80 feet up to a slightly higher terrace – the same height (and age) as the terrace across the river (Figure 4-110).

1.5   A small meadow at the top (N47.9161, W118.2928) provides an excellent view of the Jackson Springs Landslide across the river. Retrace route to trailhead at picnic area.

Trail MM. Hawk Bay Rhythmites   Flood Feature Nos. 63, 64

View some of the best exposures anywhere of multiple Ice Age flood rhythmites, each separated by dozens of annual varves laid down in quiescent Glacial Lake Columbia that persisted between outburst floods.

Length: 3.8 miles round-trip

Elevation along trail: 1,290 to 1,300 feet, depending on reservoir level

Difficulty: Easy

Best Mode of Travel: Hike or watercraft

Management/Ownership: National Park Service, U.S. Bureau of Reclamation

USGS 1:24.000 scale map: Olsen Canyon, WA

Warnings: Little shade, beaches disappear when reservoir is full (summer) making travel difficult. Spring and early summer are best times for walking the shoreline; unstable footing may exist across the steep and slumped slopes above the shoreline.

Directions: From U.S. Highway 2 at Davenport proceed north on State Route 25 for 22 miles, turn left (south) on Miles-Creston Road (Figure 4-109). Continue about seven miles before turning right (west) onto Hawk Creek Road. Park one mile farther at road's ends in boat-launch parking area just beyond the Hawk Creek Campground.

Figure 4-111. Hawk Bay. Multiple, Missoula-flood rhythmites are exposed in tall landslide scarps along the Hawk Bay shoreline. In between the rhythmites are packages of lake varves, signifying a deep Glacial Lake Columbia continued to occupy this valley for dozens of years in between Missoula flood outbursts. Looking north.

Trail Log

0.0   Park at boat launch (N47.8157, W118.3301). Follow abandoned road that leads west beyond restroom.

0.2   Hawk Creek flows through a water gap cut through the basalt. This is a superimposed canyon, one that cut through overlying Ice Age sediments and has continued to erode into the hard, buried basalt below since the last Ice Age floods.

0.6   Double-track trail descends to shoreline of Hawk Creek arm of Lake Roosevelt. Walk shoreline to the west. Note numerous large landslide scarps (Figure 4-111) that expose rhythmites composed of fine-textured, varved, Glacial Lake Columbia deposits punctuated by sandy outburst-flood rhythmites (Figures 4-112 and 4-113). Recent wave action along the shoreline often exposes interesting details of the sediment record. Look for varves – thin annual deposits of winter and summer layers of fine sediment deposited into Glacial Lake Columbia (see Figure 2-30). Each couplet represents a single year of cyclic lake sedimentation; thus, a sediment package of 50 varves indicates at least 50 years passed between outburst floods. Flood currents produced ripple lamination, graded beds, rip-up clasts and contorted bedding (e.g., see Figure 2-31) visible within rhythmites. As many as 27 separate flood-bed rhythmites from as many outbursts of Glacial Lake Missoula are interpreted in these bluffs.

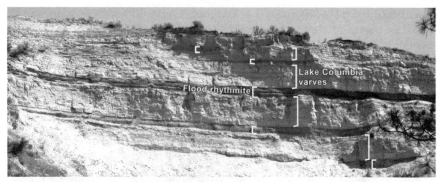

Figure 4-112. Light-toned, varved, Glacial Lake Columbia sediments (bracket open to left) alternate with darker-toned flood rhythmites (bracket open to right). A record of five separate Missoula floods, each separated by up to several dozen years is represented in this recent landslide escarpment. Looking northeast.

Cross bedding in the sandy flood deposits show flood currents moved up Hawk Bay (Figure 4-113), opposite the normal flow of water down Hawk Creek today. The reversed current direction is consistent with the surge of floodwater invading Glacial Lake Columbia. Oftentimes the floods were so powerful they would erode most, or all, the sediments laid down previously. In Hawk Bay, however, the rhythmite sequence is well-preserved since it lies in a more protected area that did not receive the full brunt of powerful flood currents from Lake Missoula outbursts (Figure 4-109). Plus Glacial Lake Columbia here was up to 1,100 feet deep, which would have reduced and buffered the erosion associated with Missoula flooding. The dampened Missoula flood currents continued up Hawk Creek before spilling south into the Telford-Crab Creek scabland.

Figure 4-113. Close up of Glacial Lake Columbia, Ice Age flood rhythmites exposed along the north side of Hawk Bay. Four separate flood rhythmites, each capped by a sequence of Lake Columbia varves are represented here. Dark sand at the base of each rhythmite was laid down in a matter of minutes or hours as a Missoula flood invaded Glacial Lake Columbia. Several dozen years of "normal" lake deposition (varved intervals) separate each flood event. Cross-bedded sand at the base of a rhythmite (lower right) indicates the flow of water surged upvalley during megaflood events.

The lake-varve sequence at the top of most rhythmites indicates many dozens of years of "normal" lake deposition occurred between each short-lived flood pulse. Altogether, more than two dozen rhythmites are exposed here in Hawk Bay. Thus the rhythmites record the passing of as many Ice Age floods, separated by decades of quiescent-lake deposition.

1.9   Beach ends at impassable rocky bluff (N47.8196, W118.3603). Retrace path to origin.

After returning to the trailhead parking lot a quick side trip is recommended to Swallow Falls (Figure 4-114). A short trail from nearby Hawk Creek Campground leads to this delightful waterfall. The falls are the result of the creek cutting through a cover of Ice Age sediments while maintaining its course into underlying basalt bedrock as it eroded downward – an example of what geologists call a superposed stream.

Figure 4-114. Swallow Falls (N47.8141, W118.3239) at the Hawk Creek Campground formed in post-glacial times when Hawk Creek eroded through unconsolidated, Ice Age sediments and incised a new channel into basalt bedrock. The old, lower channel today lies plugged with Ice Age sediment, located a few hundred yards to the left of the waterfall. Looking southeast.

Looking south from State Route 17 from the Great Blade, Lower Grand Coulee

5

Road Tours

Interpretive road tours that loop through the Channeled Scabland are custom designed to cover the greatest variety and most number of interesting flood features within the Channeled Scabland and outburst area for the Missoula floods. The five recommended routes presented in this chapter (Figure 5-1) range from about 100 miles to 152 miles and include some side spurs that lead to areas of special significance.

The five tours and starting points (in parentheses) are:

1. Spokane-Pend Oreille (Liberty Lake)
2. Cheney-Palouse Tract (Spokane)
3. Telford-Crab Creek Tract Creek (Davenport)
4. Grand Coulee (Grand Coulee)
5. Moses Coulee-Waterville Plateau (Wenatchee)

Each tour begins in a city or town with motels and restaurants to accommodate travelers wishing to explore the local flood features. To take advantage of the mileages provided in the road logs below, travelers should start in the city or town indicated with "S" in Figure 5-1. All starting points are within the state of Washington. Readers who want to create their own auto-tour routes can do so by linking any of the roads and features herein. See chapters 2 and 3 for more detail on the types and descriptions of individual features.

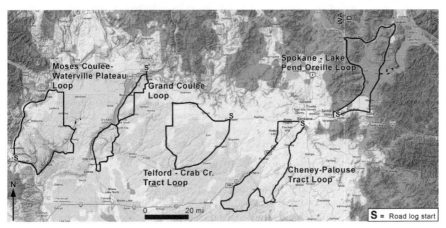

Figure 5-1. Google map showing locations of five road tours featured in this book.

Road Tour 1: Spokane-Pend Oreille Loop

*Travel to the source of the colossal Missoula floods, and explore the region imme-
diately below the breakout zone, above which an ice dam, thousands of feet tall,
once towered and repeatedly failed. Outbursts from Glacial Lake Missoula episodically unleashed a wall of water more than 1,000 feet deep. This 152-mile tour
follows roads along the streamless Rathdrum Prairie to alluring Lake Pend Oreille
before heading to Newport via an alternate escape route for the Missoula floods.
Most of this tour is located within the state of Idaho.*

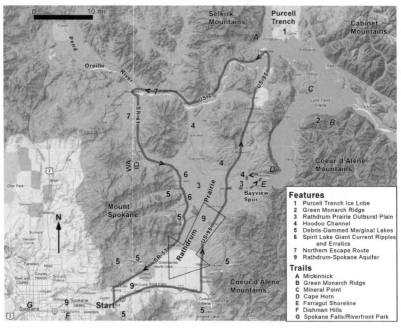

Figure 5-2 Google map with road tour (highlighted) along the Spokane-Pend Oreille Loop. Block arrow shows
the primary flood-flow direction. Features along route are described in chapter 3; nearby non-motorized trails
are presented in chapter 4.

Road Log

0.0   Tour begins at Liberty Lake along Interstate 90 (Exit 296). An old photograph of Greenacres (Figure 5-3), located just west of here, shows the flat,
featureless plain of the Spokane Valley. The Spokane Valley and its extension to
the north (Rathdrum Prairie) represent a sediment plain built up by repeated
Missoula outburst floods. Liberty Lake is one of nine lakes that formed along
the margins of the Rathdrum Prairie/Spokane Valley outburst plain (Plate 9).
Head east on I-90 through the Spokane Valley, moving against the current of
the once-800-foot-deep floodwaters from Glacial Lake Missoula. The lakes are
blocked by aprons of flood debris and bars that formed at the mouths of each
incoming tributary along the valley (see Figure 3-9, Plates 7 to 9). This buildup
of flood debris blocked the stream drainages to form the lakes.

3.8   Cross the state line into Idaho.

Figure 5-3. The expansive Spokane Valley at Greenacres, Washington, in 1910. The broad, level surface is due to the buildup of hundreds of feet of Missoula flood deposits across the valley bottom. UNIVERSITY OF WASHINGTON LIBRARIES, SPECIAL COLLECTIONS, NEGATIVE NUMBER UW6323. PHOTO BY W.E. WING

8.0   Near Post Falls, Idaho, the Spokane Valley widens, merging with the flat, featureless Rathdrum Prairie (Plate 9) entering from the northeast. The mountains that line the prairie are composed of rocks much older and different from the layered volcanic lava flows of Columbia River basalt, which make up most of the scablands to the west. These hard, old granitic and metamorphic rocks form irregular rock masses, which when attacked by the Missoula floods eroded into random rounded hills, unlike the stacked, eroded basalt flows of the Channeled Scabland. The basalts eroded into more characteristic and recognizable rock benches, mesas, buttes and basins.

12.2   Rest area along I-90.

15.5   At Coeur d'Alene, Idaho, turn north onto U.S. Highway 95 to follow the east side of the Rathdrum Prairie.

20   Hayden Lake, one of many flood-debris dammed lakes (No. 5) that lie along the margin of Rathdrum Prairie, is located just east of here. The buildup of flood deposits along Rathdrum Prairie blocked a west-flowing tributary here, causing Hayden Lake to form behind the sediment-debris dam (Plate 9). Continue north on U.S. Highway 95.

23   Notice large, rounded, light-colored boulders up to several feet in diameter used as barricades and landscaping in this area. These are boulders of mostly granite and Belt rocks that tumbled and rolled along the bottom of the Missoula flood outbursts.

28   Note how the flat Rathdrum Prairie butts up against the steep valley walls of the Coeur d'Alene Mountains just east of here. Prior to the floods this valley was occupied by a river that cut a deep valley and the surrounding mountains steadily sloped toward the valley center (see bedrock profile in Figure 3-9, right). Since then, hundreds of feet of outburst-flood deposits have backfilled and raised the level of the valley to a generally flat, featureless plain. Today, a huge and extensive underground "lake" – the Rathdrum-Spokane Aquifer (No. 9) – lies

within the coarse flood deposits not far below ground surface.

30.6   At Silverwood Theme Park the valley opens up to provide a view toward the head of the Rathdrum Prairie Outburst Plain (No. 3) along with Cape Horn located at the mouth of Lake Pend Oreille (Plate 5). In the foothills on the right is a remnant of the farthest north extent of Columbia River basalt, marking the extreme northeastern margin of the Columbia Plateau.

33.8   A man-made stockpile of huge, rounded boulders once carried by the floodwaters is visible on the right.

34.3   At Athol begin the Bayview Spur route (Figure 5-4).

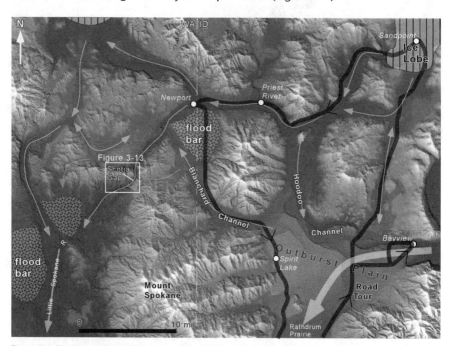

Figure 5-4. Northern spillways (light arrows) for the Missoula floods along the Spokane-Pend Oreille road tour route. During many Missoula floods the northern routes were blocked with glacial ice, which forced most of the outburst-floodwater to the south via Rathdrum Prairie (see Figure 3-11).

Bayview Spur

This 16.5-mile round-trip spur crosses the head of the Rathdrum Prairie Outburst Plain and skirts Farragut State Park before arriving at the southern tip of Lake Pend Oreille at Bayview. Tour continues along the Hoodoo Channel before returning to U.S. Highway 95.

34.3   At Athol turn right (east) onto Idaho State Highway 54.

34.9   Interpretive sign for Pen d'Oreille City that once lay a few miles east of here at the extreme southern tip of Lake Pend Oreille. Beyond the sign is a good view out across table-flat Rathdrum Prairie Outburst Plain (No. 3) to the south and east.

37.5   View of Bernard Peak with its oversteepened, glacially beveled slope (Plate 5, see Figure 4-10) that descends sharply into hidden Lake Pend Oreille below. Some of the beveling may also be due to escaping Missoula floodwaters.

38.4   Sign for entrance into Farragut State Park. The Visitor Center with interpretive exhibits, including one on the Missoula floods, and a gift shop, is 0.3 mile farther. Also available here are use permits and registration for camping. Continue north across the Rathdrum Prairie Outburst Plain on State Route 54 (Plate 6).

39.0   Here at the edge of the Rathdrum Prairie Outburst Plain is the turn off onto South Road, which runs through the heart of Farragut State Park (fees apply). Turn here if interested in hiking the Farragut Shoreline Trail (chapter 4, Trail E) or driving to Jökulhlaup Point, a peninsula of land that separates Scenic and Idlewilde bays at the mouth of Lake Pend Oreille (Plate 5; see also Figure 4-10). Otherwise this tour bypasses the state park going north on Highway 54 toward Bayview, Idaho.

41.2   Interpretive sign for "Bayview Limekilns," where lime was produced from 1904 to 1932 from 550 million-year-old limestone (see quarry location in Figure 5-5, Plate 5). Just beyond this sign, as we exit the state park, the road descends off the steep embankment at the head of the Rathdrum Prairie Outburst Plain.

41.9   End of Highway 54 in Bayview. Continue north on Main Avenue through the charming village of Bayview and past Scenic Bay, one of two prominent embayments at the south end of Lake Pend Oreille.

Figure 5-5. Scenic Bay of Lake Pend Oreille at Bayview, Idaho, looking north. An old limestone quarry (source material for limekilns) is exposed in roadcut partway up Cape Horn Peak.

42.3   Road bends west onto Perimeter Road at far end of Bayview; 0.2 mile farther, at the Bayview Post Office, is the turnoff to the Cape Horn Trail (chapter 4, Trail D) at Cherokee Road.

43.0   This straight section of Perimeter Road follows the flat-bottomed Hoodoo Channel (No. 4) that once contained a small outburst flood or perhaps the last melting of the glacier that occupied Lake Pend Oreille. Nearby, but not visible from the road, are a series of giant kettle holes (see Figure 3-7) that formed as icebergs melted beneath a cover of flood sediment.

44.7   Continue along Perimeter Road as it bends sharply to the south (left). Rise out of the Hoodoo Channel and back up onto the elevated Rathdrum Prairie Outburst Plain (No. 3).

47.1   Rejoin Highway 54. Turn right toward Athol.

51.1   At U.S. Highway 95 junction, turn right (north) towards Sandpoint. End of Spur.

53.8   At intersection with Homestead Road are dozens of huge flood-rounded boulders that lie just west of the intersection (Figure 5-6). Continue north on Highway 95 across the Hoodoo Channel before the road bends northeast (see Figure 3-7).

Figure 5-6. Enormous, rounded, bedload boulders from Rathdrum Prairie Outburst Plain above the Hoodoo Channel. These giant boulders, composed of mostly granite but with some metasedimentary Belt rocks, were tumbled and rolled along the base of the turbulent outburst flood that escaped Glacial Lake Missoula. These boulders were gathered here after excavation of an adjacent railroad cut. Looking northwest.

57.5   During the Ice Age, glacial ice extended at least this far south at Careywood.

64.0   Cocolalla Lake is dammed by a glacial moraine that piled up in front of an ice lobe that once occupied this valley. Because this valley contained glacial ice during most Missoula floods, it was bypassed and unaffected directly by the floods. Above and to the right (east) some glacial ice from the Lake Pend Oreille sublobe squeezed west through low saddles in the ridge on either side of Blacktail Mountain.

70.7   Located here at Sagle is the turnoff to the Mineral Point Trail (chapter 4, Trail C), which lies on a large, glaciated peninsula protruding out into upper Lake Pend Oreille. Most of the surface is covered with glacial till, indicating this area was still covered by the Purcell Trench Lobe, even during the last, smaller Missoula floods.

73.7   Beginning of the two-mile Long Bridge over Lake Pend Oreille.

76.7   In Sandpoint take U.S. Highway 2 west toward Priest River. Notice that the boulders in this area are generally angular, unlike the mostly rounded boulders we saw previously in Rathdrum Prairie. That's because Sandpoint lay beneath thousands of feet of glacial ice from the Purcell Trench Lobe that transported lots of ice-encased, angular boulders but relatively few rounded ones. For the most part, because of blockage by the Purcell Trench Lobe, flood-waters from Glacial Lake Missoula didn't pass through Sandpoint; therefore, no mechanism for rounding the boulders existed here.

80.0   Several nice roadcuts exposing Eocene granitic basement rocks (about 40 million years old) of the Selkirk Mountains in Dover.

83.0   Road parallels the valley, which follows the drowned Pend Oreille River behind Albeni Falls Dam.

90.5   Lots of excellent, tall roadcuts exposing metamorphic Belt rocks over the next several miles.

94.0   Hoodoo Valley joins the Pend Oreille River valley from the south (Figure 5-4). Late outburst flood(s) and glacial meltwater from Lake Pend Oreille sublobe followed the Hoodoo Channel (No. 4) to this ice-free area along the Pend Oreille River.

98.4   Town of Priest River, Idaho. This valley, occupied by the Pend Oreille River (Figure 5-7), was a northern escape route for some of the Missoula floods, when glacial ice did not fully advance into this area (see Figure 3-11, right).

Figure 5-7. View looking west down northern route for Missoula floods that flowed through the Pend Oreille River Valley past present-day Priest River, Idaho, and Newport, Washington.

102.9   The Albeni Falls Dam was constructed primarily for flood control in 1955 and to stabilize the level of Lake Pend Oreille (summer pool elevation 2,062 feet).

105.3   Temporarily reenter Washington state at east end of Newport before turning left (south) onto Idaho State Highway 41. Cross back into Idaho after 0.4 mile.

- -

110.0   After crossing a pendant flood bar, Highway 41 descends into the Blanchard Channel (Figure 5-4). Some of the Missoula floodwaters escaped north through the Newport area via the Blanchard Channel when the ice sheet was not fully advanced (see Figure 3-11, right).

124.1   Highway 41 rises up onto an older, higher flood bar covered with giant current ripples (see Figure 3-10, top) just northeast of the town of Spirit Lake (Figure 5-4, Plate 9).

127.9   Giant, ice-rafted erratic (see Figure 3-10, bottom) lies atop flood bar covered with more giant current ripples. Watch for other giant erratics scattered along roadway over the next mile.

128.8   Round Mountain (more than 3,200 feet in elevation) on the left (east) was a lonely, isolated island on Rathdrum Prairie that poked out above even the largest of the Missoula floods (Figure 3-6, Plates 7 and 9). Just beyond, along the downstream (south) side of Round Mountain, sediment accumulated onto one of the best examples of a pendant flood bar seen anywhere.

131.7   Turnoff to Twin Lakes – a pair of flood debris-dammed lakes along a western tributary into Rathdrum Prairie (Plate 7). On the left side of the road are rounded gravels, up to a several feet in diameter, exposed in a flood bar. Continue south on Highway 41.

136.3   At the town of Rathdrum turn southwest onto Highway 53 across the broad, flat and featureless Rathdrum Prairie.

142   View opens up to south. Highest point is Mica Peak (5,177 feet elevation), which was well above the maximum flood level. Missoula floodwaters spilled south out the Spokane Valley through a low saddle near Mica, on the west side of Mica Peak (see Figure 3-14) as well as through the Coeur d'Alene Lake Valley to the east.

143.9   Turnoff to Hauser Lake, another flood-debris-dammed lake that formed where Hauser Creek enters the Spokane Valley (Plate 9). At 1.4 miles farther is an interpretive sign for the Purcell Trench and its lobe of glacial ice (Figure 5-8).

Figure 5-8. Interpretive sign along the broad, featureless plain of Rathdrum Prairie. Looking east with Coeur d'Alene Mountains in background.

145.8 At the state line, Idaho State Highway 53 becomes Washington State Route 290. Continue southwest on SR 290.

147.2 Turnoff to Newman Lake, yet another flood-debris dammed lake (Plate 9). More large, flood-rounded boulders are located here at Newman Lake Community – arranged into neat rows by fastidious humans.

149.6 Turn left (south) onto Harvard Road. After 1.7 miles cross the Spokane River.

152.0 Intersection with Liberty Lake exit (No. 296) of Interstate 90. End of road tour.

Road Tour 2: Cheney-Palouse Loop

This 152-mile, round-trip tour transitions from lush wetlands and forests to the open prairie. Also lying in stark contrast are the barren basalt scablands juxtaposed with smoothed and streamlined, wheat-covered hills of windblown Palouse loess.

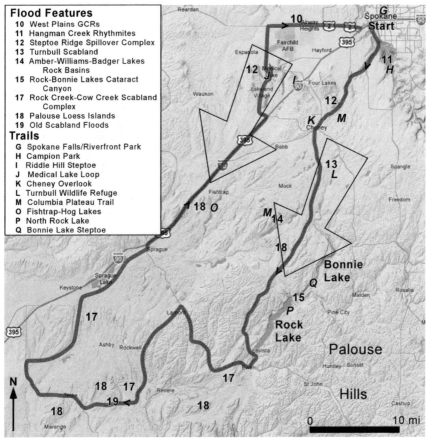

Flood Features
10 West Plains GCRs
11 Hangman Creek Rhythmites
12 Steptoe Ridge Spillover Complex
13 Turnbull Scabland
14 Amber-Williams-Badger Lakes Rock Basins
15 Rock-Bonnie Lakes Cataract Canyon
17 Rock Creek-Cow Creek Scabland Complex
18 Palouse Loess Islands
19 Old Scabland Floods

Trails
G Spokane Falls/Riverfront Park
H Campion Park
I Riddle Hill Steptoe
J Medical Lake Loop
K Cheney Overlook
L Turnbull Wildlife Refuge
M Columbia Plateau Trail
O Fishtrap-Hog Lakes
P North Rock Lake
Q Bonnie Lake Steptoe

Figure 5-9. Google map with road tour (highlighted) along the Cheney-Palouse Loop. Large block arrows indicate flood-flow direction. Features along route are described in chapter 3; nearby non-motorized trails are presented in chapter 4.

Road Log

0.0   From Spokane take Exit 279 off Interstate 90 and proceed south on U.S. Highway 195. Drive along Hangman (Latah) Creek, a backflooded valley of the Missoula floods. Earlier in the last glacial cycle, between Missoula floods, this valley lay beneath hundreds of feet of backwater from Glacial Lake Columbia (Plate 3). The last Missoula floods ran over dry ground here after the level of Lake Columbia dropped suddenly in response to a spillover breach at the head of Grand Coulee (No. 29).

2.0   Turn right onto Cheney-Spokane Road.

3.8   Rise onto hanging channel (Marshall Creek) used by floods that escaped out of the Hangman Creek valley and spilled over into the head of the Cheney-Palouse scabland.

7.2   Borrow pit on the right (closed to the public) exposes gravelly, crescent bar deposits from floods spilling out of Hangman Creek up onto the Cheney-Palouse Scabland Tract. See Figure 5-10 for evidence of multiple floods revealed in these sediments.

Figure 5-10. Four rhythmites are exposed in borrow pit several miles northeast of Cheney. Each rhythmite likely represents a separate Missoula flood event.

8.1   Another borrow pit of mostly plane-bedded deposits of flood sand. An interbedded layer of 15,400-year-old volcanic ash from Mount St. Helens (set "S") was formerly exposed in this sand pit. Looking up the valley ahead is a view of the dome-shaped Prosser Hill Steptoe, composed of Precambrian Belt rocks, which rises above the level of Columbia River basalt (see Figures 3-21 and 3-22).

9.1   Rise onto the flat, upper surface of 15 million-year-old Columbia River basalt (Priest Rapids Member).

10.6   Fish Lake lies adjacent to Prosser Hill, the easternmost of the spillovers along Steptoe Ridge (No. 12), where floods locally eroded through a thin cap of basalt into the underlying, weathered, more easily eroded Belt rocks. The Columbia Plateau trailhead (chapter 4, Trail M) is located at the north end of Fish Lake.

12.3   Regain the mostly level upper surface of the basalt plateau. To the north the view opens up onto surrounding steptoe hills (Prosser, Needham and Wrights) that rise above the younger basalt surface (Figure 5-11).

Figure 5-11. Steptoe Ridge (No. 12) near Cheney is blanketed with a thin cover of windblown, fertile Palouse loess. View looking northwest.

13.5   Enter Cheney, turn left (south) onto State Route 904.

14.8   At the west end of Cheney is the local office/ranger station for the Columbia Plateau Trail, operated by the Washington State Parks.

15.0   Turn left onto Cheney-Plaza Road and head south into tree-covered scabland. The Turnbull National Wildlife Refuge is 0.9 mile ahead.

16.4   Overpass crosses the Columbia Plateau Trail. No parking is allowed here. Over the next 10 miles the road passes through characteristic low-relief, butte-and-basin topography of the Turnbull Scabland (No. 13) and Cheney-Palouse Tract. Prior to the Ice Age floods this area was covered with perhaps a hundred feet of windblown Palouse loess, since mostly stripped off down to the bare basalt bedrock by repeated Ice Age floods.

19.2   Turnoff is located here to the Turnbull National Wildlife Refuge (Figure 5-12). The 5.5-mile-long Pine Creek Auto Tour Road, along with a number of hiking trails (chapter 4, Trail L) through wetlands and scablands, are located within the refuge, about one mile east of here. McDowell Lake, an elongated, former flood-scour channel, lies along the right (west) side of the road. Continue south on Cheney-Plaza Road. Southern boundary of Turnbull Refuge is 2.4 miles ahead.

Figure 5-12. Entrance to the Turnbull National Wildlife Refuge along Cheney-Plaza Road.

24.8   Cheney-Plaza Road bends 90 degrees to the left toward Chapman Lake. Continue straight (south) on Rock Lake Road.

26.3   Turnoff to Williams and Badger lakes (No. 14), located a couple of miles to the west. To stay en route with this road log, continue south on Rock Lake Road. One can take a detour here to access the Amber Lake Trailhead of the Columbia Plateau Trail (chapter 4, Trail M) that can be reached by following the Williams Lake Road to Mullinix Road, north to Pine Springs, and west to the trailhead at the parking area at Amber Lake (see Figure 4-29).

26.7   The pine forest disappears into open prairie; scabland channels here surround a number of Palouse Loess Islands (No. 18).

28.0   Pass down the middle of a flood channel across flood-dissected basalt flanked by a number of treeless, smoothed and streamlined Palouse hills, similar to Plate 14.

32.1   Continue straight at intersection with Belsby Road. Hole-in-the-Ground Canyon (Plate 13) and access to trails for Bonnie Lake Steptoe (Trail Q) and North Rock Lake (Trail P) are located several miles to the left (southeast) along Belsby Road. Continue southwest on Rock Lake Road. Cross over a series of giant, northwest-southeast trending, flood-gouged tectonic fractures (see Figures 1-7 and 3-29).

32.7   Rise out of basalt-floored flood channel onto a large Palouse island west of Rock Lake (see aerial image in Figure 3-32). For the next seven miles the road follows a flat-bottomed, scarped spillover channel eroded across this Palouse upland. Unlike other, lower-elevation, channels the floods were not powerful enough here to erode through the loess cover into the basalt bedrock below.

39.9   Reenter the main scabland channel that comes in from the left (northeast) via Rock Lake. More isolated, scarped and streamlined Palouse hills lie within this channel. Off to the southeast is an occasional view of Steptoe Butte (see Figure 4-24) – about 20 miles away. Crazily eroded rock buttes, mesas, benches and basins are abundant on approach to Rock Lake.

42.6   Arrive at south end of Rock Lake within Rock Creek Coulee. A primitive Washington Department of Fish and Wildlife recreation site, including a boat launch, is located here (Washington Discover Pass required). At its north end Rock Lake (Plate 13) is the deepest (400 feet) of the scabland lakes.

44.7   Rock Lake Road ends at Ewan. Turn right (west) onto State Route 23.

45.9   Cross Rock Creek, heavily scarred with scabland buttes, basins, mesas and rock benches. Over the next few miles are wonderful views to the south of streamlined and scarped Palouse hills (Plate 14) accompanied by a chaotic maze of scabland buttes, basins and channels.

49.2   Turn north rising·back up onto the huge island of Palouse loess crossed earlier, immediately west of Rock Lake. This seven-mile-wide Palouse upland divides the Rock Creek from Cow Creek scabland complexes (see Figure 3-32). The upper parts of the island remained dry even during the largest outburst floods.

53.4   Excellent, 20 to 30 feet high roadcut (N47.1558. W117.8598) exposing a thick sequence of windblown Palouse loess. Warning: Blind curve with no safe place to pull over here, so don't attempt to stop.

Within the loess sequence are multiple layers of white caliche; these represent buried soil horizons (paleosols) that formed as this Palouse upland grew very slowly over time. The elevation here (2,080 feet) was slightly higher than most of the Ice Age floods. So while floods were ravaging the landscapes all around this Palouse island, the area around this roadcut was mostly dry, and thus reveals a history dominated by wind deposition punctuated with periods of soil development.

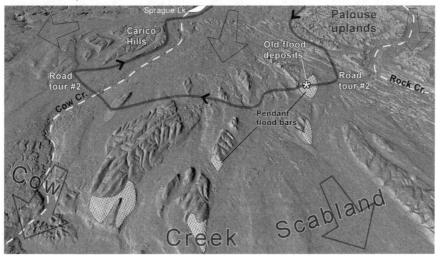

Figure 5-13. Oblique, shaded-relief image in the vicinity of the 10-mile-wide Cow Creek scabland complex along a portion of the Cheney-Palouse Road Tour. Note pendant flood bars where sand and gravel deposits accumulated at downstream ends of streamlined Palouse hills. Looking northeast. Block arrows point in the direction of flood flow. Bottom of image spans about 12 miles.

57.7   Turn left (west) onto Hardy Road. Here, after descending out of the Palouse uplands enter into the Cow Creek scablands. After 0.5 mile turn left (southwest) onto Lamont Road. Continue southwest past the grain elevators of Lamont. Follow the distinct, eastern escarpment of the eroded Palouse island along the Cow Creek scabland channel, studded with thousands of Mima mounds atop the Priest Rapids Member of Columbia River basalt.

60.4   Paved road turns to a well-maintained, straight and flat gravel road that follows a rock bench along the flood-eroded eastern margin of the Cow Creek scabland complex. The opposite side of the tract is barely visible almost 10 miles to the west (Figure 5-13; see also Figure 3-32).

62.3   Where primitive McFadden Road joins from the right Lamont Road becomes McCall Road. Continue southwest on McCall Road. Tour route approaches the steep, leading prows of several streamlined Palouse hills ahead (Figure 5-13). The prows point into the direction of ancient Ice Age flood flows. The distinct, oversteepened, eastern escarpment of the Cow Creek scabland tract is especially apparent over the next several miles.

68.1   Intersection with Gering Road. Continue straight (south) along McCall Road into the heart of the Cow Creek scabland complex of eroded flood channels and streamlined Palouse hills (Figure 5-13; see also Figure 3-32). Cross an especially well-developed scabland channel 0.7 mile beyond – buttes, mesas, basins and rock benches galore.

69.3   Interesting wavy to radiating basalt columns of the Roza Member basalt exposed in walls of flood-scoured channel. The basalt columns are the result of cooling and contracting of the once-liquid lava flow (see Figure 1-2) that flooded this area about 15 million years ago.

70.4   McCall Road bends sharply to the right (west) to become Harder Road. Over the next 15 miles, you will be driving perpendicular to the ancient flood-flow direction; therefore, the route passes over a series of low-relief flood channels, eroded into Roza Member basalt, separated by taller, streamlined and scarped Palouse islands and pendant bars (Figure 5-13).

71.1   Return of paved road. In another 0.8 mile rise out of flood channel onto a large, streamlined Palouse hill.

73.5   Roadcut exposure of old flood deposits (Figure 5-14). These older flood deposits accumulated onto a pendant flood bar that lies at the downstream end of a streamlined Palouse hill (Figure 5-13). The exposure reveals some extremely old flood gravels capped by a thick layer of white caliche (i.e., paleosol). The caliche layer here has produced an age date of more than 350,000 years. The magnetic polarity of a fine-soil sample collected between the caliche and the flood gravels is reversed. The last time the Earth experienced a reversal in its magnetic field was 780,000 years ago. Thus, the flood gravels at the base of the sequence must be more than 780,000 years old. These flood gravels apparently were laid down during an extremely old Ice Age flood that occurred during a previous glacial cycle that occurred in the early Pleistocene (see Figure 1-8). Continue west on Harder Road.

Caliche

Megaflood gravels

Figure 5-14. Old flood deposits exposed in pendant flood bar shown in Figure 5-13. Old flood gravels underlie a thick caliche paleosol along Harder Road, within the Cheney-Palouse scabland. N47.0576, W118.0637; elevation 1,730 feet.

75.1   More views of streamlined and scarped Palouse hills all around with steep prows pointing into the direction of the ancient flood flows. Figure 5-15 is an aerial view of the three Palouse islands immediately visible to the right (north).

78.5   At the railroad crossing continue straight west. Road name changes from Harder Road to Urquhart Road and is still surrounded by more stream-lined and scarped Palouse hills.

81.9   Road bends at intersection with Durry Road. Continue right (north-west) on Urquhart Road.

83.2   After driving many miles through rugged, stripped-off scabland, cross Cow Creek just downstream of Finnel Lake (elevation 1,670 feet). Low-relief scabland in the Roza Member basalt spreads out as far as the eye can see.

84.5   Road bends to the right (north) becoming Hills Road.

86.0   At stop sign turn right (east) onto Wellsandt Road. Good view to the east across the Cow Creek drainage to the streamlined Palouse hills on the opposite side of the 10-mile-wide scabland complex viewed earlier.

88.0   Drive along the flood-scarped base of the Carico Hills, a group of low Palouse hills that flank the west side of the Cow Creek scabland complex (Figure 5-13).

89.1   Bear right onto the unpaved portion of Wellsandt Road along the edge of the Palouse upland. To the right is a turnoff to flood-scoured Cow Lake Reservoir, 1.3 miles down this side road. Continue straight on Wellsandt Road.

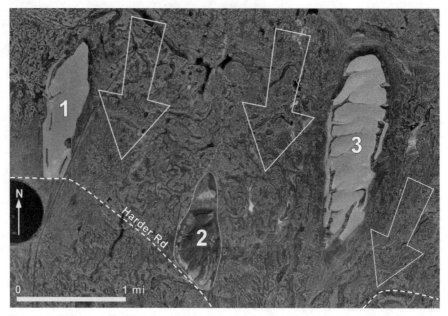

Figure 5-15. Three streamlined Palouse islands along tour route north of Harder Road. In between is the barren, flood-stripped surface of the Roza Member basalt. Block arrows indicate the ancient flood-flow direction responsible for the streamlined form of the islands. See Figure 6-6 for an oblique aerial view looking onto the upstream side of island No. 3.

94.0   Continuing north on Wellsandt Road is an expansive view across the upper Cow Creek scabland complex. Opposite side of the flood channel is still barely visible 10 miles to the east along the same Palouse uplands viewed earlier near Lamont.

96.1   Wellsandt Road terminates at Danekas Road; turn right at stop sign. Another flood channel here truncated the north end of Carico Hills to the left (west).

99.2   To the left is a short (0.5 mile) access road into a public Washington Department of Fish and Wildlife recreation site with an overlook across the south side of Sprague Lake, one of the larger, elongated, rock basins carved out during megaflooding. Sprague Lake forms the headwaters for Cow Creek (see Figure 3-32). Continue northeast on Danekas Road. Interesting flood-scoured, butte-and-basin scabland continues all the way to Sprague.

106.1   In Sprague turn right (south) on B Street, followed by a quick left to access State Route 23. Proceed left (north) onto SR 23 for 0.6 mile before connecting with the Interstate 90 on-ramp eastbound.

Figure 5-16. Abandoned barn lies along scoured-flood channel at Fishtrap. A smoothed and streamlined Palouse Loess Island (No. 18) flanks the flood channel in background. Looking south.

111.0   Between MP 249 and MP 253 are aspen-lined rock basins eroded into a scoured flood channel flanked with several classic streamlined and scarped Palouse hills. Mima mounds (see "Mysterious Mima Mounds" sidebar, page 83 in Chapter 3) are also well developed here.

113.0   Wonderful example of an isolated, streamlined and scarped Palouse hill in middle of the flood channel just north of freeway with a water-filled, rock basin (Ames Lake) along the northeast end (see Figure 4-33).

115.5   The Fishtrap-Hog Lakes Trail (chapter 4, Trail O) is only a couple of miles east of here, accessible via Fishtrap from Exit 254 (Figure 5-16).

117.0   A rather sharp boundary occurs here between the open prairie and treed scabland. Traveling northward, slowly gain elevation and enter an area that receives slightly more moisture that supports the transition from shrub-steppe vegetation to that of ponderosa pine and aspen.

125.9   Leave Interstate 90 at Exit 264 and turn left (north) onto State Route 902 (Salnave Road) toward Medical Lake. Ahead is the broad row of hills we call Steptoe Ridge (No. 12) through which megafloods scoured out a series of rock basins now occupied by lakes (see Figure 3-21).

130.0   Pass between flood-scoured Clear Lake on the right and the Booth Hill Steptoe on the left.

131.3   At the entrance to the town of Medical Lake is a view of the eastern of the two Medical Lakes. Here, at Waterfront Park, is the trailhead for the Medical Lake Loop Trail (chapter 4, Trail J). Continue north through Medical Lake.

132.9   At north end of Medical Lake turn left (west) onto Brooks Road. After one-half mile Brooks Road bends right (north) heading into the broad expanse of the West Plains. Another steptoe, Olsen Hill, lies a short distance to the northeast (Figure 5-17). Olsen Hill is an island of Eocene-age granitic rock surrounded by a sea of Columbia River basalt that covered the West Plains about 15 million years ago. The youngest basalt flow beneath the West Plains is the Priest Rapids Member (upper Wanapum Basalt).

- -

Figure 5-17. Olson Hill, looking northeast from Medical Lake, is divided by a prominent spillover flood channel. The base of the channel lies at 2,560 feet (120 feet above the surrounding plains). Flood-scarped slopes above the spillover channel indicate that the maximum flood depth over the West Plains probably exceeded 250 feet (2,700 feet elevation).

135.0   Ice Age floods moving rapidly across the West Plains stripped off most of the topsoil that once blanketed the West Plains. In places the floods left behind a thin layer of flood gravel, sometimes molded into giant current ripples (Figure 5-18; see also Figures 3-18, 6-10).

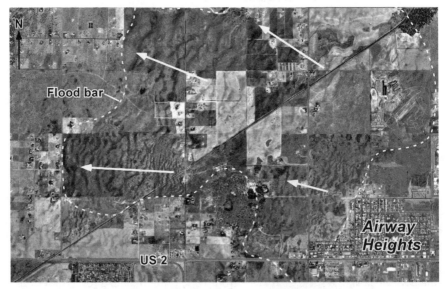

Figure 5-18. West Plains giant current ripples along U.S. Highway 2 near Airway Heights. Arrows indicate flood flow direction, transverse to the orientation of the ripples.

137.7   Turn right (east) at intersection with U.S. Highway 2.

140.8   Rambo Road intersection.

Color Plates

- - - - - - -

Ice Age Floods in the Pacific Northwest

Legend
- Glaciers
- Flood Extent
- Glacial Lake
- Pleistocene Coastline
- Present Coastline

N

0 5 10   20   30   40 Miles
0 5 10 20 30 40 Kilometers

Used with permission, © Ice Age Floods Institute

Prints of this map measuring 24x36 inches may be purchased from the Ice Age Floods Institute, www.iafi.org

Plate 1. Map of Glacial Lake Missoula and the Channeled Scabland. Modified version issued by the Ice Age Floods Institute in 2010. Shown here is the Cordilleran Ice Sheet at its maximum extent around 20,000 years ago.

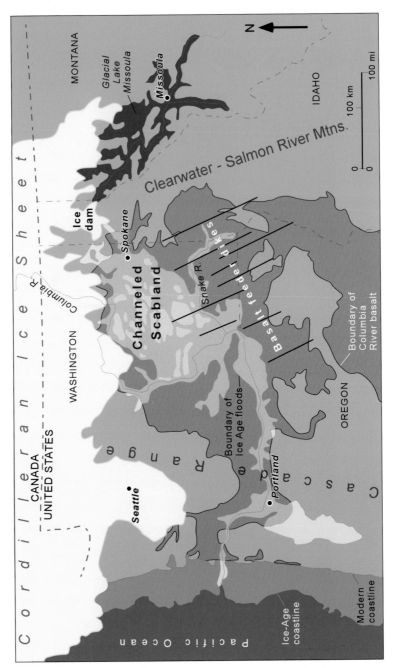

Plate 2. Map of the Pacific Northwest showing coverage of Columbia River basalt and the area impacted by Ice Age floods. The basalt flowed from thousands of feeder dikes (dark lines), filling an intermontane province called the Columbia Plateau. The continental flood basalts extended southward beyond the edge of the map to cover a large part of southeastern Oregon as well.

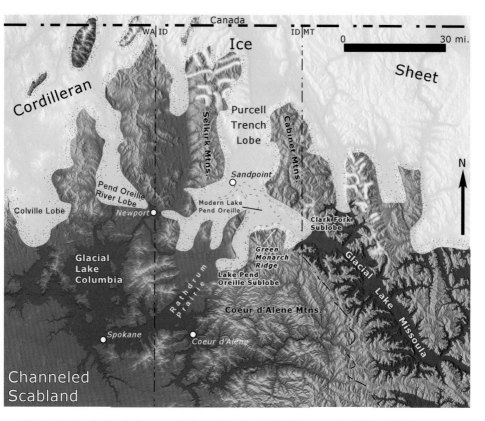

Plate 3. Shaded-relief map of glacial ice dam that impounded Glacial Lake Missoula, which rose to a maximum elevation of 4,250 feet. To the west the surface of Glacial Lake Columbia lay 1,950 feet lower (2,300 feet elevation) when it backed up behind another ice dam near Grand Coulee Dam, 75 miles west of Spokane.

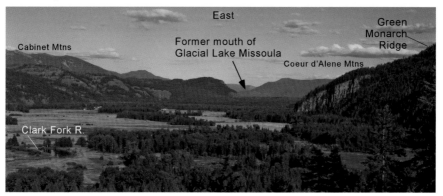

Plate 4. Clark Fork River Valley looking across area of former ice dam that created Glacial Lake Missoula. N48.1358, W116.2273.

Plate 5. Mouth of Lake Pend Oreille and head of the Rathdrum Prairie Outburst Plain – the breakout zone for floods from Glacial Lake Missoula. Looking northeast. The beveled slope at right was planed off by the grinding action of the ancient ice lobe, perhaps in combination with the outburst floods. A non-motorized trail climbs to near the summit of Cape Horn Peak to an impressive northern view of Lake Pend Oreille (chapter 4, Trail D).

Plate 6. Aerial view over south end of Lake Pend Oreille and breakout area for the Missoula floods. The broad outburst plain merges with Rathdrum Prairie (Feature No. 3), each covered with hundreds of feet of bouldery flood sediment. A non-motorized trail follows the shoreline of stunning Idlewilde and Buttonhook bays of Lake Pend Oreille within Farragut State Park (chapter 4, Trail E).

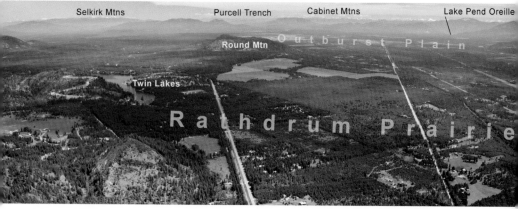

Plate 7. Looking north across Rathdrum Prairie toward outburst area for the Missoula floods. Twin Lakes and other lakes along the margins (No. 5) of Rathdrum Prairie were dammed by outburst flood debris that filled the central part of the valley more than the margins.

Plate 8. Flood-debris dammed Spirit Lake along the western margin of Rathdrum Prairie. The top of Mount Spokane (elevation 5,883 feet) was more than 3,000 feet above the maximum flood level. Looking west.

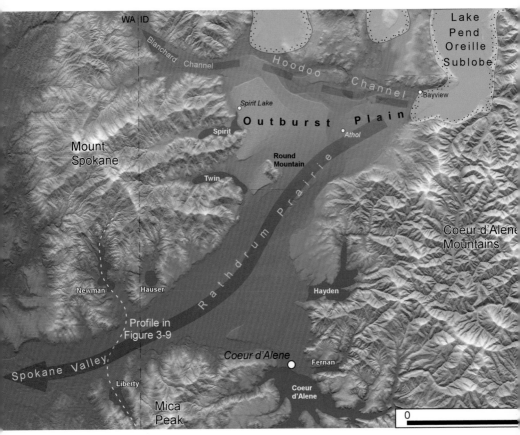

Plate 9. Shaded-relief map showing ice lobes and sediment buildup in the Rathdrum Prairie Outburst Plain (No. 3) immediately downstream. Glacial ice of the Lake Pend Oreille sublobe was the southern limit for the Purcell Trench Lobe (No. 1). Sediment buildup along Rathdrum Prairie partially blocked tributary valleys, forming a series of flood-debris-dammed lakes (No. 5) along its margins. See Figure 3-9 for a cross-sectional profile across the Spokane Valley-Rathdrum Prairie. Blue arrows show flood-flow direction. Most floods were directed southwest via Rathdrum Prairie; however, when glacial ice was not fully advanced, some Missoula floodwaters also escaped northwestward via the Blanchard Channel. Today, the slow flow of groundwater through the huge, underground Rathdrum-Spokane Aquifer generally parallels that of the southern route for the Missoula floods.

Plate 10. Satellite image of the eastern Channeled Scabland, which includes the Cheney-Palouse and Telford-Crab Creek Scabland Tracts. Darker areas are flood coulees and channels eroded into basalt bedrock by the Ice Age floods. Intervening lighter-colored, patchwork areas are fertile Palouse uplands of wind-blown loess, which were generally above flood level and thus escaped erosion.

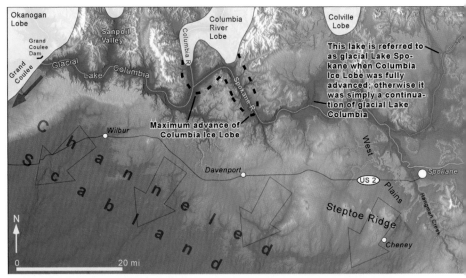

Plate 11. Glacial lakes of the Spokane and Columbia valley during the last glacial cycle. Lake level (blue area) in this image is elevation 2,300 feet based on the inferred height of Glacial Lake Columbia during the last glacial cycle. Large block arrows show direction of outburst floodwaters that spilled out onto the Channeled Scabland after quickly overfilling the pre-existing glacial lake(s). During an earlier glacial cycle, evidence exists to suggest another ice dam formed when the Columbia Lobe extended completely across the Columbia valley (bold dashed line), creating what is known as Glacial Lake Spokane.

Plate 12. Solitary Pine Creek Coulee (No. 16) winds through the Palouse country at the eastern edge of the Cheney-Palouse scablands. Flow of water (arrow) was away from viewer. Looking south.

Plate 13. Rock Lake (No. 15), the deepest lake within the Channeled Scabland, lies beyond Hole-in-the-Ground Canyon. Pine Creek Coulee joins in at lower left. Note flood-streamlined loess hills and uneroded Palouse uplands on either side of Rock Lake. Flood flow was away from viewer. A non-motorized trail follows an abandoned railroad along the east (left) side Rock Lake (chapter 4, Trail P). Looking south.

Plate 14. Streamlined and scarped Palouse Loess Islands (No. 18) and tiered rock benches of Roza Member basalt were eroded along a flood channel of the Cow Creek Scabland Complex (No. 17) near Marengo. Block arrows indicate flood-flow direction. Looking northeast.

Plate 15. Islands of Palouse loess eroded and streamlined by Ice Age floods along the Cheney-Palouse Scabland Tract, looking northeast. Low areas are Mima mound-studded flood channels with a floor of scoured basalt bedrock of the Roza Member. The flow of floodwater, toward the viewer, rose above the tops of faceted, channel escarpments (arrows) that run diagonally across the image.

Plate 16. The non-motorized BLM trail to Towell Falls (chapter 4, Trail R) parallels Rock Creek. Mima mound-covered flood bars line the valley floor. In the background a trenched spur isolates a prominent butte (circled) from the basalt mesa in the upper right. View looking northwest from N46.9986, W117.9288.

Plate 17a. Late summer flowers atop potholed bench at south end of Deep Lake.

Plate 17b. Banks Lake from the top of Salishan Mesa, looking north into the Upper Grand Coulee. Paynes Gulch flood bar, blanketed with Lake Columbia silt, and Steamboat Rock lie at upper right.

Plate 18a. The desolate Odessa Towers lie along a flood-dissected mesa within lower Lake Creek Coulee (No. 23). Looking west. The towers are eroded remnants of once-continuous basalt flows of the Roza Member. A non-motorized trail along Lake Creek Coulee is featured in chapter 4 (Trail V).

former
Bobs Lak

Plate 18b. Remote lower Lake Creek Coulee looking north toward the now mostly desiccated Bobs Lake. N47.3773, W118.7667

Plate 19. Natural bridges are rare in the Channeled Scabland. This one, in Marlin Hollow (No. 25), formed where two closely spaced potholes coalesced during flooding. As the potholes expanded, the stronger basalt-flow entablature proved more resistant to the plucking and undercutting action of the floods, leaving behind the bridge.

Plate 20. Telford-Crab Creek Scabland Tract. Left: Crab Creek Coulee (No. 22), one of the main Ice Age flood channels, flows toward Sylvan Lake (background). Looking west. Note giant current ripples (GCRs) that line the valley; arrows indicate flow direction. Right: A calling card of the Ice Age floods, this ice-rafted erratic of granite lies in the Marlin Hollow (No. 25) flood coulee.

Plate 21. A one-mile-long longitudinal flood bar, blanketed with giant current ripples, lies at the west end of Sylvan Lake along Crab Creek. Flood flow was from left to right. Two concentric Odessa Ring Craters (No. 24) in basalt bedrock were etched out by rushing floodwaters. Today, sand and gravel is being removed from an active borrow pit at the right end of the bar (see close-up in Figure 2-29). Looking southeast.

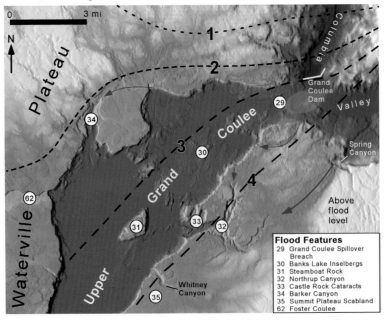

Flood Features
29 Grand Coulee Spillover Breach
30 Banks Lake Inselbergs
31 Steamboat Rock
32 Northrup Canyon
33 Castle Rock Cataracts
34 Barker Canyon
35 Summit Plateau Scabland
62 Foster Coulee

Plate 22. Flood flow into Grand Coulee funneled between uplands to the southeast and glacial ice to the north and west (dashed lines). During maximum ice advance (position 4) when most of the main coulee was plugged with ice, some floodwater flowed southwest across the Summit Plateau Scabland (No. 35). At other less-advanced glacial-ice positions (1 through 3) floodwaters invaded and eroded wider swaths of Grand Coulee.

Plate 23. These parallel scratches in granite bedrock are glacial striations left behind from thousands of years of slowly creeping ice of the Okanogan Lobe moving over this rock surface. This area is thought to have become free of ice somewhere between 14,000 to 15,000 years ago. Looking south from Crown Point Vista towards Grand Coulee Dam and Lake Roosevelt (upper left). Candy Point (chapter 4, Trail W) is at upper right.

Plate 24. Steamboat Rock rises up to 900 feet above the Banks Lake reservoir within the Upper Grand Coulee. Looking southwest onto leading prow of the monolith parallel to the flood-flow direction. Glacial erratics and remnants of a glacial moraine atop Steamboat Rock indicate that the monolith was once covered by glacial ice of the Okanogan Lobe. Glacial moraines preserved on the monolith suggest the last megafloods did not completely overtop the monolith. Curvilinear grooves in basalt of the Priest Rapids Member, atop the leading edge of the monolith, were etched out during earlier episodes of flooding. Gravity pulled down a slump block off the steep prow of the monolith during, or soon after, a megaflood event. An awe-inspiring hike that circumvents the top of Steamboat Rock is featured in chapter 4 (Trail Z).

Plate 25. Grand Coulee Dam lies near the head of the Upper Grand Coulee, which was finally breached by a recessional cataract about 17,000 years ago. Foundation of the dam is built into 40 million- to 60 million-year-old granitic basement rock. The Banks Lake reservoir is filled with water pumped from Lake Roosevelt (left center) as part of the Columbia Basin Irrigation Project. In the distance are Banks Lake Inselbergs (No. 30) and the Steamboat Rock Monolith (No. 31). Looking southwest.

Plate 26. The most significant flood features of the Upper Grand Coulee include Steamboat Rock Monolith (No. 31), Northrup Canyon (No. 32), Castle Rock Cataracts (No. 33) and Banks Lake Inselbergs (No. 30). Arrows signify a pair of high flood spillover channels incised into the grooved upland plateau at the head of the Castle Rock Cataracts. Before Ice Age flooding, the Waterville Plateau once continued, uninterrupted, across the entire width of Grand Coulee (see Figure 3-54, Stage 1). Lying above the granitic inselbergs are multiple flows of Grande Ronde and Wanapum basalt. Looking southwest.

Plate 27. State Route 155 and the Coulee Corridor follow the east side of the Upper Grand Coulee. A series of faint giant current ripples are visible through a thin cover of post-last-flood Glacial Lake Columbia silt deposits, which blanket the Paynes Gulch flood bar. An unusual ringed crater in basalt was etched out by floodwaters sweeping across the summit plateau scabland up to the erosional limit (trimline) for the coulee. Looking northeast.

Plate 28. Salishan Mesa from the edge of the Summit Plateau Scabland (No. 35). Looking southwest across State Route 155 and the Upper Grand Coulee. See chapter 4 for a featured hike to the top of precipitous Salishan Mesa (Trail BB).

Plate 29. End of the rainbow over the 400-foot-high Dry Falls Cataract and Plunge Pool (No. 41). Looking northeast from the J Harlen Bretz Memorial (Dry Falls) Visitor Center.

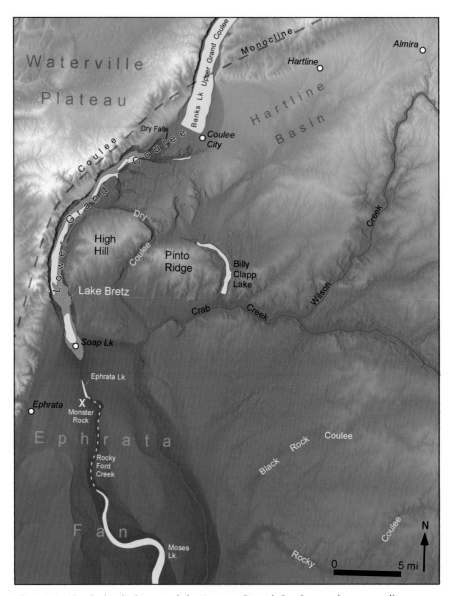

Plate 30. Shaded-relief map of the Lower Grand Coulee and surrounding area. Because of the flood debris at Ephrata Fan (No. 58) that built up at the mouth of Grand Coulee, a single lake, called Lake Bretz and shown in dark blue, occupied the full length of the lower coulee for many years after the last Missoula flood. Over time the lake shrank, leaving behind the present chain of isolated lakes (light blue), which become progressively more alkaline down the coulee.

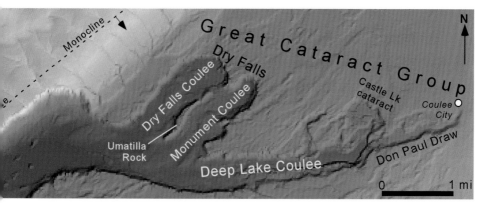

Plate 31. Shaded-relief map of the four-mile-wide Great Cataract Group. At the west end, the Umatilla Rock Blade (No. 43) neatly divides the Dry Falls (No. 41) and Monument (No. 42) recessional cataract canyons. Farther east lies the Castle Lake recessional cataract. The east end of the Great Cataract Group extends a mile farther to the head of Don Paul Draw at Coulee City.

Plate 32. Looking south over Dry Falls and the Lower Grand Coulee. Note pockmarked and grooved upland plateau (No. 45) in foreground. The Umatilla Rock Blade (No. 43) neatly divides the cataract complex into two major alcoves. The Dry Falls Visitor Center is circled at right.

Plate 33. View looking south down the Lower Grand Coulee. Sun Lakes State Park is at lower left along the shores of Park Lake. The Coulee Monocline (No. 36) at right tilts down toward a flood-swept upland plateau that spreads out for many miles to the east.

Plate 34. Deep Lake Coulee. Deep Lake is the deepest (120 feet) of the lakes within Grand Coulee. Left: Looking west toward the Lower Grand Coulee. Right: A string of three cavernous potholes (No. 46), plucked out by swirling megaflood vortices, on a rock bench above Deep Lake. Looking northeast.

Plate 35. View down the throat of Monument Coulee (No. 42) from Dry Falls cataract. Below lies the Red Alkali Lake plungepool with Green Lake just beyond. The Umatilla Rock Blade (No. 43) is at top center. Looking south.

Plate 36. Upland scabland plateau adjacent to Blue Lake, Lower Grand Coulee. Massive flood bars (outlined) surround the plateau including a huge pendant-crescent bar, which nearly fills the canyon with flood sediment at lower right. Looking north.

Plate 37. Lower Grand Coulee, looking south. Jasper Canyon (No. 48) divides and rejoins the coulee downstream. Note how whitish volcanic ash from the 1980 eruption of Mount St. Helens collected in swale between flood bars at lower left.

Plate 38. A castle-like promontory of The Great Blade (No. 54) and Hogback Islands (No. 53) are reflected in Lake Lenore. Lake Lenore Caves (No. 52) are located about halfway up the west side of the rocky rib of basalt. Looking south.

Plate 39. Like a giant snake, The Great Blade (No. 54) winds through Lower Grand Coulee. The rock blade divides Lake Lenore (left) from East Lenore Coulee (No. 55) on the right. A trail leading from Lake Lenore Caves (No. 52) to East Lenore Coulee (Trail II, chapter 4) runs through a notch in The Great Blade. Looking north.

Plate 40. Remote and desolate scabland of East Lenore Coulee parallels Lower Grand Coulee along the east side of The Great Blade. N47.5303, W119.4727.

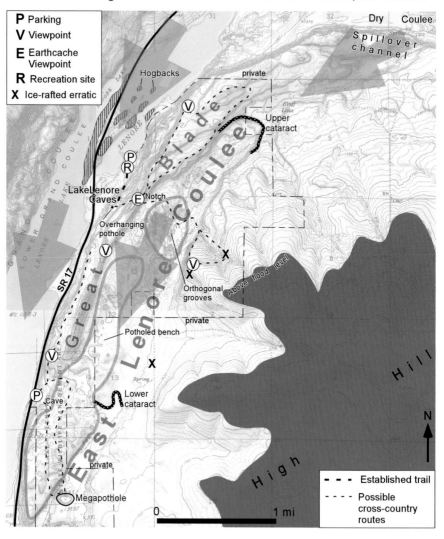

P Parking
V Viewpoint
E Earthcache Viewpoint
R Recreation site
X Ice-rafted erratic

Hogbacks
private
Dry Coulee
Spillover channel
Upper cataract
Blue Lake
The Great Blade
Lake Lenore Caves
Notch
Overhanging pothole
Orthogonal grooves
Above flood level
private
Potholed bench
private
Cave
Lower cataract
Megapothole
SR 17
GRAND COULEE
LOWER GRAND COULEE
LENORE LAKE
East Lenore Coulee
Great Lenore Coulee
High Hill
N

- - - Established trail
- - - - Possible cross-country routes

0   1 mi

Plate 41. Coauthor Bjornstad looks over the crisscrossing, giant grooves of East Lenore Coulee from The Great Blade. Faceted channel escarpments are eroded into High Hill (No. 51) along opposite side of the coulee. N47.5146, W119.4907. Looking southeast. TOM FOSTER PHOTO

Plate 42. An 800-foot-wide megapothole was plucked out of a flow of Grande Ronde Basalt within East Lenore Coulee. Water flow was from left to right. Note how pothole is steeper, deeper and slightly undercut on the downstream (right) side. Hiker (circled) is shown for scale. N47.4781, W119.5082.

Plate 43. Castle Lake basin (No. 44) at the east end of the Great Cataract Group. Located here is one of the three Castle Rocks located within the Channeled Scabland. N47.6005, W119.3060. Looking southwest.

Plate 44. Spring Coulee (No. 40), now occupied by Billy Clapp Reservoir, carried floodwaters diverted out of Lower Grand Coulee and around the east side of elevated and unflooded Pinto Ridge. Looking south.

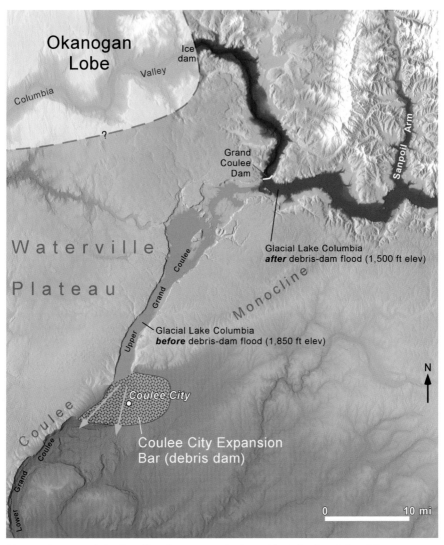

Plate 45. One of the last floods occurred when Glacial Lake Columbia over-topped a debris dam at the south end of Upper Grand Coulee. The ensuing flood drained south into the Lower Grand Coulee altogether lowering the level of Lake Columbia by more than 300 feet.

west   Badger Mountain

Plate 46. A portion of the rugged Three Devils scabland complex along Moses Coulee (No. 61). N47.4357, W119.7897. Canyon walls exposed here are mostly Wanapum Basalt. Note hiker at upper right for scale.

US 2

Plate 47. U.S. Highway 2 crosses the 250-foot-tall Great Bar of Moses Coulee (outlined) one of five recognized National Natural Landmarks within the Channeled Scabland region. Looking south.

Plate 48. Picturesque Jameson Lake was dammed by a glacial moraine during retreat of the Okanogan Lobe after the last flood down Moses Coulee. Looking north. BARBARA KIVER PHOTO

Plate 49. Looking up lower Moses Coulee (No. 61) toward Palisades. A group of flood-deposited giant current ripples (outlined) lies atop a flood bar along the coulee bottom, streamless since the Ice Age. Note the faceted walls and hanging valleys along coulee margins exposing ancient flows of Grande Ronde Basalt. Looking northeast.

Plate 50. Man-made Lake Roosevelt (surface elevation 1,300 feet) extends to near the Canadian border behind Grand Coulee Dam. This lake conforms to the area where much-larger Glacial Lake Columbia used to reside, which once filled this valley with an additional 1,100 feet of ice-dammed glacial meltwater. A number of nested sediment terraces built up within the valley during multiple stages of Glacial Lake Columbia and Ice Age flooding. Looking north.

Rambo Road Spur

Take a short four-mile detour to drive across a series of gently undulating giant current ripples, hundreds of feet apart, that spread for almost a mile along Rambo Road.

140.8   Turn left (north) on Rambo Road.

141.9   Start of undulating giant current ripples (Figure 5-19) that blanket a broad flood bar. Notice the abundance of cobbles and boulders exposed in road-cuts along ripple crests, deposited as the ripples migrated forward during flooding.

Figure 5-19. A series of undulating megaripples along Rambo Road near Airway Heights. Looking south. N47.6691, W117.6253

142.8   Turn around at Deno Road and return to U.S. Highway 2, passing over the same ripples in the opposite direction.

144.8   Turn left (east) on U.S. Highway 2 toward Airway Heights. End of spur.

151.8   Staying on U.S. Highway 2, pass the Spokane Airport before rejoining Interstate 90, 1.5 miles west of the starting point for this tour. End of road tour.

Road Tour 3: Telford-Crab Creek Loop

Explore an approximately 100-mile, round-trip tour through some of the most remote, scarred, and arid regions of the Channeled Scabland. Along the way examine low-relief scabland at the head of the Telford tract as well as flood bars and giant current ripples along Crab Creek and some unusual and unique, flood-scoured ring structures (Odessa Craters).

Road Log

0.0   Start at intersection between U.S. Highway 2 and State Route 28 in Davenport, Washington (see Figure 3-35). Head south on SR 28 toward Harrington. Just west of Davenport floodwaters spilled southward after overfilling Glacial Lake Columbia (No. 20) via a low divide at the head of Hawk Creek into Bluestem Creek. Low-relief, flood-swept scabland (Priest Rapids Member basalt) divides Palouse uplands on either side of the valley.

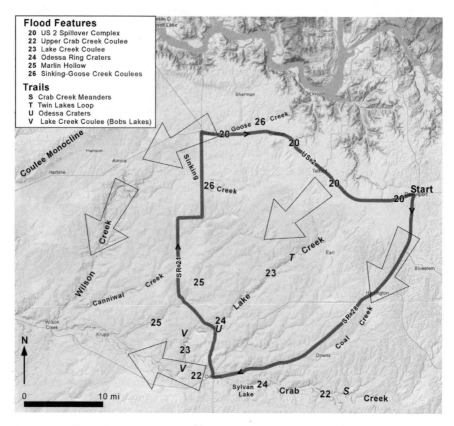

Figure 5-20. Google map with road tour (highlighted) of the Telford-Crab Creek Loop. Block arrows indicate flood-flow directions. Features along route are described in chapter 3; nearby non-motorized trails are presented in chapter 4.

6.2   Cross Bluestem Creek that heads off to the southeast.

7.3   SR 28 follows a narrow, scarped Palouse-lined flood coulee that splits off from Bluestem Creek to the southwest.

Figure 5-21. Abandoned farm that straddles a scabland channel and fertile prairie along Palouse hills of the upper Telford Tract.

10.7   Junction with wider Coal Creek Coulee. After 0.7 mile railroad cuts reveal layers of windblown loess exposed in scarped Palouse hills lining coulee on the left.

13.1   Pass through the sleepy town of Harrington. Slowly rise out of Coal Creek Coulee into adjoining Palouse uplands.

24.0   Begin descent back into Coal Creek Coulee.

26.0   Exposed in roadcut to the right is 10 to 20 feet of pillow basalt (similar to Figure 1-4) floating in a matrix of yellow-brown palagonite that formed 15 million years ago when an advancing basalt flow of the Priest Rapids Member explosively poured into a small pond or stream. Ahead Coal Creek Coulee deepens as we approach the junction with upper Crab Creek Coulee (No. 22).

32.6   Some faint giant current ripples are visible in a flood bar above and to the right. To the left, across the railroad, is a broad, low flood bar where Coal Creek Coulee merges with Crab Creek Coulee. Coulee widens suddenly upon entering the Crab Creek Valley. Flood bars along Sylvan Lake, with some of the best examples of giant current ripples anywhere, lie about 1.5 miles south of here (Plate 21). Also in this area are dozens of flood-eroded, Odessa Ring Craters (No. 24). Continue west on State Route 28.

37.4   In downtown Odessa turn right (north) onto State Route 21. The turn-off to the trailhead for the South Lake Creek Coulee Trail (chapter 4, Trail V2) is 0.1 mile on the left at grain silos. This road tour continues north on SR 21.

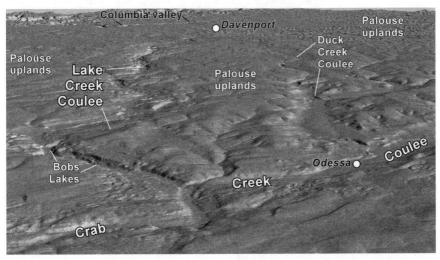

Figure 5-22. Oblique aerial view, looking northeast, across the Telford-Crab Creek scabland. Floodwaters spilled over from the Columbia River Valley at the top of the image. See also Figure 3-43 for a different aerial view in the vertical direction.

38.6   A flat-topped flood bar fills the bottom of Duck Creek Coulee (Figure 5-22) on the right (northeast). Several borrow pits expose coarse gravel and sand deposits within the bar. Giant current ripples blanket the bar about a mile up the coulee. Continue north onto gently rolling Palouse uplands that were generally above maximum flood level.

41.9   Enter a flat-bottomed, hanging, side coulee lined with flood-scarped Palouse loess. This channel carried floodwaters that spilled southwest out of Lake Creek Coulee before rejoining the same coulee 2.5 miles west of here. At the head of the hanging, side coulee the road descends into Lake Creek Coulee (No. 23).

43.4   The Cinnamon Roll (see Figures 4-53 and 4-54), a partially formed Odessa Ring Crater, is located just north of intersection with Trejabal Back Road. Ahead another ringed crater is visible around Wederspahn Lake (Figure 5-23).

Figure 5-23. Odessa Ring Craters (No. 24) in a basalt flow of the Roza Member along State Route 21 within Lake Creek Coulee. See Figures 4-53 through 4-55 for U.S. Bureau of Land Management hiking trails to some of these ringed craters. Looking northeast.

43.6   Cross the bottom of Lake Creek Coulee. Located here is the inter-section with Coffeepot Road that heads northeast toward upper Lake Creek Coulee. Up this coulee is Coffeepot Lake (see Figure 6-9) and the Twin Lakes Loop Trail (chapter 4, Trail T). To the west was once a sizable water body called Pacific Lake (Figure 5-24), but it has since gone dry due to overpumping of irri-gation wells in the area (see "Disappearing Lakes and Aquifers" sidebar, page 99 in chapter 3).

44.1   Trailhead for the U.S. Bureau of Land Management's Odessa Craters Trail (chapter 4, Trail U2, see Figures 4-53 and 4-54). Only 0.3 mile farther is a second trailhead to circular Cache Crater (Trail U1).

Figure 5-24. Entrance to the U.S. Bureau of Land Management's Pacific Lake recreation area, now only a forlorn, dry lake bed.

45.2 Nice view to the left (southwest) into dark, ragged Lake Creek Coulee scabland is in sharp contrast with the smoothed Palouse uplands along the coulee margins.

46.0 Turnoff to Lakeview Ranch Loop Road on the left. About 1.8 miles down this road is the north trailhead for North Lake Creek Coulee (Bobs Lakes) (chapter 4, Trail V1, see Figure 4-58).

47.6 After rising up and over more Palouse uplands, descend into Marlin Hollow (No. 25), another southwest trending flood coulee (see Figure 3-43). Some of the most impressive potholes and one of the few natural bridges (see Figure 3-44, Plate 19) are located near here (on private land). Continue north on State Route 21 over another ridge of Palouse loess that escaped erosion by the raging floodwaters.

53.6 Follow low-relief, Canniwai Creek Coulee for 1.5 miles before rising up onto more broad, gently undulating, Palouse uplands covered with dryland wheat.

59.6 Follow SR 21 as it bends sharply to the right (east) at grain elevator. After three miles is another right-angle turn to the north at edge of Canniwai Creek Coulee.

64.8 Crest Palouse upland out of the Lake Creek drainage and into Sinking Creek Coulee (No. 26, see Figure 3-45). The isolated prairie town of Wilbur is visible eight miles to the north and beyond are mountains of the Okanogan Uplands that lie north of the Columbia River Valley (see Figure 5-25). In between is the spillover area along U.S. Highway 2 (No. 20) after megaflood outbursts rapidly overfilled Glacial Lake Columbia (Plate 11).

65.7 Good view of ragged, dark scabland on the right up into Sinking Creek Coulee, which unlike the other coulees we've crossed, drains west into Wilson Creek (see Figure 3-45). The head of Sinking Creek drained floodwaters that spilled over from Welsh Creek near Creston.

Figure 5-25. The Okanogan Lobe blocked the Columbia River near present-day Grand Coulee Dam, creating Glacial Lake Columbia. Outburst floodwater (large block arrows) encountering this lake quickly overfilled it, forcing the floodwaters south across the scablands via the Cheney-Palouse and Telford Crab Creek tracts, as well as Grand Coulee. Looking south.

70.7   Gain yet another hill of Palouse loess that extends north into the town of Wilbur.

73.3   At Wilbur, Goose Creek Coulee enters from the right (east) after spilling over from the Columbia Valley via Redwine and Jump Canyons (see Figure 3-45). Turn right (east) onto U.S. Highway 2 toward Davenport that follows the bottom of Goose Creek Coulee for a couple of miles.

75.2   Good view of Goose Creek Coulee scabland to the north as we rise up onto more Palouse uplands between Wilbur and Creston. The floor of Goose Creek Coulee is pitted with dozens of flood-scoured potholes where the floods spilled over the divide from Redwine Canyon into the head of Goose Creek (see Figure 3-46).

78.4   Ahead and to the right, south of Creston, lies Creston Butte Steptoe (elevation 2,680 feet) composed of extremely hard quartzite rock at least 500 million years old (Figure 5-25, see Figure 3-45). Probably only the uppermost 100 feet of this butte poked out above the largest of the megafloods.

82.0   Scattered trees begin to appear here in the scabland areas due to the higher elevation and moister conditions that exist here. The open ponderosa pine and aspen forests preferentially grow in the rubbly, rocky scabland soils unlike the finer-textured, windblown soils within the adjacent Palouse hills, which are generally treeless.

84.3   Just east of Creston enter the main flood spillway complex for the Telford scabland. Treed areas lie within butte-and-basin scabland where all the fine Palouse soil was stripped away during flooding, leaving behind large patches of basalt bedrock covered only with a locally thin veneer of basalt rubble. Here also is the head of Sinking Creek where floods spilled over from Welsh Creek (see Figure 3-45).

87.0   Continue east through the broad (approximately 12 miles wide), low-relief Telford tract, which drains into the head of Lake Creek Coulee. Here the floods barely eroded through the uppermost basalt flow (Priest Rapids Member), producing only low mesas and buttes; this is in sharp contrast to the lower part of the same coulee – where Lake Creek Coulee is hundreds of feet deep.

89.8   Turnoff into the Telford Rest Area. Just east of here the floods scoured to their lowest level (about elevation 2,300 feet) anywhere across the width of the Telford-Crab Creek Scabland Tract (see profile in Figure 3-37). Near here, just south of Telford are some great examples of curvilinear grooves etched out by Ice Age floodwaters and partially filled with elongated, post-flood, Mima-like mounds.

94.4   Butte-and-basin scabland continues here across Bachelor Prairie, where floodwaters spilled over from Glacial Lake Columbia at the head of Hawk Creek only a few miles north of here.

96.3   The heights of the scabland spillover channels rise as you approach the east margin of the Telford tract. A flood-streamlined and scarped Palouse hill lies just to the right (south).

98.8   U.S. Highway 2 crosses the head of another branching arm of Hawk Creek. From here floods spilled southward into the heads of Bluestem, Coal and upper Crab Creek coulees.

102.8   Complete loop at Davenport, Washington. End of road tour.

Road Tour 4: Grand Coulee Loop

Along this 125-mile tour follow the path of the floodwaters down the full, 50-mile length of Grand Coulee via the Coulee Corridor. Traverse Ephrata Fan where the coulee expands into the broad Quincy Basin before heading north again to get a different perspective of the lower coulee complex from the lofty heights of Pinto Ridge. Retrace route through the Upper Grand Coulee or take an alternate route up and over the Coulee Monocline to the wild spillover area above Northrup Canyon to complete the loop.

Road Log

0.0   Road tour begins at the Grand Coulee Dam Visitor Center, just below towering Grand Coulee Dam. Drive south on the Grand Coulee Highway (State Route 155) to traverse up the steep hanging wall of Grand Coulee (Plate 25). Near here Lieutenant Thomas Symons, surveying the Columbia River for the U.S. Army Corps of Engineers, on October 4, 1881, wrote in his journal:

> 10 A.M.: After about eleven miles are passed we come to the mouth of the Grand Coulee, which, however, would not have been noticed if old Pierre had not told us, as it presents the same appearance as the rest of the left bank, the Coulee bottom being high above the river.

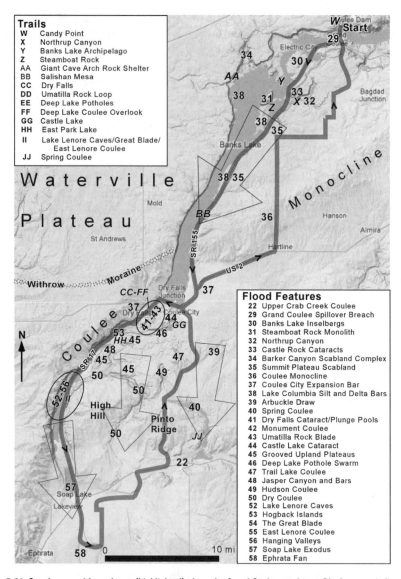

Figure 5-26. Google map with road tour (highlighted) along the Grand Coulee road tour. Block arrows indicate paleoflow direction of megafloods. Features along route are described in chapter 3; non-motorized trails are presented in chapter 4.

1.6   At the top of the grade is the town of Grand Coulee located at the head of the Grand Coulee canyon (elevation 1,500 feet). During most of the Ice Age floods, while the cataract that formed Grand Coulee was receding northward, the head of the coulee was much higher than it is today. Only late in the last glacial cycle, did the cataract finally recede across the full length of the coulee, breaching and dramatically lowering the divide with the Columbia River Valley by 900 feet (see Figures 3-55 and 3-56). Most, or all, the waters from later out-burst floods were hijacked through this suddenly lowered Grand Coulee divide.

The Coulee Corridor

The Coulee Corridor is a 150-mile-long National Scenic Byway that winds past many of the most spectacular features of the Ice Age floods, including the full length of the 50-mile-long Grand Coulee (see Figure 3-50). Of special interest along the route, besides the flood-scarred landscape, are abundant boating and fishing opportunities, a rich American Indian history, and wildlife viewing. Branching off both State Routes 155 and 17, are a number of non-motorized trails, including Northrup Canyon (chapter 4, Trail X), Steamboat Rock (Trail Z), Banks Lake Archipelago (Trail Y), Salishan Mesa (Trail BB), Dry Falls (Trail CC) and Lake Lenore Caves (Trail II). The corridor continues south through even more megaflood terrain beyond Grand Coulee for another 50 miles to Othello.

The corridor has its roots in the nonprofit, volunteer-based Coulee Corridor Consortium established in 1999 by a group of local, private individuals as well as civic and business leaders to "promote sustainable tourism along with appreciation, interpretation and stewardship of natural and heritage resources along the byway."

Figure 5-27. State Route 155, along the Coulee Corridor, runs the full length of stunning Upper Grand Coulee, including Steamboat Rock at upper left. Looking northwest.

2.1   Continue on SR 155 south into the Upper Grand Coulee.

2.6   A man-made dam (North Dam) blocks the upper end of Banks Lake. Continue southwest through Electric City and a series of granite-rock outcroppings, called the Banks Lake Inselbergs (No. 30), scattered across the floor of Upper Grand Coulee (see Figure 3-57).

4.2   Visible directly ahead is a flat, basalt-capped mesa, into which the Castle Rock Cataracts (No. 33) are eroded. The low saddle just left (east) of Castle Rock is a flood-spillover channel at the head of one of the cataracts (see Figure 3-62, Plate 26). Laminated, pale yellow sediment visible in roadcuts and the shoreline of Banks Lake for the next few miles is Lake Columbia Silt

(No. 38). These sediments were deposited in the Upper Grand Coulee within an ancient lake, 200 feet higher than Banks Lake, for up to several hundred years after the last Missoula flood.

5.9   Rounded knobs of the Banks Lake Inselbergs (No. 30) protrude up from coulee bottom.

7.5   Pass through a modern, deep roadcut, which freshly exposes the core of granitic inselbergs, 40 million to 60 million years old, west of Castle Rock. At the opposite end of the roadcut, find flat-topped, basaltic Steamboat Rock (No. 31) and granite inselbergs sometimes reflected within Banks Lake (Figure 5-28).

Figure 5-28. Reflection of flood-exhumed granitic inselberg within Banks Lake along State Route 155, looking north.

The inselbergs were once buried under lava flows of the Columbia River basalt and later exhumed by the Ice Age floods about 17,000 years ago, toward the end of the Ice Age.

8.6   Exposure of pale yellow, lake-deposited silt visible within a low terrace along the eroded shoreline of Banks Lake. These laminated, fine-grained sediments were deposited within Glacial Lake Columbia at the close of the Ice Age (No. 38). Only 0.4 mile farther is the entrance to Northrup Canyon (No. 32) State Park, where two hiking trails are featured in chapter 4 (Trail X). Continuing south on SR 155, Steamboat Rock (Plates 24 and 26; see Figures 3-58 and 3-59) dominates the skyline to the west across an embayment of Banks Lake called the Devils Punch Bowl. The Punch Bowl may be a plunge pool left behind as the recessional cataract that formed the Upper Grand Coulee receded northward past former Steamboat Falls (see Figure 3-54, Stage 4).

10.6   Granitic rocks and inselbergs disappear beneath the thickening cover of Columbia River basalt (see Figure 3-53). At 0.5 mile farther, on the left, is a plunge pool where Martin Falls (dry much of the year) drops below Whitney Canyon (Devils Creek), an out-of-sight canyon that transects the Summit Plateau Scabland (No. 35) high above the steep east wall of the coulee (Figure 5-29).

Figure 5-29. Looking north at Martin Falls (dry), which drops 400 feet over a cataract cliff at the mouth of Whitney Canyon. PHOTO TAKEN IN 1930 BY OTIS W. FREEMAN. IMAGE SPC 988-0293

12.3   Pass turnoff to Steamboat Rock State Park and the Steamboat Rock Trail (chapter 4, Trail Z). Continue southwest on SR 155.

13.2   On the opposite side of Grand Coulee, a side coulee called Horse Lake Coulee hangs 550 feet above Banks Lake (see Figures 3-74 and 3-75). A sizable delta bar lies at the base of the hanging coulee, derived from an ancient glacial stream and waterfall that once flowed into Grand Coulee from the west via melting of the Okanogan Lobe (see Figures 3-112 and 3-113).

14.9   Notch in the east wall of Grand Coulee, immediately to the left, is the short, hanging, side-cataract canyon, which seasonally drops water from Ladds Creek (see Figures 3-73, right, and 6-20).

15.9   SR 155 rises up onto Paynes Gulch bar, a longitudinal-type flood bar. Around the lower margins of this bar are well-laminated, yellow-colored lake deposits of silt laid down at the end of the last Ice Age within Glacial Lake Columbia (No. 38). The lower part of the bar is covered with silt deposits from the ancient lake, which once partially flooded the bar (Plate 27). From the air, giant current ripples from the last Missoula flood are faintly visible atop the flood bar through the thin blanket of silt.

17.1   Huge, rounded boulders of basalt and granite are scattered here at the crest of the bar that lay above the level of former Glacial Lake Columbia (Figure 5-30).

Figure 5-30. Rounded basalt and granite boulders litter the crest of Paynes Gulch flood bar along SR 155 at an elevation of 1,630 feet. Around the lower margins of the bar, these boulders lie buried beneath a covering of silt deposited within former Glacial Lake Columbia. The granite boulders likely derive from flood erosion of the Banks Lake Inselbergs (No. 30) toward the end of the Ice Age. Looking southwest.

18.5   A truncated high promontory of basalt protrudes above the east wall of the coulee on the left. The largest floods completely filled Grand Coulee, spilling over its east edge for a mile or more along the Summit Plateau Scabland (No. 35), which lies out of view above and to the left (Plate 27). Slightly tilted Salishan Mesa (chapter 4, Trail BB) is visible ahead – perched high above the east side of Banks Lake (see Figure 4-83, Plate 28).

19.1   Paynes Gulch (with seasonal waterfall draining Lewis Creek) hangs 300 feet above the coulee floor on the left.

19.9   Wide pullout along right side of SR 155 with excellent view to the north across Paynes Gulch flood bar and the Upper Grand Coulee (Plate 27). From here megaripples are faintly visible through the veneer of ancient Glacial Lake Columbia silt deposits. Spectacular examples of columnar basalt are exposed in the near-vertical coulee walls above and east of the pullout.

20.1   SR 155 begins its ascent up into the blasted east wall of Upper Grand Coulee. This is the beginning of the so-called Million Dollar Mile Highway (Plate 28, see Figure 3-66), a costly construction project undertaken in 1948 to redirect the highway around Banks Lake reservoir.

20.6   Wide spot along SR 155 for parking and primitive hiking routes to the top of Salishan Mesa (chapter 4, Trail BB). See Figure 4-82 for a trail map.

22.0   South end of the Million Dollar Mile Highway as SR 155 descends to the level of Banks Lake (Figure 5-31).

Figure 5-31. South end of the Million Dollar Mile Highway (SR 155), blasted through volcanic lava flows of Columbia River basalt after the central coulee was flooded by Banks Lake (in background). Looking southwest.

24.0   Rock shelters eroded into one particular basalt flow near the top of the east coulee wall (see Figure 2-12). In another 0.6 mile are some unusually shaped basalt pillars along left coulee wall. The mouth of Upper Grand Coulee begins to open up into the Hartline Basin (see Figure 3-77).

25.7   The mouth of Upper Grand Coulee crosses the Coulee Monocline (No. 36). Here the ancient basalt lava flows (see Figure 3-70) were bent by geologic forces originating deep within the Earth's crust. The end result was the Coulee Monocline, a long ridge of tilted basalt (see Figure 3-50) that crosses the Upper Grand Coulee at this location. Earlier in the Ice Age this was the beginning point of the cataract (see Figure 3-54, Stage 2) that eventually receded northward 25 miles before breaching the divide with the Columbia River Valley (Stage 6). Here also is the beginning of the ancient Coulee City Expansion Bar (No. 37), created as Missoula floodwaters suddenly expanded outward from the confines of the Upper Grand Coulee into the broad expanse of the Hartline Basin and Coulee City area (see Figure 3-77). Notice how the flood bar is plastered against the tilted layers of basalt where it crosses the monocline. Also notice how, traveling south, the size of the flood-transported boulders get smaller farther from the mouth of the coulee. This is because of the slowing currents and dissipating energy associated with the spreading floodwaters.

26.7   The last Ice Age flood incised into the Coulee City expansion bar, leaving behind high remnants of the former bar on either side (see Figure 3-77). The long, eroded escarpment of the approximately 300-foot-tall bar is visible to the left (see Figure 3-72), north of the intersection with U.S. Highway 2.

27.8   End of SR 155. Continue south on U.S. Highway 2.

30.4   Dry Falls Dam at Coulee City is the southern boundary for Banks Lake Reservoir. Cross the Main Canal of the Columbia Basin Project that transports water southward from Banks Lake to irrigate 671,000 acres of farmland downstream across much of southeastern Washington (see "The Columbia Basin Project" sidebar, page 144 in chapter 3). Below the dam to the left are Table Rock and the flood-scoured upland plateau immediately behind Dry Falls (Figure 5-32, Plate 32).

Figure 5-32. Flood-scarred upland plateaus spread out behind and beyond Dry Falls. The popular Dry Falls Visitor Center along State Route 17 is circled at upper right. Aerial view looking south.

32.1   At the west end of Dry Falls Dam turn left (southwest) onto SR 17. Wide, heavily scarred scabland-basalt plateau lies to the left.

34.2   Dry Falls Cataract (No. 41) and Visitor Center. This is perhaps the premiere public vantage point for witnessing the megafloods' destruction (Plates 29 and 32, see Figures 3-80 to 3-82, top). After soaking in the incredible views, be sure to check out the flood displays, videos and books within the J Harlen Bretz Memorial Visitor Center. For some different views farther south of the falls, take a hike along a primitive trail that follows the coulee rim south of the visitor center (chapter 4, Trail CC).

34.4   Another erosional remnant of the gravelly flood sediments of the Coulee City Expansion Bar (No. 37) is visible as an elevated terrace along the west side of SR 17, against the west wall of the coulee. The gravels in this bar are 100 percent basalt; therefore, it must be an older flood feature that developed before the cataract had receded all the way to the head of the upper Grand Coulee, breaching and exposing the granitic inselbergs present there today.

35.5   Wide pullout along left side of SR 17 with scenic view over Sun Lakes State Park, Park Lake and the Lower Grand Coulee (Plate 33). Tilted Hogback Islands (No. 53) lie within the lake below (see Figure 2-21). Above and to left of the coulee are dissected and Grooved Upland Plateaus (No. 45).

36.0   Pass turnoff to Sun Lakes State Park, with access to Deep Lake (No. 46), Monument Coulee (No. 42) and Umatilla Rock (No. 43). Non-motorized trails into these areas lie along the Umatilla Rock Loop (DD), Deep Lake Potholes (EE), Deep Lake Coulee Overlook (FF) and East Park Lake (HH) Trails (see chapter 4 for detailed maps and descriptions). Also notice long series of Hanging Valleys (No. 56) notched into the flood-faceted, high, upper west wall of the coulee (see Figure 2-23, right). Continue southwest on SR 17.

38.2   Across the north end of Blue Lake lies the entrance to Jasper Canyon, whose entrance is plugged with an 80-foot-tall flood bar (see Figure 3-87). Above the steep walls of Jasper Canyon are scarred and Grooved Upland Plateaus (see Figure 3-84, bottom, 3-88, Plates 36 and 37). Looking back up the Lower Grand Coulee, tilted basalt flows along the Coulee Monocline are visible in the high, steep coulee walls (see Figure 3-69).

40.8   A 300-foot-tall pendant-crescent-type flood bar lies at the downstream end of Blue Lake and Jasper Canyon (Figure 5-33, Plate 36). A side entrance to Dry Coulee hangs about 150 feet above Lower Grand Coulee at the south end of the flood bar (see Figure 3-88).

Figure 5-33. As floods flowed over and around the jagged upland plateau on the left, 300 feet of flood deposits of gravel and sand collected to form the smooth surface of a pendant-crescent bar extending to the right. View looking east from State Route 17 (MP 87.5) at south end of Blue Lake. See Plate 36 (lower right) for an aerial view of this same flood bar.

42.5   Pass through a series of tilted basalt flows (hogbacks) folded along the Coulee Monocline, exposed along the shores of Lake Lenore. Ahead is the tall, castellated ridge forming the west wall of The Great Blade (No. 54, see Plates 38 and 39).

43.9   Pass turnoff to Lake Lenore Caves (No. 52) that connects up with hiking trail (Trail II) into East Lenore Coulee (No. 55) via a notch in The Great Blade (see Figure 4-99, Plates 39 and 40). Continue south on SR 17.

44.5   Hanging Valleys (No. 56) of the Lower Grand Coulee are prominently displayed along the west side of the coulee here (see Figure 2-23, right).

45.8   At MP 83 is another trailhead (Plate 40) with access into East Lenore Coulee (Trail II). Just beyond is a small exposure of stratified-silt deposits plastered against the coulee wall at eye level on the left side of the road (see Figure 3-101). These are ancient deposits from so-called Lake Bretz that once filled the Lower Grand Coulee up to an elevation of 1,160 feet. This height, which is 80 feet above present-day Lake Lenore, is the same height as the flood-debris dam (Ephrata Fan, No. 58) that controlled the outlet for Lake Bretz at the end of the Ice Age (Plate 30). During that time there was apparently only a single, continuous lake within the Lower Grand Coulee that extended all the way from Soap Lake to Park Lake. Since the Ice Age, water levels have dropped significantly in the coulee leaving behind the series of isolated, shallower lakes visible today.

Terracettes

Travelers cannot pass through the Channeled Scabland without noticing the unusual, sub-horizontal, mini terraces (terracettes) etched into the coulee walls. They are most visible on grassy slopes of moderately steep coulees (Figure 5-34). The step-like terracettes parallel each other along the slope contour, while others divide, reconnect or crisscross one another. These features are not unique to the Channeled Scabland – many other examples of terracettes are reported worldwide.

Figure 5-34. Terracettes (arrows). The slope on the right, which was created in 1968 during the construction of Little Goose Dam (Snake River), has never seen grazing animals; this suggests an alternate mechanism such as rapid soil creep must be at work – at least for some terracettes.

One idea for their formation is that they formed from grazing animals, similar to those in Figure 5-34 (top), who constantly traverse the slopes back and forth as they feed. An alternate explanation is that they represent scarps from slumping soil pulled down by gravity as the soil undergoes constant expansion and contraction via heating and cooling as well as wetting and drying. Or perhaps some terracettes form from a combination of these (or other) processes. One thing we know for sure is they are much younger than the Ice Age floods and may form relatively quickly (e.g., Figure 5-34, above right).

50.4   At the north end of Soap Lake, irrigation water from the Columbia Basin Project's West Canal (see "Columbia Basin Project" sidebar, page 144 in chapter 3), is delivered from the east to west sides of Soap Lake, completely bypassing the lake via a huge, underground siphon that passes through the basalt bedrock deep beneath the road here (Figure 5-35).

Figure 5-35. A 25-foot diameter siphon, part of the Columbia Basin Irrigation Project, delivers water 2.4 miles underground across Lower Grand Coulee at the north end of Soap Lake. This photo was taken during construction of the siphon in 1942. U.S. BUREAU OF RECLAMATION PHOTO, UNIVERSITY OF WASHINGTON COLLECTION

52.8   As you approach Soap Lake, the steep walls of Grand Coulee suddenly drop away into the broad, expansive Quincy Basin.

53.6   After passing through the town of Soap Lake (see "Eccentric Soap Lake" sidebar, page 167 in Chapter 3) continue south on SR 17. Notice the flat, featureless, gently north-dipping plain that covers the area south of Soap Lake. Also notice all the cultivated fields and lack of any flood-deposited boulders on this north side of the Ephrata Fan. This area was covered in a thick blanket of lake silt (like that in Figure 3-101), laid down after the last megaflood. This is a depositional remnant of the large lake (referred to as Lake Bretz) that temporarily occupied the Lower Grand Coulee up to an elevation of 1,160 feet behind the flood-debris dam of the Ephrata Fan (Plate 30). (Note: This was not a glacial lake, since it wasn't dammed by glacial ice). Apparently the bouldery flood debris (like that in Figure 5-36), more typical of Ephrata Fan, lies buried beneath the silty blanket of lake deposits along this part of the fan.

Figure 5-36. Boulder-strewn Ephrata Fan. These somewhat rounded boulders were transported as bedload along the base of the flood flow and are composed of about 90 percent basalt and 10 percent granite. Most of the granite boulders are likely derived from erosion of the Banks Lake Inselbergs (No. 30) that occurred at the head of the coulee, during floods from the last glacial cycle. Since these boulders were not transported by or encased in ice they are not true erratics, as some have reported previously. View looking northwest toward the mouth of Grand Coulee.

55.1   Where a railroad overpass crosses SR 17 just above Ephrata Lake (Plate 30), at about 1,160-foot elevation, is a single, modest outlet for Lake Bretz that once spilled into present-day Rocky Ford Creek soon after the last flood down Grand Coulee. This last flood, from Glacial Lake Columbia, occurred when a different debris dam (i.e., Coulee City Expansion Bar, No. 37) failed halfway up Grand Coulee and lowered Lake Columbia by 300 feet (See "Lake Columbia Floods" sidebar in Chapter 3, page 130). The ensuing flood further eroded the Lower Grand Coulee while adding bouldery flood depostis (Figure 5-36) onto Ephrata Fan (No. 58) as the flood expanded into the Quincy Basin. Only briefly after this last flood did a small amount of glacial meltwater off the Okanogan Lobe continue to flow into Grand Coulee, allowing a full Lake Bretz to drain south temporarily. This spillover did not last long, however, before the rapidly melting Okanogan Lobe wasted away and ultimately broke apart, sending the remainder of Glacial Lake Columbia down the Columbia Valley to the west.

57.3   Turn left off SR 17 onto unpaved Trout Lodge Road NE (also known as Hatchery Road).

58.0   A giant boulder of basalt deposited onto Ephrata Fan, Monster Rock (see Figure 3-103) looms up to the left.

58.7   View north into Rocky Ford Creek (Plate 30), that once carried meltwater that overfilled Lake Bretz at the end of the last Ice Age.

59.4   At this, our most distant southern point, turn left at "T" intersection past the privately owned and operated Trout Lodge Fish Hatchery along Rocky Ford Creek. At 0.3 mile farther the gravel road changes back to pavement and ascends up the steep east bank of Rocky Ford Creek. Coarse, gravelly deposits that make up the interior of Ephrata Fan expansion flood bar are visible in the roadcut going up the embankment. At top of the grade, turn north onto Road B.5 NE across the relatively flat upper surface of Ephrata Fan strewn with thousands of rounded, flood-tossed boulders. Notice how the size of the boulders increases as we head north toward the mouth of Grand Coulee.

63.1   Follow road as it bends 90 degrees to the west to become Road 19 NE. After one-half mile turn right (north) onto Road B NE for 0.7 mile and then northeast on Road B7/10 NE.

64.8   Bear right (east) onto Road 20 NE. At 2.7 miles turn left (north) onto Adrian Road to State Route 28, which is 2.5 miles farther, crossing over Crab Creek and a tall flood bar along the way. Turn right (east) onto SR 28.

72.6   Turn left (north) off SR 28 onto Pinto Ridge Road that ascends the south side of Pinto Ridge (Plate 30). After one mile cross over the Main Canal for the Columbia Basin Project that delivers water from Billy Clapp Lake Reservoir located several miles northeast of here.

75.3   Several shallow roadcuts expose fertile, windblown Palouse loess that mostly escaped flood erosion and blankets the upper Pinto Ridge where row crops are grown today.

77.5   Summit of Pinto Ridge (elevation 1,945 feet) was only about 100 feet above the maximum flood levels in this area. Immediately upon cresting the summit are wonderful views of scablands to the north (see Figure 3-90). On the left is deep, dark Dry Coulee (No. 50) and straight ahead is the mouth of Hudson Coulee (No. 49, Figure 5-37). Far off in the distance straight ahead is Banks Lake and to left are the high, Hanging Valleys (No. 56) above Lower Grand Coulee. Far below, to the right of Hudson Coulee, is flood-swept Arbuckle Flats. Continue down north flank of Pinto Ridge.

Figure 5-37. The gaping mouth of Hudson Coulee looking north from Pinto Ridge summit.

78.7   Road intersection. To the right is a turnoff to Summer Falls Park (closed in winter) located at the north end of Billy Clapp Lake. The road dead ends after 1.2 miles. The east-west trending, ruler-straight canyon leading to Summer Falls follows a flood-scoured fault plane along the northern end of Pinto Ridge. At Summer Falls is one end of a primitive trail (chapter 4, Trail JJ) that runs along the west side of Spring Coulee. Just ahead a left turn off Pinto Ridge Road follows an unpaved road for another interesting drive through the lower part of Dry Coulee, eventually reconnecting with State Route 28 after 9.6 miles. Continue straight (northeast) on Pinto Ridge Road.

79.2   Drive across an expansion flood bar that formed as floods spread out of Hudson Coulee into the area of Arbuckle Flats (see Figures 3-78 and 3-90). Arbuckle Flats itself is underlain by a flat, flood-swept basalt surface covered with a thin veneer of coarse flood deposits locally molded into megaripples (see Figure 3-78).

80.0   Road runs along the base of a taller flood-scarped, flood bar, 250 feet high that lies to the left between Hudson Coulee and Arbuckle Flats.

81.3   Pinto Ridge Road crosses the Main Canal again, flowing out of Trail Lake Coulee (No. 47) on its way to Summer Falls to the south. The dual outlet of man-made Bacon Tunnel (see Figure 3-86) lies 2.4 miles up this coulee via an unpaved road. Continue northeast on Pinto Ridge Road toward Coulee City.

82.7   Northeast of here the mouth of Arbuckle Draw (No. 39) is visible. The road begins to rise above Arbuckle Flats to gain the upland plateau south of Coulee City.

86.7   On the left is a quick peek into the head of Don Paul Draw cataract canyon, located at the extreme east end of the four-mile-wide Great Cataract Group (Plate 31).

87.8   Where Pinto Ridge Road terminates in Coulee City turn left on Main Street, then take a quick right onto 4th Street to reconnect with U.S. Highway 2. Turn right (northeast) onto U.S. Highway 2.

90.5   Intersection with State Route 155. From here one may retrace the

27.5 miles (along SR 155), followed at the beginning of this tour to return to Grand Coulee Dam, or take a different, alternate route via Hartline and over the Coulee Monocline. The directions that follow are for the slightly longer (about five miles), alternate route over the Coulee Monocline (see Figure 5-26).

90.8   Ascend the incised, eastern escarpment of the Coulee City Expansion Bar (No. 37) along U.S. Highway 2 (see Figure 3-77). Notice flood gravels exposed within the bar as well as the huge boulders (mostly basalt) that litter the broad, flat, upper surface of the bar after 0.5 mile.

93.8   The eastern margin of the Coulee City Expansion Bar lies near a railroad crossing here. Some borrow pits expose mostly coarse sands that make up the inside of the bar. Note that the western portion of the bar, closer to the mouth of the Upper Grand Coulee, contained mostly gravel, but here at the distal east end of the bar are only sandy deposits. This is because farther from the mouth of Upper Grand Coulee, the floods were less energetic here; thus, only sands were transported and deposited. The steeper slopes of the Coulee Monocline (No. 36) rise up just to the north (left).

98.7   Turn left off U.S. Highway 2 onto Road R NE at Hartline. Arrow-straight road heads north, making a steady ascent across the steeper, south limb of the Coulee Monocline (No. 36).

103.2   Near a power line, rise over the crest of the monoclinal ridge (elevation 2,596 feet). Here the ridge was about 1,100 feet above the largest Ice Age floods; therefore, all floods were prevented from washing over this monoclinal ridge. The single exception was within the Upper Grand Coulee (see Figure 3-50) where the floods carved a 25-mile-long recessional cataract canyon. The Coulee Monocline is blanketed with a thin cover of windblown Palouse loess that supports cropland farming along the ridge.

107.7   Begin a series of right-angle turns for the next 10 miles that take us in a net northeasterly direction. The first turn is to the right onto Road 50 NE. Here we are close to the head of Whitney Canyon and the Summit Plateau Scabland (No. 35) located only 1.5 miles north of here (see Figure 6-20).

111.7   After four miles turn north (left) onto Road V NE. Scabland of the southern arm of upper Northrup Canyon (No. 32) is visible only a few miles northwest of here.

113.7   Turn right onto Road 52 NE, proceed another mile before making a last right-angle turn onto Road W NE heading north. Make final descent off Palouse uplands onto the flood-swept upland plateau that spreads out northeastward above Northrup Canyon (Plate 22).

115.9   First sign of erratics (Figure 5-38) along the left side of Road W NE at elevation 2,390 feet. Here, in a drainage culvert that separates the road from adjacent wheat fields, are a number of erratics up to 2 to 3 feet in diameter. Most of the erratics are of granitic composition, although a few smaller, argillite-type Belt rocks are also present. These erratics lie near the trimline for the floods and therefore probably ice rafted into place during one of the largest floods.

Figure 5-38. Highest observed angular erratic (arrow) along upland plateau behind Northrup Canyon (N47.8618, W118.9966). This angular, granodiorite erratic may have been moved slightly from the adjacent wheat field. Looking north.

116.8   Road descends onto the flats of a flood-swept upland plateau east of Northrup Canyon (Plate 22).

118.0   Intersection with Grand Coulee Hill Road. Turn left (northwest) to head across low-relief, butte-and-basin scabland along the central portion of the flood-scoured upland plateau.

118.9   Long Lake (see Figure 3-61) is visible on the right. Long Lake and adjacent scabland were carved out by floods that spilled over this plateau via Spring Canyon during earlier floods either before breaching of the cataract at the head of Grand Coulee (No. 29), and/or when the Upper Grand Coulee was partially to completely filled with glacial ice from the Okanogan Lobe (see Figure 3-65, Plate 22).

120.7   Begin switchback descent northward off upland plateau into the head of Grand Coulee.

122.1   Good view down onto breached spillover channel at head of Grand Coulee (see Figures 3-55 and 3-56).

122.8   At bottom of grade, road name changes to Spokane Way; turn left at intersection with State Route 174. Make final one-half mile descent into the town of Grand Coulee, and turn right onto State Route 155 toward Grand Coulee Dam Visitor Center.

125.6   Grand Coulee Dam Visitor Center. End of road tour.

Road Tour 5: Moses Coulee-Waterville Plateau Loop

From Wenatchee this 136-mile loop follows most of the 50-mile-long Moses Coulee before heading up onto the unflooded uplands of the Waterville Plateau, covered by glacial ice during most outburst floods. The Withrow Moraine defines the edge of the vanished ice sheet and is viewed in several places before the route descends into the Columbia Valley. Here is more dramatic evidence for the Okanogan Lobe and at least two megafloods (one early and one late) that escaped down the entrenched Columbia Valley during the last cycle of glaciation.

Road Log

0.0　　Start in East Wenatchee at intersection of State Route 28 and Grant Road, at elevation 750 feet. Head south on SR 28. Large, rounded boulders along highway were carried via a last flood from the final break up of the Okanogan Lobe, which released the contents of Glacial Lake Columbia hundreds of years after the last Missoula flood.

3.1　　SR 28 runs along a lower of two flood bars perched 120 feet above the Columbia River. This bar is littered with more huge, rounded boulders tumbled and rolled along by the Lake Columbia outburst flood. On the left is the face of another, much taller bar, called the Pangborn Bar (No. 65). This bar was created from one of the largest Ice Age floods that took place early in the last glacial cycle – before the Okanogan Lobe had advanced across the Columbia River (see Figure 1-11, position A). The top of Pangborn Bar lies 500 feet above the road here (see Figure 3-117). Ahead and to the right is the tall, steep, north face of basaltic Jumpoff Ridge.

5.7　　Megafloods coming down the Columbia River were funneled along the north side of the Jumpoff Ridge before flowing through a constriction at its east end. Here, the floodwaters flowed counterclockwise around the southern end of Pangborn Bar where a huge, circulating (counterclockwise) eddy, up to two miles in diameter, left behind an eddy scar at the downstream end of the bar (see Figure 3-118).

7.0　　The steep, 600-foot-tall eddy scar at the south end of Pangborn Bar is visible to the left near Rock Island. This flood bar came from one or more very large floods that occurred early in the last glacial cycle, perhaps around 25,000 to 28,000 years ago, before the Okanogan Lobe had advanced over the "big bend" of the Columbia River (position A in Figure 1-11).

10.0　　Visible downvalley is another tall (300 to 400 feet) flood bar perched high above either side of the Columbia River. This is the northern extension of Moses Coulee Bar (No. 2 in Figure 3-118) that extends for more than 11 miles along the Columbia River from Rock Island Dam almost all the way to Trinidad. The interior of the bar is composed of coarse flood deposits from at least five floods derived from Moses Coulee. The deposits from Moses Coulee making up this expansion bar are composed of almost purely basaltic gravel and sand, formed via erosion of Moses Coulee, which is exclusively underlain by dark basalt. This is in contrast to flood deposits transported down the Columbia River that contain lots of other non-basalt rock fragments, including a large proportion of light-colored granite.

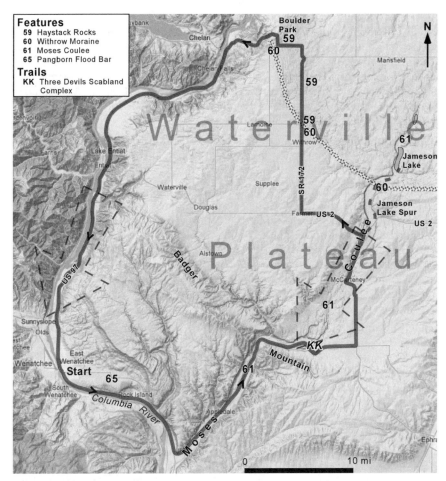

Figure 5-39. Google map with road tour (highlighted) along the Moses Coulee-Waterville Plateau road tour. Only a few floods escaped down Moses Coulee and the Columbia Valley to the west. Most floods were diverted across the eastern Channeled Scabland by the Okanogan Lobe (Plate 1). Features along route are described in chapter 3; nearby non-motorized trails are presented in chapter 4.

Across the top of Moses Coulee Bar is a different type of deposit (sandy rhythmites) derived from later floods directed down the Channeled Scabland that backflooded up the Columbia River from the scabland coulees at the west side of the Quincy Basin (e.g., Potholes Coulee in Figure 3-118). These later floods were restricted to the Channeled Scabland during a time when the Okanogan Lobe blocked flood flow to the Columbia Valley as well as Moses Coulee. The last event to affect Moses Coulee Bar was a last outburst flood (i.e., from Glacial Lake Columbia). This last flood incised and bisected Moses Coulee Bar (the northwestern part of the bar on the other side of the river is called Rock Island Bar). The last outburst flood from Glacial Lake Columbia locally blanketed Moses Coulee Bar with more coarse sediment that contains much less basalt, since it was diluted with non-basalt rock fragments exposed around the margins of the Columbia Plateau.

11.9   SR 28 rises up onto the Moses Coulee Bar. A short distance farther roadcuts expose laminated, fine sand and silt deposits along the north side of the bar. These were deposited after the last floods down Moses Coulee built up the Moses Coulee Bar. Later, floods from the Channeled Scabland backflooded the valley, depositing these fine sediments into a standing lake that formed behind the Moses Coulee Bar obstruction. The lake was subsequently drained after the last flood – a Glacial Lake Columbia outburst that cut through Moses Coulee Bar and breached the silt-laden lake.

13.2   Undulating surface atop the flat, upper surface of Moses Coulee Bar shows some weakly developed giant current ripples left behind by the Glacial Lake Columbia flood.

14.2   At the gaping mouth of Moses Coulee turn left (east) onto Palisades Road. As you head into Moses Coulee, notice how the surface of the Moses Coulee Bar continues to descend up the coulee. This is an indication that the floodwaters last responsible for the bar came from the direction of the Columbia Valley (i.e., the last Glacial Lake Columbia flood). If the last floods had come down Moses Coulee, the sediment buildup would be higher in Moses Coulee, which is not the case. Canyon walls expose multiple flows of Grande Ronde Basalt along the base of the coulee.

14.5   For the next several miles, a long series of hanging valleys lies high above the south side of Moses Coulee (Plate 49). These hanging valleys formed in much the same way as those in the Lower Grand Coulee (No. 56). They mark the former levels of tributary streams that once gradually drained into McCarteney Creek (precursor to Moses Coulee). Ice Age floods since reamed out, deepened and oversteepened the walls of Moses Coulee, leaving the tributary valleys perched high above the valley bottom.

15.8   A layer of white volcanic ash, about 1 foot thick, is exposed in a steep talus slope along the coulee wall at left. This ash was deposited during the volcanic eruption of Mount Mazama (southern Oregon's Crater Lake) about 7,700 years ago, long after the last Ice Age flood. Since that time the ash was buried under several more feet of talus and subsequently exposed to reveal this record.

18.3   Borrow pit on the right exposes coarse flood deposits within a flood bar along the coulee bottom. In another mile pass by a whale-backed flood bar on the right within the center of the coulee.

19.8   At the base of the north coulee wall on the left is Chief Moses Council Cave, an overhanging, hollowed out rock shelter (Figure 5-40). Apparently a wonderfully preserved, American Indian smoking pipe was discovered within this cave.

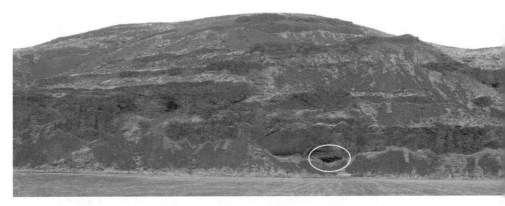

Figure 5-40. Chief Moses Council Cave, Moses Coulee. The rock shelter cave (circled), on private land, is almost filled in with an apron of talus shed off the cliffs of Grande Ronde Basalt from above, slowly deposited over the millennia since the last megaflood down Moses Coulee. Looking northwest.

21.6   A flood bar with giant current ripples blankets the coulee bottom on the right (Plate 49). Ahead a rock bench (100 to 200 feet tall), with wonderfully exposed basalt columns, flanks either side of the coulee bottom. More hanging valleys are perched high above the coulee walls on either side.

24.0   Immediately ahead is a longitudinal-type flood bar that runs along the east side of the coulee. Roadcut into the bar exposes rounded, basalt boulders up to 10 feet in diameter that testify to the debacles that once passed through Moses Coulee.

25.0   Pass through tiny, downtown Palisades (established 1908).

26.8   A 130-foot-tall crescent flood bar, with a distinct leading edge, lies along the inside of a sharp bend in the coulee (see Figure 3-109). A borrow pit on its east side exposes the coarse detritus inside. This is also where Moses Coulee cuts through the upwarped Badger Mountain anticline (see Figure 6-13).

28.6   Near the mouth of Douglas Creek notice how the basalt layers dip to the northeast and southwest on either side of the anticlinal ridge (Figure 5-41). Coming in from the opposite side is a post-flood alluvial fan from Douglas Creek, a major tributary of Moses Coulee. The alluvial fan and crescent flood bar merge toward the coulee center. At the end of the Ice Age as meltwater from the Okanogan Lobe drained down Moses Coulee, the glacial meltwater appears to have pooled behind this bar-fan dam. Behind the dam today is a broad, very flat, surface (i.e., ancient lake bottom) that extends upvalley for four miles, all the way to the base of the Three Devils cataract at Billingsley Ranch (Figure 5-42).

Figure 5-41. Canyon country of lower Moses Coulee near the mouth of Douglas Creek. Looking up the coulee to the southeast at the dogleg in Moses Coulee (see Figure 3-109).

29.3   Three Devils scabland complex, with a number of hanging coulees, comes into view (Figure 5-42).

30.0   End of pavement. A wide, well-maintained gravel road continues. Going 0.4 mile farther prominent buttes appear to the right; they formed from floods spilling over hanging coulees from above. Note the extremely flat bottom of the coulee here; this is the ancient lake bottom that developed as glacial meltwater collected behind a flood bar-fan dam at the mouth of Douglas Creek described above.

Figure 5-42. Aerial view toward the Three Devils scabland complex. The extremely flat nature of lower Moses Coulee suggests a post-flood lake once filled in the valley here.

32.2   The 200-foot-tall Steamboat Rock (Figure 5-42) lies along the edge of the cataract that divides lower from upper Moses Coulee. The broad, flat field at the base of the cataract is a giant, sediment-filled plunge pool. Water wells in the plunge pool have been drilled to 400 feet without hitting basalt bedrock, suggesting a cataract and waterfall at least 600 feet tall existed here during formation of the cataract! After another one-half mile, this public county road bends right (south) to go through the Billingsley Ranch before ascending into the Three Devils Coulee (Figure 5-42, Plate 46).

33.1   Road levels off in the Three Devils Coulee. To the right is a pullout with parking at the trailhead for the Three Devils Extension Trail (chapter 4, Trail KK1, see Figures 4-106 and 4-107).

33.7   Huge columns of basalt, characteristic of the Roza Member basalt, are exposed to the left. Immediately above the columns is a zone of wavy, curving, platy basalt. Both the columnar and curving, platy fracture patterns developed 15 million years ago as this basalt flow solidified from molten lava.

34.6   Pass over the stair-stepped cataract that lies at the head of the Three Devils Coulee.

35.0   Just past a cattle guard, to the right, is a gravel road leading to the trailhead for the Three Devils Overlook Trail (chapter 4, Trail KK2, see Figures 4-106 and 4-108). About 0.1 mile farther the road straightens to become Road 12 SE. Moses Coulee widens into a broad, open valley along central Moses Coulee called Sagebrush Flat (see Figures 3-109 and 6-13).

35.2   After 0.4 mile road flattens out atop flood bar and heads straight east across the expansive Sagebrush Flat. As Ice Age floods spread out into this broad basin, they lost much of their power and ability to erode, which explains the general lack of dramatic flood features along this stretch of the coulee. Instead of eroding, the floods deposited expansive flood bars of sand and gravel. Ahead is a broad, low flood bar with borrow pits and roadcuts exposing the coarse flood sediment within the bar.

36.7   Gravel road turns back to pavement.

38.0   Four-way road intersection. From Road 12 SE turn left (north) onto Coulee Meadows Road (also signed as Road B SE).

40.0   Pass through Rimrock Meadows – a struggling real estate development atop a rocky bench out in the middle of the dry, barren, treeless desert.

42.1   Descend off the rock bench into butte-and-basin scabland of the Coyote Canyon-McCarteney Creek canyons. At 0.4 mile farther is a borrow pit on the right exposing a portion of a huge flood bar within Coyote Canyon.

44.0   Descend onto the flat bottom of the upper Moses Coulee. Here, where the coulee narrows, the canyon walls once again rise to form a single, well-defined, inner coulee canyon.

45.1   The three-mile-long Great Bar of Moses Coulee (Plate 47; see also Figures 3-109 and 3-111) is visible ahead, hugging the west wall of Moses Coulee. The Great Bar begins as a pendant-type bar below a basalt headland and transitions to a longitudinal-crescent flood bar along the inside of a broad bend in Moses Coulee where flood currents were less energetic and allowed sediment buildup to occur.

47.1   Moses Coulee Road (Coulee Meadows Road) begins its ascent onto the south end of the Great Bar.

48.3   Traverse the top of the 250-foot-tall flood bar (see Figure 3-111).

49.4   Coulee Meadows Road ends atop the Great Bar at intersection with U.S. Highway 2.

Jameson Lake Spur

This 7.5-mile one-way spur continues up Moses Coulee, over the outwash train for the Okanogan Lobe, before crossing the Withrow Moraine and on to serene Jameson Lake, where abundant recreational opportunities await, including camping, picnicking, boating and fishing.

Figure 5-43. Upper Moses Coulee. Frozen Dutch Henry Falls in winter, looking west.

49.4   Turn right (northeast) onto U.S. Highway 2. Descend off the Great Bar (Plate 47) and proceed 1.1 miles to Jameson Lake Road. Turn left (north). For the next several miles, the valley bottom is covered with a network of abandoned stream channels that are not very visible at road level but are striking on aerial photographs (see Figures 3-111 and 6-14). The channels are meltwater channels that meandered back and forth along the valley floor as the Okanogan Lobe melted away at the close of the Ice Age.

51.3   Pavement ends; continue on wide, flat, well-maintained gravel road through upper Moses Coulee.

52.0   Rise up onto large pendant flood bar that formed downstream of the rocky ridge in the middle of Moses Coulee just to the north.

53.1   View of the Withrow Moraine ahead and to the right, characterized by the uneven, hummocky mounds that lie along the coulee bottom as well as on top of the mid-canyon basalt ridge (see Figure 3-108). The moraine represents the farthest extent of glacial ice from the Okanogan Lobe (Figure 5-44, see Figure 3-105). Notice how the morainal mounds are superimposed on top of the relatively flat, smooth flood bar. This indicates that the Okanogan Lobe occupied this valley with ice after the last flood that deposited the bar! If another flood had come afterward, it would have certainly destroyed or severely modified the hummocky moraine, which is not the case. Therefore, we can say with certainty that Moses Coulee was used only during earlier floods before the Okanogan Lobe had reached its maximum extent (i.e., more than 20,000 years ago) and subsequent Ice Age floods were diverted away from Moses Coulee.

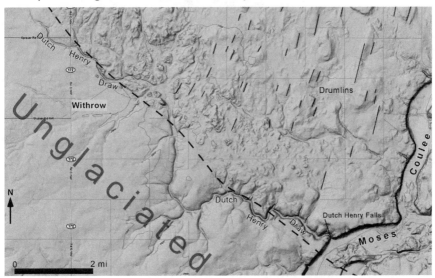

Figure 5-44. Google map showing the edge of the former Okanogan Lobe at the Withrow Moraine (dashed line). Notice the well-developed meltwater channel (Dutch Henry Draw) that developed along the leading edge of the glacier. Note also how drumlins and lineaments are aligned with the direction of flow (from the northeast) for the massive ice sheet. The Withrow Moraine and Jameson Lake Drumlin Field together are recognized as a National Natural Landmark (see www.nature.nps.gov/nnl/).

54.4   On the right is a roadcut exposing the glacial till that makes up the Withrow Moraine (Figure 5-45). Just ahead, across the road, is a short (one-quarter mile) hiking trail, maintained by The Nature Conservancy, to Dutch Henry Falls (Figure 5-43). As the Okanogan Lobe melted back at the end of the last Ice Age, a prominent channel called Dutch Henry Draw carried meltwater along the Withrow Moraine and the leading edge of the melting glacier (Figure 5-44). At that time Dutch Henry Falls must have been fully gorged with the milky meltwater as the flow shot over the falls into Moses Coulee.

Figure 5-45. Chaotic, unsorted glacial till of the Withrow Moraine exposed along the public road to Jameson Lake. Small notebook (circled) for scale. See Figure 3-108 for a nearby view showing the characteristic hummocky morphology of the Withrow Moraine. Looking southeast.

56.3   Arrive at south end of Jameson Lake (Plate 48). A gate (closed in winter) lies 0.6 mile ahead, which provides access into the recreation area.

57.0   Road ends at the recreation area and boat launch, managed by the Washington Department of Fish and Wildlife (Washington Discover Pass required), along east side of Jameson Lake. End of spur. Retrace route to U.S. Highway 2.

64.8   Turn right (southwest) onto U.S. Highway 2. Recross floor of Moses Coulee and the Great Bar before exiting coulee to the west via Armour Draw.

69.3   At the head of Armour Draw continue west across the broad uplands of the Waterville Plateau. This relatively flat upland reflects the surface of the Columbia River basalt, which is covered with a thin mantle of fine-textured, windblown, Palouse loess. This fertile, fine-soil mantle supports an abundance of agriculture here south of the Withrow Moraine (see Figure 3-105).

72.7   At Farmer (Figure 5-46), turn right (north) onto State Route 172 toward Withrow. Over the next six miles cross more fertile, crop-covered high plains of the Waterville Plateau. A huge sky spreads out in all directions as far as the eye can see.

Figure 5-46. U.S. Highway 2 spreads out across the expansive, elevated Waterville Plateau at Farmer. This area that lies beyond the Withrow Moraine consists of relatively smooth and flat, productive farmland. Looking west.

77.4   Visible ahead, beyond the lonely town of Withrow, is the distinct hummocky edge of the Withrow Moraine. Notice how the mounded moraine contrasts with the almost flat, even surface on this side of the moraine. After another 1.4 mile pass the remote and isolated hamlet of Withrow.

80.2   First huge, basalt boulders (Haystack Rocks, No. 59) are visible along the glacial moraine that developed near the front of the Okanogan Lobe.

80.6   Cross Dutch Henry Draw, a channel that once carried glacial melt-water eastward, toward Moses Coulee, along the edge of the Okanogan Lobe (Figure 5-44). Rising up onto the elevated moraine, notice the abundance of Haystack Rocks, as well as granitic glacial erratics, littering the surface.

81.8   The land surface levels off somewhat north of the moraine's edge but is still chaotic, undulating and irregular. Haystack Rocks (No. 59) spread out across the glacial-debris-covered Waterville Plateau in all directions. Imagine, during the Ice Age, this area was completely covered with a thousand feet or more of slowly moving, grinding ice that, like a conveyor belt, brought down a steady stream of debris from the north. Lineaments and aligned, streamlined hills of glacial till (drumlins) visible to the right were molded into shape under the tremendous weight and pressure of the massive, slowly moving ice sheet (Figure 5-44).

86.7   Turn left onto McNeil Canyon Road (Road C NW) toward Chelan. After 1.3 miles road bends left (west) onto Road 15 NW (Mud Springs Road).

88.9   Hummocky upland ahead and to the right is Boulder Park (Figure 5-47), which defines the northwest end of the Withrow Moraine (see Figure 5-39). Huge haystack boulders of basalt litter its surface. The tour route passes the southern end of Boulder Park after about a mile.

Figure 5-47. Boulder Park (private land) is located at the northwest end of the Withrow Moraine. House-sized boulders are basaltic Haystack Rocks (No. 59) that were carried along and dumped along the edge of the Okanogan Lobe ice sheet. Looking northwest. This area is included in the Boulder Park and McNeil Canyon Haystack Rocks National Natural Landmark.

90.3   Follow McNeil Canyon Road as it bends to the right (north). After one mile road begins its long descent down McNeil Canyon to the Columbia River Valley. Here, at the west end of the Columbia Plateau, the basalt is relatively thin and the strongly weathered, pre-basalt, crystalline rocks are exposed. Most of McNeil Canyon is covered with hummocky glacial debris and Haystack Rocks, suggesting the Okanogan Lobe once occupied this canyon at the same time the Withrow Moraine was forming atop the Waterville Plateau to the east.

93.3   Several miles ahead, across the Columbia Valley, is a view looking down onto the mouth of the bedrock basin holding back Lake Chelan. During the Ice Age a tongue of slowly creeping ice (an extension of the Okanogan Lobe) descended into the Columbia Valley. This tongue of ice backed up into the lower Lake Chelan Valley, leaving behind a tall dam of glacial debris (sand and gravel) that today holds back Lake Chelan.

95.6   Cross a narrow, flat bench that lies several hundred feet above the river along the east wall of the Columbia Valley. A couple of borrow pits excavated into the bench expose water-worn gravels and sand with relatively few basalt fragments. This is the so-called "Great Terrace" that formed as glacial debris accumulated along the edge, as well as in front, of the retreating Columbia River tongue of the Okanogan Lobe. North of here the glacier did not come into contact with very much dark basalt, which explains the low basalt content within the glacial debris. Instead there is an abundance of light-colored sediment clasts derived from granitic and gneissic rocks that crop out around the perimeter of the Columbia Plateau. Today the Great Terrace can be intermittently traced northward into the Okanogan River Valley all the way to British Columbia.

98.2   At the bridge that crosses the Columbia River turn left (south) onto U.S. Highway 97. Ahead the 700-foot-high Great Terrace (Figure 5-48, lower left) is distinctly visible lining the sides of the Columbia Valley.

101.5   The Great Terrace ends temporarily. The road continues to parallel a lower terrace only about 100 to 200 feet above river level. This lower terrace is associated with the last outburst flood, from the sudden breakup of the Okanogan Lobe that drained the contents of Glacial Lake Columbia at the very end of the Ice Age about 14,000 years ago. Near this point was the maximum extent of an ice tongue of the Okanogan Lobe that extended down the Columbia Valley from the north.

107.4   The Great Terrace reappears on the left as a high bench along the inside of a large bend in the Columbia Valley (Figure 5-48, upper right). The road parallels the edge of the Great Terrace atop a lower bench – a Glacial Lake Columbia flood bar that slopes toward the river 250 feet below the Great Terrace. The Lake Columbia flood bar is littered with huge, rounded, mostly non-basalt boulders that rolled and tumbled along the bar surface during the last Ice Age flood.

116.5   Entiat River enters the Columbia River from the west. A couple of miles farther is Orondo. Continue south on U.S. Highway 97.

Figure 5-48. Two bench-like sediment terraces line the Columbia River Valley. The narrow, flat, upper terrace (i.e., Great Terrace) was derived from the slow melting of the Okanogan Lobe that occupied this valley late into the last Ice Age. The lower terrace, which slopes toward the river, is a flood bar that formed later during an outburst flood from Glacial Lake Columbia at the very end of the Ice Age.

122.6   Across the river is a large eddy flood bar, also known as a "gulch fill," covered with giant current ripples (Figure 5-49) at the mouth of the Tenas George Canyon. The ripples are slightly steeper on their north sides suggesting the flow was upvalley – opposite the direction of the floods. The ripples probably formed as water circulated around in an eddy that formed at the entrance to this canyon. The bar is higher nearer the mouth of the side canyon and slopes down away from the Columbia Valley – an indication it was deposited by water moving down the Columbia Valley rather than down the tributary. As the floodwaters expanded and swirled around in the mouth of this side canyon, the bar was slightly more protected from the ravaging flood currents. This bar was deposited during one or more of the early, especially large Ice Age floods, which swept down the Columbia Valley before the Okanogan Lobe had advanced far enough to block the "Big Bend" of the Columbia River (see Figure 1-11, position A). This was probably the same megaflood(s) that formed the huge Pangborn Bar (No. 65) – downstream in Wenatchee, which rises to a similar height (about elevation 1,200 feet).

Figure 5-49. Flat-topped, eddy flood bar (arrows) rises 500 feet above the Columbia River (foreground). Regularly spaced giant current ripples cover the sloping surface of the bar facing the viewer. Since the Ice Age erosion by a side stream has eroded and divided the bar into two segments. Looking northwest.

123.6   Good view of Turtle Rock, a large island within the Columbia River channel. Turtle Rock, composed of a metamorphic rock called gneiss, probably originated as a pre-flood landslide block that slid into the Columbia River from the east.

125.9   Road passes over another longitudinal-crescent-type flood bar derived from a Glacial Lake Columbia flood. Rounded, non-basaltic boulders lie atop the surface of the flood bar. The rounded boulders are mostly derived from non-basaltic (i.e., granite and gneiss) rocks exposed along the Columbia Valley north of Wenatchee. These boulders arrived here as bedload that rolled and tumbled along with the flood outburst that drained Lake Columbia at the very end of the Ice Age.

131   Continue straight (south) on State Route 28 through East Wenatchee.

133.6   Descending into East Wenatchee notice the high, flat leading edge of the Pangborn Bar (No. 65) as it comes into view on the left. Over the next couple of miles notice more huge, light-colored (i.e., non-basalt), flood-transported boulders used in retaining walls and landscaping within the city.

135.0   More huge boulders are scattered across a 150-foot-tall flood bar that underlies most of East Wenatchee. Many of the boulders lie along a public, paved path located here between the highway and the Columbia River (Figure 5-50). The largest flood-displaced boulders are an incredible 40 feet in diameter!

Figure 5-50. In East Wenatchee huge boulders on a flood bar lie above the Columbia River, derived from an outburst flood from Glacial Lake Columbia – the last great flood to move through this area at the very end of the Ice Age. Looking south.

135.6   Exit toward Quincy continuing on SR 28.

136.3   Intersection with Grant Road. End of road tour.

Above Lenore Caves and The Great Blade, Lower Grand Coulee

6

Aerial Tours

Two aerial tours are custom designed to fly over the widest range and most spectacular flood features of the Channeled Scabland in the least amount of time (Figure 6-1). The tours are 1) Cheney-Palouse/Telford-Crab Creek Tour, starting in Spokane and covering the eastern Scabland, and 2) Moses Coulee-Grand Coulee Tour starting in Wenatchee and encompassing the western Scabland. It is also possible to connect the two aerial tours into a single, longer (335 mile) flight via the dashed routes shown in Figure 6-1. Flood features visible along these aerial routes are described in more detail in chapter 3.

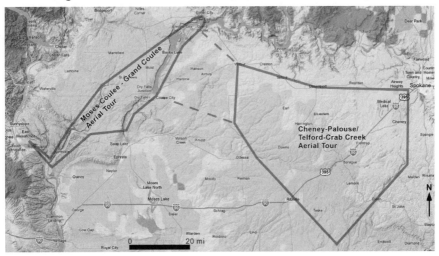

Figure 6-1 Google map with locations of two aerial tours featured in this chapter.

To charter a scenic flight, contact a pilot or air charter company in the vicinity of either Spokane (Spokane International or Felts Field) or Wenatchee (Pangborn Memorial), both in Washington. Other smaller municipal airports in the area include Wilbur, Davenport, Odessa, Lind, Ritzville, Mead, Moses Lake, Ephrata, Mansfield, Waterville, Wilson Creek, Quincy, Rosalia and Grand Coulee Dam. Additional municipal airports are located in Coeur d'Alene, Sandpoint and Bonners Ferry, Idaho. For anyone flying their own plane, be sure to contact a Flight Service Station for an up-to-date briefing on weather conditions and Temporary Flight Restrictions. For the two routes shown in this guide, the most likely features to generate restrictions are the Grand Coulee Dam and Fairchild Air Force Base in Spokane. Currently, it is generally prohibited to circle over these sensitive areas, but overflights along a straight flight path were unrestricted at the time of this writing.

Whether chartering with a professional pilot or flying in a personal aircraft, here are some tips for optimizing the views, photographic opportunities and enjoyment of the flight:

- When flying in a clockwise direction, recommended for most small planes, the best views of most flood features will be out the right (i.e., passenger) side of the aircraft.

- Fly during the morning or evening hours, when the air tends to be more stable and the ride smoother. Morning and evening hours also provide the best lighting conditions and least amount of haze. During spring and fall, plant foliage provides more pleasing color contrasts.

- An altitude of several thousand feet is a good compromise for viewing large- and small-scale features. A cruise power setting for the engine contributes to a smoother and quieter flight experience.

- For the most pleasing photographic results, use a moderately fast shutter speed (1/250th second or faster) and fix the focus on infinity, so the autofocus feature doesn't disappoint by fixing on the window. Carefully clean the window viewing area before the flight and pay close attention to reflections that may appear while shooting. When photographing through windows of the aircraft, it is best to have the sun behind you.

- Additional options to improve photographic results include shooting through an open window; using a polarizing filter; and approaching as close as possible to the scene you wish to photograph. Wide-angle lenses, up to 35 millimeter, are helpful. It is difficult to obtain pleasing aerial images with a telephoto lens.

- While photographing features, try to keep the horizon in your peripheral vision and in the image frame of the camera.

Table 6-1. Geographic coordinates, bearings and distances for the seven legs of the Cheney-Palouse/Telford-Crab Creek Aerial Tour.

Leg No.	Destination Along Route	Latitude	Longitude	Bearing (degrees from true north)	Leg Distance (miles)	Cumulative Distance (miles)
Start	Spokane Airport	N47.6197	W117.5320			
1	NE side Bonnie Lake	47.2874	117.5100	177	23.0	23.0
2	East Benge	46.9135	118.0276	223	35.5	58.5
3	Sylvan Lake	47.3214	118.5964	316	38.6	97.1
4	Marlin Hollow	47.4907	118.7470	329	13.0	110.1
5	Wilbur	47.7541	118.7176	4	17.6	127.7
6	Davenport	47.6529	118.1377	104	27.7	155.4
7	Spokane Airport	47.6197	117.5320	94	28.3	183.7

1. Cheney-Palouse/Telford-Crab Creek Aerial Tour

Figure 6-2 shows the aerial tour route for the eastern Channeled Scabland. The total length is about 184 miles. This tour takes about 2.5 hours to complete at an average speed of 75 miles per hour. Table 6-1 presents specific directions for the seven legs of this tour that loop in a clockwise direction starting at the Spokane International Airport.

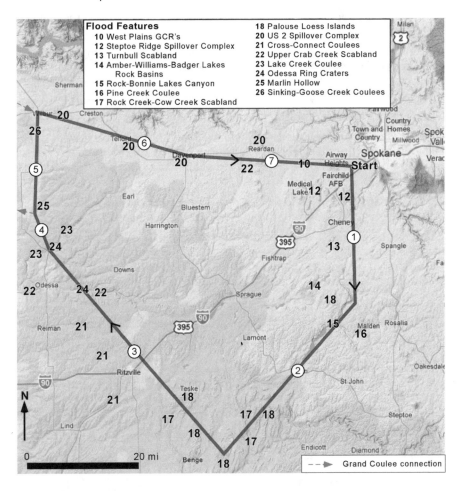

Flood Features
10 West Plains GCR's
12 Steptoe Ridge Spillover Complex
13 Turnbull Scabland
14 Amber-Williams-Badger Lakes
   Rock Basins
15 Rock-Bonnie Lakes Canyon
16 Pine Creek Coulee
17 Rock Creek-Cow Creek Scabland
18 Palouse Loess Islands
20 US 2 Spillover Complex
21 Cross-Connect Coulees
22 Upper Crab Creek Scabland
23 Lake Creek Coulee
24 Odessa Ring Craters
25 Marlin Hollow
26 Sinking-Goose Creek Coulees

Grand Coulee connection

Figure 6-2. The Cheney-Palouse/Telford-Crab Creek Aerial Tour. See chapter 3 for more detailed descriptions of numbered flood features along route.

Flight Log

Leg 1

Start: Spokane Airport

Destination: Bonnie Lake

Cumulative Distance

0   Depart Spokane Airport and immediately head south into the head of the Cheney-Palouse Scabland Tract (Plate 10).

6   Fly across the east end of the Steptoe Ridge Spillover Complex (No. 12), a series of rounded hills that resisted the attack of floodwaters, except in the low gaps between the hills (see Figure 3-21). Many flood-scoured lakes, like Fish Lake below, occupy flood-scoured rock basins between the steptoe hills.

8   Enter forested scabland beyond the treeless Palouse north of Cheney.

12   Fly over Kepple Lake (see Figure 4-25) and other flood-scoured wetlands of the Turnbull National Wildlife Refuge (No. 13) for the next several miles. The Pine Creek Auto Tour Road and several hiking trails are located in the refuge below (chapter 4, Trail L).

17   Rolling Palouse hills (see Figure 1-9) spread out to the east (left) untouched by and beyond the influence of the Ice Age floods.

23   Where Rock Creek enters the north end of Bonnie Lake, a canyon follows a linear, northwest-trending fracture zone in the basalt (see Figure 3-28). The weaker rock along fractures was etched out by powerful flood forces. Turn southwest to fly over the east side of Rock Lake (Figure 6-3, Plate 13).

Figure 6-3. Hole-in-the-Ground Canyon connects Bonnie and Rock lakes (No. 15). Today, only the grossly underfit Rock Creek flows through this steep-walled, multitiered cataract canyon.

Leg 2

Start: Bonnie Lake

Destination: East Benge

26 More gently rolling Palouse uplands that escaped the floods' wrath spread out to the left (east). An isolated steptoe island at the lower end of Bonnie Lake is composed of about 1.5 billion-year-old basement rock of the Belt Supergroup that lies beneath a thin cover of 15 million-year-old basalt lava in this region (see Figure 3-30). Consider for a moment the mind-boggling disparity in age – the rocks of the steptoe island are one-thousandth that of the overlying Columbia River basalt!

28 "Hole in the Ground" is the name given the dry portion of the canyon separating Bonnie Lake from Rock Lake along Rock Creek Coulee (Figure 6-3). Pine Creek Coulee (No. 16), a side coulee coming in from the east, enters near the head of Rock Lake (Plate 13). A well-developed recessional cataract and rock blade lie near this juncture (see Figure 4-39). Two non-motorized trails, North Rock Lake (Trail P) and Bonnie Lake Steptoe (Trail Q) visible below, are featured in chapter 4.

31 Flood-sculpted Castle Rock butte and Castle Rock Lake lie atop a rock bench high above the east side of Rock Lake. Castle Rock is a lone remnant of a basalt layer that was scrubbed away from the surrounding area by the turbulent flow of cataclysmic floodwaters.

47 Several parallel scabland channels, separated by Palouse Loess Islands (No. 18), lie just downstream of Rock Lake along Rock Creek. One of these streamlined islands is shown in Figure 6-4. See Plate 15 for another perspective looking toward Rock Creek from the south.

Figure 6-4. Streamlined and scarped Palouse hills of the Rock Creek Scabland Complex (No. 17) at Texas Lake. Note steep prow at upstream end and secondary cross channel (solid white arrow) that crosses the head of the loess island in foreground. In contrast, are the rough, flood-gouged channels on either side, dotted with post-flood Mima mounds (see "Mysterious Mima Mounds" sidebar in chapter 3, page 83). Large block arrows indicate primary direction of floodwaters. Looking southeast.

52   Towell Falls (Figure 6-5) drops over a rocky ledge along Rock Creek Coulee (see Figure 4-45).

Figure 6-5. Double Towell Falls drop over a basalt ledge along Rock Creek. These falls can be accessed on the ground via Trail R (see chapter 4). Looking northwest.

54   Some of the best examples of Palouse Loess Islands (No. 18) are visible over the next dozen miles to Benge and beyond on either side of the aircraft. Notice the smoothed hills with their steep prows (Figure 6-6; see also Figures 2-22, 3-32 and 3-33, Plates 14 and 15) – all aligned and pointing in the direction of floodwater flow like a "flotilla of ships."

Figure 6-6. Steep prow at upstream end of Palouse island in the Cow Creek Scabland Complex (No. 17). See Figure 5-15 for another aerial perspective of this streamlined and scarped hill. Floods, hundreds of feet deep, rushed along either side of the island; some of the flow also overtopped the island (indicated with smaller arrows). Looking southeast.

58   Just east of Benge alter course to the northwest (see new bearings in Table 6-1). Up until now this aerial route has been parallel to the ancient flood flows; the next leg of the tour trends perpendicular to the flood flow. As a result the next leg crosses a long series of scabland channels separated by flood-molded islands of Palouse loess within the lower Rock Creek-Cow Creek Scabland Complex (No. 17, see Figure 3-32).

"Literally hundreds of isolated groups of maturely eroded hills of loess stand in the scablands. Their gentle interior slopes are identical with those far from scabland tracts. But their marginal slopes, descending to the scablands, commonly are very steep."

– J Harlen Bretz (1923)

Leg 3

Start: East Benge

Destination: Sylvan Lake

68   Near Marengo (see Figure 3-32) fly over a dissected Palouse upland that was eroded and divided into three separate streamlined and scarped Palouse hills.

74   Fly over Cow Creek with more bizarre scabland and Palouse islands south of Ritzville.

79   Pass over Interstate 90 with Ritzville on the left (west).

87   Below are several Cross-Connect Coulees (No. 21) including Bauer and Rocky coulees (see Figure 3-38) that carried excess floodwater out of the Cheney-Palouse scablands westward into the Quincy Basin.

94   After passing over an elevated Palouse upland area, untouched by the floods, Upper Crab Creek Coulee (No. 22) comes into view on the right (east).

97   Perhaps the highest density of giant current ripples and exposed Odessa Ring Craters (No. 24) occur along Crab Creek near Sylvan Lake (see Figure 2-34 and 3-40). One of the flood bars blanketed with megaripples is shown in (Figure 6-7). Alter course slightly to the northwest to begin Leg 4 (see new bearings in Table 6-1).

Figure 6-7. Giant current ripples atop flood bar (dashed line) south of Sylvan Lake. Asymmetric ripples indicate flow direction for the floods (block arrow). Three flood-scoured ringed craters are also visible (white arrows). See Plate 21 for another view of this flood bar and surrounding ringed craters. Looking east.

Leg 4

Start: Sylvan Lake

Destination: Marlin Hollow

104   Along Lake Creek Coulee (No. 23) pass over another group of Odessa Ring Craters (Figure 6-8). The general distribution of ringed craters in the Odessa area is shown in Figure 3-43. For other images of these same craters see Figures 4-53 through 4-55. About six miles up the coulee to the right (northeast) lies the deep, flood-scoured rock basin of Coffeepot Lake (Figure 6-9). Just down coulee off the left side of the aircraft lies Pacific Lake, today totally dry due to a drastic drop in the groundwater level over the last few decades (see "Disappearing Lakes and Aquifers" sidebar, page 99 in chapter 3).

Figure 6-8. Cluster of three Odessa Ring craters along Lake Creek Coulee. Looking northeast. These craters are accessible via Trail U2 in chapter 4.

Figure 6-9. Coffeepot Lake, located midway along Lake Creek Coulee within the Telford-Crab Creek scablands. Looking southwest.

108   Cross Marlin Hollow (No. 25), another coulee of the Telford-Crab Creek Tract (see Figure 3-43). In the heavily scoured coulee below are lots of wonderful potholes, rock basins and benches along with one of the few natural bridges (see Figure 3-44, Plate 19) in all the floods' terrain. At Marlin Hollow alter course to fly north-northeast towards Wilbur (see new bearings in Table 6-1).

To combine both aerial tours featured in this book into a single flight, fly west-northwest (bearing of 288 degrees) from Marlin Hollow for 26 miles to join the fourth leg of the Moses Coulee-Grand Coulee tour at Coulee City (see Figure 6-1). Otherwise continue north toward Wilbur to complete only the eastern loop.

Leg 5

Start: Marlin Hollow

Destination: Wilbur

117   Palouse uplands are briefly interrupted by a minor, shallow flood spillway that follows Canniwai Creek.

123   Cross Sinking Creek Coulee (No. 26) that joins Wilson Creek Coulee a few miles to the northwest (see Figure 3-45).

128   Turn right (east) in Wilbur to follow Goose Creek Coulee (see new bearings in Table 6-1).

Leg 6

Start: Wilbur

Destination: Davenport

136   Flight path for the remainder of the tour heads east-southeast parallel to U.S. Highway 2. During the largest floods Creston Butte Steptoe (see Figure 3-45) on the left was an isolated island that barely poked out above the rushing floodwaters heading south and west into the head of the Telford-Crab Creek Scabland Tract.

144   Cross a series of spillover flood channels that delivered floodwaters into the Telford Tract after overfilling the Columbia Valley (Plate 11).

146   At the head of Hawk Creek, which drains northward into the Columbia Valley is the low point for floods spilling southward into the Telford scabland.

155   At Davenport (Plate 11) is more low-relief scabland with spillover channels feeding south into the Upper Crab Creek Scabland Complex (No. 22). Alter course slightly toward the Spokane International Airport (see new bearings in Table 6-1).

Leg 7

Start: Davenport

Destination: Spokane International Airport

164   To the left (north) lies the head of Crab Creek and its flood coulee near Reardan (Plate 10). Continue to fly over the Palouse uplands that divide the Telford-Crab-Creek from the Cheney-Palouse Tracts.

173   Just beyond Deep Creek on the West Plains is a huge, one-mile-wide flood bar blanketed with giant current ripples (Figure 6-10), created as floodwaters flowed southwest into the head of the Cheney-Palouse Tract. Several miles to the south lies double-peaked Fancher Butte and Riddle Hill, two of the many hills making up Steptoe Ridge (No. 12, see Figure 3-21). Floodwater funneled through these older, more flood-resistant rocky hillocks (i.e., steptoes), carving out several visible rock basins in between, today occupied by East and West Medical and Silver lakes (Figure 6-11).

- -

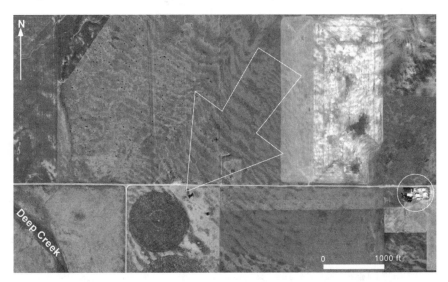

Figure 6-10. Vertical aerial photograph of flood bar blanketed with giant current ripples along Deep Creek just south of U.S. Highway 2. Ripples are up to several hundred feet apart. Block arrow indicates flood-flow direction. Note farm at right (circled) for scale. Figure 3-18 shows these same ripples at an oblique angle.

Figure 6-11. View southeast toward the Medical Lakes (left) and Fancher Butte. East and West Medical Lake lie along flood channels that spilled through gaps in Steptoe Ridge (No. 12) at the head of the Cheney-Palouse Tract. Looking southeast.

177   Fly over Fairchild Air Force Base located atop the flood-swept West Plains.

184   Land at the Spokane International Airport. End of aerial tour.

Table 6-2. Geographic coordinates, bearings and distances for the 11 legs of the Moses Coulee-Grand Coulee Aerial Tour.

Leg No.	Destination Along Route	Latitude	Longitude	Bearing (degrees from true north)	Leg Distance (miles)	Cumulative Distance (miles)
Start	Pangborn (Wenatchee) Airport	N47.3953	W120.1969			
1	Mouth Moses Coulee, N. side	47.3245	120.0514	127	8.6	8.6
2	Jameson Lake	47.7037	119.6257	37	32.0	40.6
3	Coulee Dam	47.9808	119.0173	56	33.7	74.3
4	NE side Grand Coulee	47.9287	118.9771	157	6.1	80.4
5	Mouth of Whitney Canyon	47.8454	119.0978	224	7.8	88.2
6	Coulee City	47.6125	119.3006	208	19.4	107.6
7	Head E. Lenore Coulee	47.5303	119.4616	233	8.7	116.3
8	S. end Lake Lenore	47.4516	119.4957	198	5.8	122.1
9	Three Devils of Moses Coulee	47.4324	119.7996	263	12.8	134.9
10	Mouth Moses Coulee, S. side	47.2818	120.0421	227	15.9	150.8
11	Pangborn (Wenatchee) Airport	47.3953	120.1969	320	11.1	161.9

2. Moses Coulee-Grand Coulee Aerial Tour

Figure 6-12 shows the route for this 160-mile aerial tour. A little over two hours of flight time are required at an average speed of 75 mph. Table 6-2 presents specific directions for the 11 legs of this tour that loop in a clockwise direction starting from the Pangborn Memorial (Wenatchee Valley) Airport in East Wenatchee, Washington.

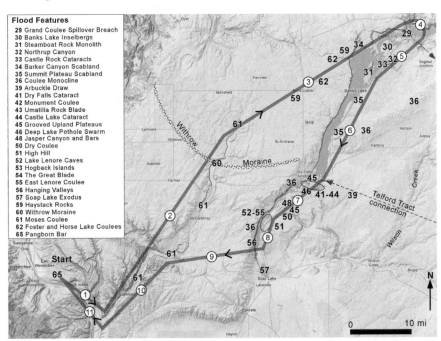

Flood Features
29 Grand Coulee Spillover Breach
30 Banks Lake Inselbergs
31 Steamboat Rock Monolith
32 Northrup Canyon
33 Castle Rock Cataracts
34 Barker Canyon Scabland
35 Summit Plateau Scabland
36 Coulee Monocline
39 Arbuckle Draw
41 Dry Falls Cataract
42 Monument Coulee
43 Umatilla Rock Blade
44 Castle Lake Cataract
45 Grooved Upland Plateaus
46 Deep Lake Pothole Swarm
48 Jasper Canyon and Bars
50 Dry Coulee
51 High Hill
52 Lake Lenore Caves
53 Hogback Islands
54 The Great Blade
55 East Lenore Coulee
56 Hanging Valleys
57 Soap Lake Exodus
59 Haystack Rocks
60 Withrow Moraine
61 Moses Coulee
62 Foster and Horse Lake Coulees
65 Pangborn Bar

Figure 6-12. The Moses Coulee-Grand Coulee Aerial Tour. See chapter 3 for more detailed descriptions of numbered flood features along route.

Flight Log

Leg 1

Start: Pangborn Memorial Airport

Destination: Mouth of Moses Coulee, north side

Cumulative Distance

0   Depart Pangborn Memorial Airport in East Wenatchee, the regional airport for the Wenatchee Valley. Airport is located atop Pangborn Bar (No. 65), a 600-foot-tall, ancient flood bar (see Figures 3-117 and 3-118) locally covered with giant current ripples and ice-rafted erratics. Fly southeast over the Columbia River towards the mouth of Moses Coulee (Figure 6-13).

8   Turn northeast to fly up the north side of Moses Coulee (see new bearings in Table 6-2).

Figure 6-13. Oblique shaded-relief map of 50-mile-long Moses Coulee (No. 61), looking northeast. The Three Devils scabland complex divides the lower part of Moses Coulee from the upper. See Figure 3-109 for different (vertical) perspective of this image.

Leg 2

Start: North side of Moses Coulee

Destination: Jameson Lake

11   Lower Moses Coulee is the deepest and straightest of the flood cou-lees (Plate 49). Notice the high hanging valleys, similar to the Hanging Valleys (No. 56) of Lower Grand Coulee, resulting from Ice Age floods that reamed out and oversteepened the sides of the coulee. The flat bottom of the coulee is totally devoid of any surface water and has been since the end of the Ice Age.

20   Fly over the crest of Badger Mountain (Figure 6-13) – an upfolded ridge of the Yakima Fold Belt. Just beyond, the coulee takes a sharp bend to the right (east).

25   On the right is the rugged scabland around the Three Devils scab-land complex and Rattlesnake Creek (see Figures 5-42 and 4-105). A few miles farther north lies the human-scarred Rimrock Meadows housing development.

31   The Great Bar of Moses Coulee (see Figure 3-111), a giant crescent flood bar along the west side of Moses Coulee, spans out to the right. Just north of the bar, covering the coulee bottom, is a train of glacial outwash (Figure 6-14) left behind as the Okanogan Lobe melted northward at the end of the last Ice Age. The meltwater streams naturally followed the path of least resistance, which was down the already established, relict flood coulee.

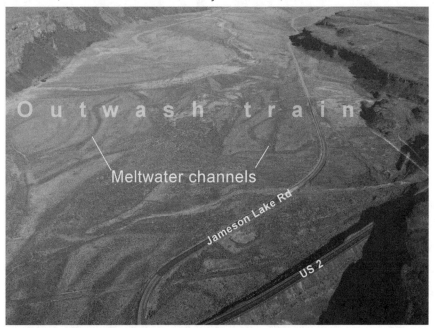

Figure 6-14. Abandoned, braided stream channels of glacial outwash that lies just downstream of the former Okanogan Lobe (marked by the Withrow Moraine), located just a few miles upvalley from here. The Great Bar of Moses Coulee lies below the lower left corner of this image. Looking northeast.

37   The Withrow Moraine (No. 60) stretches out across Moses Coulee and the basalt plateau on either side (see Figures 3-108 and 3-109).

41   At Jameson Lake (Figure 6-15, Plate 48), near the northern end of Moses Coulee, alter course toward Coulee Dam (see new bearings in Table 6-2).

Figure 6-15. Jameson Lake is a natural lake near the head of upper Moses Coulee, dammed by the Withrow Moraine that developed along the front of the Okanogan Lobe. Looking northwest.

Leg 3

Start: Jameson Lake

Destination: Coulee Dam

43   Fly over Grimes Lake at the head of Moses Coulee. Moses Coulee soon loses definition to the north where it merges with the low-relief Mansfield Channels (see Figure 3-109) spreading out across the glaciated Waterville Plateau. Here Haystack Rocks (No. 59) and other glacial deposits were laid down toward the end of the last Ice Age (about 15,000 years ago) by the retreating Okanogan Lobe (Figure 6-16; see also Figure 3-104).

Figure 6-16. Glacial features on the Waterville Plateau. Sinuous eskers near Sims Corner are a recognized National Natural Landmark (Sims Corner Esker and Kame Complex). Block arrow indicates direction of movement (southeast) of the Okanogan Lobe during the last Ice Age.

55   Lots of glacial features are visible on the Waterville Plateau in the vicinity of Sims Corner, including Haystack Rocks and drumlins (see Figure 5-44) molded by the moving ice sheet (Figure 6-16). Also present are an occasional esker, a sinuous ridge of sediment that once partially filled a sub-glacial meltwater channel beneath the Okanogan Lobe. While these features did not result from Ice Age flooding, they are discussed here because they help to define the exact locations of the ice sheet that strongly affected the paths of Ice Age floods.

57   Fly over Horse Lake Coulee (No. 62), which along with Foster Coulee to the north, once carried glacial meltwater eastward, away from the edge of the wasting Okanogan Lobe (see Figures 3-112 and 3-113).

63   Cross the mouth of meandering Foster Coulee (Figure 6-17), which hangs several hundred feet above the floor of the Upper Grand Coulee. At one time, before Grand Coulee was carved out by cataract recession by Ice Age floods, Foster Creek may have extended all the way to the head of Grand Coulee (see Figure 3-54, Stage 1). Since then Foster Coulee was cut off by cataract recession that created Upper Grand Coulee.

Figure 6-17. Foster Coulee meanders across the Waterville Plateau above the west side of Grand Coulee. The delta bar below the hanging coulee formed as meltwater streams coming off the Okanogan Lobe drained into a Glacial Lake Columbia that occupied Upper Grand Coulee at the end of the last Ice Age (see Figure 3-113). Looking northwest.

66   Fly over the mouth of Barker Canyon (No. 34), a side coulee that enters Grand Coulee from the north (Plate 22). Steamboat Rock (No. 31) prominently protrudes from the middle of Grand Coulee on the right (Plates 24 and 26).

71   Here in the Upper Grand Coulee, the floods exhumed the irregular knobs of granitic basement rock, referred to here as the Banks Lake Inselbergs (No. 30), that lay beneath layered basalt flows, like those near Steamboat Rock (Figure 6-18). We are in an area where the Columbia River basalt thins and pinches out against basement rocks along the northern perimeter of the Columbia Plateau.

Figure 6-18. The round rock mounds in the foreground are granitic inselbergs exhumed by Ice Age floods. Before the floods the granite rock lay beneath several hundred feet of layered, basaltic lava rocks like those capping Steamboat Rock in background. Looking southeast. Lake Columbia silt (No. 38) covers the low area between Banks Lake and the inselbergs.

Leg 4

Start: Coulee Dam

Destination: NE side of Grand Coulee

74   Circle clockwise around Grand Coulee Dam (Figure 6-19) before heading southwest down the east side of Upper Grand Coulee (see map on Figure 6-12). Note how the eroded head of Grand Coulee was finally breached (No. 29) and lowered by 900 feet when Ice Age floods spilled over from the Columbia Valley (see Figures 3-55 and 3-56).

Figure 6-19. The Columbia River and Grand Coulee Dam looking east toward Lake Roosevelt, modern equivalent to the much deeper, ancient Glacial Lake Columbia. The Okanogan Lobe of glacial ice once blocked the Columbia River here, forcing most floodwaters down other, eastern scabland tracts. It may have not been until late in the Ice Age that Grand Coulee became a dominant flood coulee.

To combine both aerial tours featured in this book into a single flight, fly southeast (bearing of 46 degrees) from the northeast corner of Grand Coulee for 17 miles to join the sixth leg of the Cheney-Palouse/Telford-Crab Creek tour at Wilbur (see Figure 6-1). Otherwise continue southwest toward Coulee City to complete the Moses Coulee-Grand Coulee tour through the western Channeled Scabland.

Leg 5

Start: Northeast side of Grand Coulee

Destination: Mouth of Whitney Canyon

81   Below is a flood-swept, upland plateau along the east side of Upper Grand Coulee (Figure 6-20, see Figure 3-65). Floods feeding Northrup Canyon spilled over onto this plateau from Spring Canyon, especially when ice of the Okanogan Lobe periodically filled and blocked floods from passing directly down Upper Grand Coulee.

84   Fly over Northrup Lake plunge pool (see Figure 4-70) and cataract at the head of Northrup Canyon. Like Barker Canyon, seen earlier, Northrup Canyon is a side, spillover coulee feeding into Grand Coulee. Notice the granite basement rock that crops out along the valley axis.

86   A flood-swept Summit Plateau Scabland (No. 35) spreads south of Northrup Canyon. This elevated plateau lines the east side of Upper Grand Coulee, marking the paths of floods that flowed between the edge of the Okanogan Lobe and the high Coulee Monocline (Figure 6-20). Steamboat Rock looms above the deep coulee floor on the right (Figure 6-21).

Figure 6-20. Floodwaters indicated by block arrows were funneled across the Summit Plateau Scabland at times when the Okanogan Lobe blocked the Upper Grand Coulee. The trimline marks the approximate high water mark and level of erosion by Ice Age floods.

Figure 6-21. View looking west across Northrup Canyon, Castle Rock and Steamboat Rock into the Upper Grand Coulee.

88   Alter course slightly (see new bearings in Table 6-2) at Whitney Canyon (Figure 6-20), a deep side canyon that cuts into the Summit Plateau Scabland hanging high above Grand Coulee. Notice the many curvilinear grooves etched into the upper surface of the plateau here (see Figures 1-6 and 3-67). Many of the grooves run transverse to flood flow, indicating they are primarily the result of large-scale flow or fracture features inherent to the basalt.

Leg 6

Start: Mouth of Whitney Canyon

Destination: Coulee City

92   A short, side-cataract canyon at hanging Ladds Creek (see Figure 3-73, right) formed where floods moving across the Summit Plateau Scabland dropped into the Upper Grand Coulee (Figure 6-20).

95   Cross Paynes Gulch, another hanging side canyon that feeds into Grand Coulee from the east.

100   Here at the south end of the Upper Grand Coulee, the Coulee Monocline (No. 36) dips steeply into the Hartline Basin. Notice the basalt flows that were long ago folded and tilted on edge along the monocline (see Figures 3-70 and 3-72).

106   Over Coulee City, at the south end of Banks Lake, change to a more westerly flight path (see new bearings in Table 6-2).

Leg 7

Start: Coulee City

Destination: Head of East Lenore Coulee

108   Fly parallel to distinct grooves in upland plateau (No. 45) above and behind Dry Falls (No. 41) (Figure 6-22, Plate 32). The Great Cataract Group (Plate 31), including the 400-foot-tall Dry Falls cataract on the right, drops away into the deep inner channel of Lower Grand Coulee. A prominent, elongated rock blade (Umatilla Rock) extends beyond, separating Dry Falls and Monument coulees. To the left, at the head of Deep Lake, is the Castle Lake cataract and Don Paul Draw present at the far eastern end of the four-mile-wide Great Cataract Group (see Figure 4-92).

109   Crossing Deep Lake notice the rock benches above the lake riddled with potholes (Figure 6-22) of the Deep Lake Pothole Swarm (No. 46). An expansive, scarred and Grooved Upland Plateau (No. 45) lies beyond Deep Lake all the way to Jasper Canyon (No. 48).

Figure 6-22. Flood-swept and Grooved Upland Plateau between Deep Lake and Dry Falls. Note swarm of deep potholes on rock bench in foreground (see also Figures 4-88 and 4-89). Coulee walls expose lava flows of the Wanapum Basalt. The base of Dry Falls and the potholed rock bench in foreground lie atop older Grande Ronde Basalt. Flow of floodwater was from right to left.

112   A couple of side cataracts join Jasper Canyon on either side of the aircraft. Flood bars, including eddy bars at the mouths of the side cataracts, fill the canyon bottoms (see Figures 3-87 to 3-89).

113   Cross the head of 300-foot-deep Jasper Canyon (Figure 6-23).

- -

Figure 6-23. Head of Jasper Canyon divides the upland plateau along the east side of Lower Grand Coulee. Blue Lake in background. Flood bar of coarse gravel and sand (see Figure 3-87) partially fills the bottom of Jasper Canyon. Looking west.

114   A huge pendant-crescent flood bar lies immediately below (see Figures 3-88, Plate 36). Flood bars are recognized by their smoothed surfaces without any of the jagged rocky slopes that typify eroded-basalt scabland. Note how the flood bar has built up almost to the same height as the upland plateau on the right. Another long-abandoned coulee, Dry Coulee (No. 50), comes into view from the left and merges with Jasper Canyon before reentering the Lower Grand Coulee (Plate 37).

115   Cross Dry Coulee (Figure 6-24) with its southern wall that rises sharply up into the head of East Lenore Coulee (see Figure 3-95). This is also the beginning point for The Great Blade (No. 54) that divides East Lenore Coulee from the main portion of Lower Grand Coulee, where Lake Lenore is located to the west (Figure 6-25, Plate 39). Change course slightly (see new bearings in Table 6-2) to fly down the east side of East Lenore Coulee (No. 55).

Figure 6-24. Desolate upper Dry Coulee, looking east. Floor of the coulee is partially filled with flood sediment, including a sizable flood bar in lower left.

Leg 8

Start: Head of East Lenore Coulee

Destination: South end of Lake Lenore

116   Upper cataract at head of East Lenore Coulee is to the right (Figure 6-25). Palouse-covered uplands of High Hill (No. 51), generally above the highest flood levels, are on the left (see Figure 3-97).

117   The deeply scoured floor of East Lenore Coulee is riddled with criss-crossing grooves and potholes (Plates 39 to 41). Beyond, The Great Blade narrows to only a few tens of feet in places. Hiking trails that access the primitive

wilds of the Great Blade and East Lenore Coulee are described in chapter 4 (Trail II).

118   Lower cataract drop-off for East Lenore Coulee (Plate 40). An almost one-mile-wide rock bench, cratered with deep potholes lies south of The Great Blade. A mile farther is an 800-foot wide megapothole (Plate 42) along the coulee floor.

Figure 6-25. The Great Blade divides Lower Grand Coulee (Lake Lenore) from East Lenore Coulee. Looking southwest. DAVID WYATT PHOTO

121   At the mouth of East Lenore Coulee, turn west-southwest while gaining elevation to cross the south end of Lake Lenore and the tall western wall of the Lower Grand Coulee (see new bearings in Table 6-2).

Leg 9

Start: South end of Lake Lenore

Destination: Three Devils Scabland of Moses Coulee

124   Cross the Coulee Monocline ridge again along the west side of Grand Coulee; slope descends onto the relatively featureless Sagebrush Flat (see Figure 3-109) before dropping into Moses Coulee.

132   To the right is an expansive view into the upper Moses Coulee across the scarred, dry and barren Rimrock Meadows development. To the left is the Badger Mountain anticlinal ridge.

134   On the right is the Three Devils scabland complex within central Moses Coulee (Figure 6-26, see also Figures 4-105 to 4-108). Here lies a bewildering, complex maze of recessional cataract canyons, hanging coulees and flood-swept mesas and buttes (Plate 46). Publically accessible, non-motorized trails into the

Three Devils scabland complex are described in chapter 4 (Trail KK), and a road tour through the area is presented in chapter 5 (Road Tour No. 5).

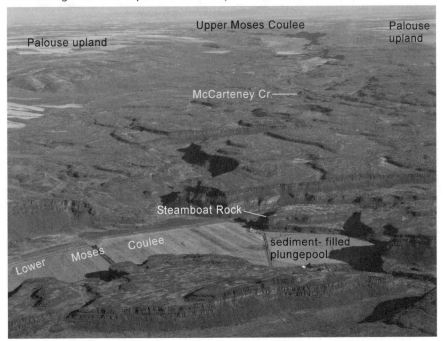

Figure 6-26. Three Devils scabland complex located about midway along Moses Coulee (see Figure 3-109). Looking northeast. Steamboat Rock of Moses Coulee is a much less prominent feature than the one in Grand Coulee (Plate 24).

135   Change course to fly southwest over the top of Badger Mountain and then parallel to the southeast side of lower Moses Coulee (see new bearings in Table 6-2).

Leg 10

Start: Three Devils Scabland of Moses Coulee

Destination: Mouth of Moses Coulee (south side)

144   Valleys on either side of the coulee were left hanging after floods reamed out and oversteepened the coulee walls (Figure 6-27, Plate 49).

Figure 6-27. Lower Moses Coulee, looking down coulee to the southwest. Notice flood-faceted escarpments and hanging valleys on left side of coulee.

150   At the mouth of Moses Coulee, turn northwest to fly over the Columbia River and onto Pangborn Memorial Airport in East Wenatchee (see new bearings in Table 6-2). For those starting in Spokane and wishing to combine the two aerial tours in Figure 6-1, skip the next leg and fly directly across the mouth of Moses Coulee to connect up with start of Leg 2 for the Moses Coulee-Grand Coulee aerial tour. Otherwise complete the last leg by flying into the Pangborn (Wenatchee) Airport.

Leg 11

Start: Mouth of Moses Coulee (south side)

Destination: Pangborn Memorial Airport

159   Tall Pangborn flood bar (No. 65) lies 600 feet above the valley floor (see Figure 3-117). Note eddy scar carved into the south end of Pangborn Bar where floods swirled around the east side of Jumpoff Ridge (see Figure 3-118).

162   Land at Pangborn Memorial Airport. End of aerial tour.

Glossary

abrasion: the mechanical wearing, grinding, scraping and rubbing down of the land surface by friction and impact, in which the solid rock particles transported by wind, ice or running water are the tools of abrasion.

alcove: a deep, horseshoe-shaped **inner canyon** that forms below a recessional **cataract.**

anastomosis: a braided, interlacing network of branching and reuniting flood channels.

anticline: a fold in the Earth's crust, arched upward, whose core contains older rocks than its sides.

aquifer: a subsurface body of rock or sediment that is sufficiently permeable to conduct ground water and yield significant quantities of water to wells and springs.

argillite: a kind of metamorphic rock, originally a mudstone or shale, that has since been transformed into an extremely hard, compact, rock tightly cemented with silica. Locally, argillite and associated **quartzite** come from a group of rocks known as the Belt Supergroup (1.4 billion to 1.6 billion years old) that crops out in northern Washington, Idaho and Montana.

basalt: a dark, fine-grained, volcanic-**igneous** rock composed primarily of two minerals, plagioclase and pyroxene. Between about 6 million and 17 million years ago, hundreds of lava flows of **Columbia River basalt** flowed out of long, linear vents in southeastern Washington, eastern Oregon and west-central Idaho and traveled hundreds of miles before cooling and solidifying to form the **Columbia Plateau.**

basalt member: a grouping of individual basalt lava flows with similar characteristics, erupted around the same time.

bedload: the sediment moved or transported by a flood or stream immediately at or above the bottom of the flow. Usually consists of the larger or heavier rocks, which may become rounded as they tumble and roll along the bottom of the flood flow.

beds: discrete layers of sediment or rock of varying thickness and character. Individual beds are laid down sequentially, so that beds at the bottom of a sequence are older than those on top.

bedrock: a general term for solid rock that underlies the soil or other loose, unconsolidated materials found on the surface.

Belt rock: 1.4 billion- to 1.6 billion-year-old rocks of the Belt Supergroup. Mostly composed of metamorphosed ancient marine sandstone (**quartzite**) and mudstone (**argillite**). They are so old they lack fossils of any complex life forms. Belt rocks are a mind-boggling 1,000 times older than the **Columbia River basalt** they underlie.

bioturbation: the burrowing, churning and stirring of loose sediment by plants and/or animals near the land surface. Bioturbation is often observed in and associated with **paleosols.**

borrow pit: man-made excavation to remove loose sand and gravel materials for use in roads, construction, etc.

breakout area: the area along and immediately in front of the ice dam for **Glacial Lake Missoula.**

butte: an isolated, often flat-topped landform that is taller than it is wide. The sides are steep and the lower slopes are often covered with **talus.** Ice Age floods eroded flat-lying basalt flows to form isolated buttes. The more flood-resistant basalt **entablature** usually caps the top of buttes.

butte-and-basin topography: a general term coined by J Harlen Bretz to describe all landforms created by extreme flood erosion, including rock basins, benches, buttes and mesas within the **Channeled Scabland.**

calendar year: the time required for the Earth to complete one revolution around the Sun.

caliche: a secondary chemical deposit of calcium carbonate that binds sediment or soil together into a rock-like mass. Caliche, which slowly develops in arid to semi-arid climates, may take many thousands of years to form.

Cambrian: a period of geologic time spanning the interval between 500-570 million years ago. The earliest period of the Paleozoic Era.

cataract: a waterfall, especially one of great volume in which the vertical descent has been concentrated in one sheer drop over a precipice. Used in areas of Ice Age floods to describe a tall, now-dry cliff formed during cataract recession.

cataract canyon: the deep, steep-walled canyon that extends below a **recessional cataract**.

catastrophism: the doctrine that sudden, violent, short-lived events outside our present experience or knowledge of nature have greatly modified the surface of the Earth. J Harlen Bretz promoted catastrophism, unpopular at the time, to his peers to explain the features he observed in the **Channeled Scabland**. Opposite of **uniformitarianism** (or gradualism), which was the popular theory at the time. Both concepts have validity.

Channeled Scabland: a region of interconnected **flood channels, coulees** and **cataracts** eroded through Palouse **loess** and into **basalt** by cataclysmic floods in eastern Washington. The **Channeled Scabland** has been used as an analog for similar channelized features on the planet Mars.

Cheney-Palouse Scabland Tract: a network of interconnected flood channels and coulees, separated by uplands of **Palouse loess**, that trends south across the eastern portion of the **Channeled Scabland**.

clast: an individual **particle** or fragment of sediment or rock, several inches or more in diameter, produced from the physical and/or chemical breakdown of a larger rock mass.

clay: extremely small **sedimentary** particles that are less than 0.004 millimeters in diameter.

coarse-grained: pertains to **sedimentary** material that is composed of relatively large particles of **sand** and/or **gravel**.

colonnade: columnar basalt that forms in the lower, interior cooling zone of a basalt lava flow that contains larger, more massive columns, most of which are bounded by vertically oriented cooling fractures. Polygonal columns up to several feet in diameter are common to some flows. Opposite of entablature that forms in the upper cooling zone of a basalt flow (see Figure 1-2).

Columbia River basalt: general name given to **Miocene** age (6 million to 17 million years ago) basalt lava flows of the Columbia Plateau.

Columbia River Lobe: lobe of glacial ice from the **Cordilleran Ice Sheet** that sometimes extended down the Columbia River Valley from the north. Glacial Lake Spokane would form behind the Columbia River Lobe when the ice dam blocked the Spokane River.

Columbia Plateau: the broad area underlain by Columbia River basalt in eastern Washington, western Idaho and north-central Oregon.

columnar: a lava flow that displays columnar jointing.

convoluted bedding: localized wavy, crumpled or twisted layering in sedimentary beds. Such bedding can form as one bed was suddenly laid on top of another while underwater. Convoluted bedding can also form as a result of earthquake shaking, landsliding or squeezing under the massive weight of a glacier. A type of soft-sediment deformation. Flame structures may result during convolution (see Figure 2-31).

Cordilleran Ice Sheet: name for the ice sheet, thousands of feet thick, that extended across western North America from the Canadian Arctic periodically during the Pleistocene Epoch (see Plate 1).

coulee: a long, deep, steep-walled, Ice Age flood channel, now completely dry or occupied by an **underfit stream**. French for "flow or rush of a torrent." Recessional cataracts may lie along, or at the head of, the coulee.

Coulee Monocline: a long flexure in the surface of the Columbia River basalt that trends along and across Grand Coulee. Along the monocline a narrow band of basalt rock was tilted uniformly to the east and south by **tectonic** stresses applied within the Earth's crust.

crescent bar: a giant flood bar that formed along the inside of bends or curves in flood channels or coulees where floodwaters moved a little more slowly.

cross stratification: where the internal layering within a bed is inclined at an angle with respect to normal horizontal bedding above and below.

curvilinear: a term given to **fractures** that sometimes appear as broad, curving lines atop flood-swept basalt surfaces. These curving fractures probably resulted from the last movements or the cooling and contraction of the once-molten basalt lava.

delta bar: a lobate landform that forms where a vigorous, sediment-rich, glacial-meltwater stream empties into a standing body of water such as a lake.

dike: a near-vertical, tabular igneous intrusion that cuts across the bedding or layering in the rock that is intruded.

divide crossing: where deep floodwater flowed over a low divide separating two drainages, often eroding a notch or **spillover channel** across the abandoned spillway.

drumlin: a low, smoothly rounded, elongate oval hill, mound or ridge of glacial sediment including till built under the margin of glacial ice and shaped by the flow of the ice; the long axis of drumlins is generally parallel to the flow of ice. Drumlins sometimes display a blunt upper end that points in the upstream direction of the ice and a gentler tapered end that points in the opposite direction.

eddy bar: a flood bar that forms where eddy currents develop along a flood route. Often found in the more protected mouths of tributary valleys where they join main flood coulees.

entablature: the upper portion of basalt flows that show a more dense and random distribution of cooling fractures. In contrast to colonnade that forms at or toward the bottom of flows (see Figure 1-2).

Eocene: an epoch of geologic time spanning an interval from 34 million to 56 million years ago.

eolian: refers to sediment transported and deposited by the wind. Includes deposits of **loess** and dune sand.

erratic: an out-of-place rock (often boulder size) that is of a different rock type than the bedrock beneath it and transported to its present location by glaciers or icebergs. Edges of erratics are typically, but not always, angular.

erratic cluster: a grouping of ice-rafted erratics that probably melted out from the same iceberg after becoming grounded.

esker: a long, narrow, sinuous, steep-sided ridge composed of irregularly stratified sand and gravel that was deposited by a stream flowing beneath a melting glacier. Eskers may branch and are often discontinuous (see Figure 6-16).

expansion bar: a giant flood bar that forms where flood channels or coulees suddenly widen or expand. As the water expands it also slows down from the **venturi effect**, which results in sediment buildup and bar formation.

faceted escarpment: an over-steepened slope or cliff planed off by the movement of strong currents along a flood channel. Often a series of individual escarpments may align along channel margins (see Plate 15).

feature: as used here, a landform produced by Ice Age floods.

fen: a watery bog.

fine-grained: pertains to sedimentary material in flood deposits composed of mostly small particles of silt and/or fine sand.

flame structure: a sedimentary structure consisting of wave- or flame-shaped plumes of sediment squeezed irregularly upward into an overlying sediment layer. See **convoluted bedding**.

flood bar: an accumulation of sediment, most often composed of sand and/or gravel, that occurs along flood channels where the currents temporarily slowed for various reasons. Different types of flood bars from the Ice Age floods in the Channeled Scabland include eddy, expansion, longitudinal, crescent and pendant bars (see Figure 2-32).

flood channel: straight to curved paths scoured out by the floods. Deep flood channels are called coulees.

foreset bedding: internal bedding within a sedimentary deposit that is inclined to the principal surface of accumulation. Foreset beds generally dip in the direction of water flow.

fosse: a long narrow depression or trough-like hollow that sometimes develops along the edge of a flood bar near where it extends up to a coulee wall. It may represent slightly higher flow velocity for floods along the side of the coulee.

fracture: a general term for any naturally broken surface in rock. In the Channeled Scabland, small fractures developed during cooling and contraction of basalt lava. Larger, curving fractures (curvilinear) also sometimes developed as the lava cooled. Later, long after the lava hardened, more extensive parallel sets of fractures occasionally developed locally from large tectonic stresses within the crust (see Figure 3-28).

giant current ripples: waves of sand and gravel deposited by deep, fast moving cataclysmic flood currents, similar to ripples along a river or on the beach, but much, much larger.

gneiss: a light- and dark-banded **metamorphic** rock composed predominantly of quartz, feldspar and hornblende.

goat island: the rocky upland that divides a pair of **recessional cataracts**. Originally named for the rocky upland separating American and Horseshoe falls at Niagara Falls. Synonym for "**rock blade**."

grading: refers to a progressive shift in the size of sedimentary particles within a bed. Normal grading is a shift from larger to smaller particles upward within the bed; reverse grading is the opposite.

Grand Coulee: a 50-mile-long coulee within the western Channeled Scabland that displays some of the most recent and intense erosional flood features anywhere on Earth.

granite: a light-colored, crystalline, intrusive-**igneous** rock that contains abundant minerals of gray to white quartz and feldspar, in addition to pink-colored alkali feldspar.

granitic: a general term for any light-colored intrusive-igneous rock that formed deep underground from a cooling body of liquid magma. Granitic rocks include granite and granodiorite. Most ice-rafted erratics in the Channeled Scabland are granitic in origin; granitic rocks underlie the head of Grand Coulee and also occur north and east of the Channeled Scabland.

granodiorite: a light-colored, crystalline, intrusive-igneous rock that contains abundant minerals of gray to white quartz and feldspar.

gravel: sedimentary particles larger than sand (more than 2 millimeters in diameter). Gravel clasts are referred to, in increasing size, as granules, pebbles, cobbles and boulders.

grooves: in the Columbia Plateau, refers to a series of long, roughly parallel ridges or flutings on the land surface due to intense flood erosion. Straight to **curvilinear** grooves are often visible on flood-swept upland plateaus.

grus: fragmented products of in-situ granular disintegration of granite through weathering at the surface.

hanging coulee: a side coulee that enters a larger coulee at a higher elevation. Characteristic of the Channeled Scabland, where flat valley floors suddenly drop off into nothingness at either one or both ends.

Haystack Rocks: large basalt boulders scattered across the Waterville Plateau by the **Okanogan Lobe**.

Holocene: an epoch of geologic time between the present and the end of the last Ice Age (about 13,000 years ago).

hydraulic constriction: places along the flood route where a large volume of water was forced to go through a narrow opening. If more water enters the opening than can drain through, then the constriction will cause water to back up, creating a type of hydraulic dam (e.g., Wallula Gap, Steptoe Ridge). Because of the **venturi effect**, water moved much faster through hydraulic constrictions.

ice lobe: a finger of ice that extends south from an ice sheet. Two ice lobes of the Cordilleran Ice Sheet, the Purcell Trench Lobe and Okanogan Lobe, had a direct impact on the timing and frequency of Ice Age floods in the Pacific Northwest.

ice dam: formed where an ice lobe moved across and blocked normal stream drainage. Glacial lakes, up to thousands of feet deep, filled behind ice dams (see Plate 1).

igneous: rock that solidified from molten or partly molten material, including both intrusive and extrusive rock types. One of the three principal rock types, along with **sedimentary** and **metamorphic**.

inner canyon: steep-walled, deep canyon or coulee below a **recessional cataract** or incised into a larger canyon.

inselberg: as used here, a granitic hill or ridge exhumed at the head of Grand Coulee by Ice Age floods after being buried beneath basalt.

jökulhlaup: an Icelandic term for glacial-outburst flood.

kame terrace: an elevated bench of glacially transported sediment perched along the side wall of a valley that collected along the edge of a glacier that once filled the valley center. The kame terrace, composed of sand and gravel, remained after melting of the glacier.

kettle: a steep-sided, bowl-shaped depression in glacial-outwash or flood-**outburst plain**. Kettles form by the melting of large, detached blocks of glacial ice that are partly to wholly buried beneath glacial or outburst-flood deposits. The bowl-shaped depression forms later as the soil cover collapses into the void created by the melting block of ice.

knickpoint: a sudden interruption or break in slope along a stream profile.

kolk: the whirlpool-like, eddying current created by extremely high-velocity, turbulent floodwaters that drilled deep potholes along scabland channels and coulees.

lacustrine: pertaining to, produced by or formed in a lake.

Lake Columbia: a glacial lake that formed behind the Okanogan Lobe of glacial ice (see Plate 1).

Lake Spokane: a glacial lake that formed behind the Columbia River Lobe of glacial ice (see Plate 11), near the junction of the Columbia and Spokane rivers.

Lake Missoula: the glacial lake responsible for most, but not all, of the Ice Age floods. The lake formed as the Purcell Trench Lobe blocked the Clark Fork River, creating an ice dam up to 2,000 feet high in the Idaho Panhandle (Plate 1). The lake failed episodically, sending up to 500 cubic miles of water downstream. At its maximum, Lake Missoula was 200 miles long and covered a 3,000-square-mile area. It took up to 60 years for glacial meltwater to fill the lake but only a few days to empty.

landslide: the downslope movement of weakened soil or rock en masse under the influence of gravity.

loess: windblown silt and fine sand. Among flood routes it has collected downwind of sedimentary basins, especially in the **Palouse** country where it occurs as rolling hills up to 250 feet thick. Loess deposition began forming about the same time as the earliest Ice Age floods (about 2 million years ago) and continues to form today.

longitudinal bar: an elongated giant flood bar that forms along the sides of flood channels or coulees. Also referred to as a shoulder bar.

longitudinal groove: long, parallel grooves eroded into rock benches and mesas and upland plateaus in areas experiencing extreme velocities and turbulence associated with **scabland floods** (see Plate 32).

magnetic polarity reversal: refers to a flip in the Earth's magnetic field that has occurred periodically through geologic time. The last magnetic-polarity shift that caused a reversal in the magnetic field occurred 780,000 years ago.

marker bed: a layer of distinctive sediment or rock that can be traced over long distances. Volcanic ash beds are particularly useful marker beds because they are also time markers (see Figure 4-50).

mass wasting: processes and products produced by downslope movements such as soil creep or landslides.

mesa: an isolated, nearly level rock mass standing distinctly above the surrounding countryside; mesas are bounded by abrupt, steep-sided slopes on all sides and capped by erosion-resistant rock such as entablature basalt. Width of a mesa is always much greater than its height, which distinguishes it from a **butte**.

metamorphic: a rock derived from pre-existing, deeply buried rocks and altered due to intense heat and/or pressure. One of the three principal rock types, along with **sedimentary** and **igneous**.

metasedimentary: sedimentary rocks that show both sedimentary and metamorphic characteristics. Most rocks of the 1.5 billion-year-old Belt Supergroup fit into this category.

Mima mounds: small circular to oval masses of sediment several to tens of feet wide that occur in large groups. Mima mounds on the Columbia Plateau are composed of a mixture of silt and basalt rubble.

Miocene: an epoch of geologic time spanning an interval from 5 million to 24 million years ago. The Columbia River basalt all poured out of vents during the Miocene Epoch between about 6 million and 17 million years ago.

Missoula flood: an outburst flood derived from the sudden release of ice-dammed Glacial Lake Missoula, after the lower end of the **Purcell Trench Lobe** of ice failed.

monolith: a large, upstanding mass of rock. Within the Channeled Scabland, Grand Coulee's Steamboat Rock is the best example.

- -

moraine: an accumulation of glacial **till** with a distinct hummocky form carried and deposited directly by glacial ice.

Moses Coulee: a 50-mile-long coulee in the western Channeled Scabland used during some earlier floods but blocked from most later floods by the **Okanogan Lobe**.

natural bridge: used here as a rock span across an opening produced mostly via erosion by water, including Ice Age floods.

Okanogan Lobe: a lobe of the Cordilleran Ice Sheet that extended south from Canada along the Okanogan River Valley and blocked the Columbia River near present-day Grand Coulee Dam. Glacial Lake Columbia was the ice-dammed lake that backed up behind the Okanogan Lobe (Plate 1).

outburst plain: used here to describe the broad plain of outburst-flood sediments deposited immediately downstream of the **breakout area** for the Missoula floods along Rathdrum Prairie.

paleochannel: a remnant of a channel cut into older rock or sediments that later became filled with younger sediments.

paleomagnetic: pertains to the natural magnetization that resides in rock and sediment material and records the intensity and direction of the Earth's magnetic field when the material was emplaced.

paleosol: a buried soil horizon of the geologic past.

Palouse: name given the treeless rolling hills of up to 250-foot-thick windblown loess of eastern Washington. Derived from the French word "pelouse" meaning "lawn" or "grassy plains." Palouse soils originally supported native bunch grass but today are used to grow mostly wheat.

Palouse Formation: the geologic name given to the windblown deposits of loess in the Palouse region of southeastern Washington.

Palouse Slope: a gentle, southwest-sloping surface that underlies the Palouse region. The surface is a reflection of the top of the Columbia River basalt, which has a similar attitude. The Palouse Slope merges with the **Yakima Folds** to the west.

particle: a discrete, individual sedimentary grain or fragment.

patterned ground: arrangements of surface materials produced by frost action or other natural processes into various geometric forms, including **Mima mounds**.

pendant bar: a type of flood bar that forms immediately downstream of a flow obstruction within a flood channel or coulee.

periglacial: pertains to natural processes active in cold envionments such as those found near the present or former margins of a glacier.

pillar: used here to describe a tall, narrow eroded basalt monolith with an irregular top. Height of a pillar is much greater than its width.

pillow basalt: pillows appear as large, rounded balls of glassy basalt at the base of the lava flow. The pillows indicate the lava cooled very suddenly after coming in contact with a lake or stream.

Pleistocene: an epoch of geologic time between about 13,000 years and 2.6 million years ago. The Pleistocene essentially spans the same time period known as the Ice Age (see Figure 1-8).

plunge pool: a deep, circular hole eroded at the base of a **cataract**, scoured out by the force of up to hundreds of feet of floodwater rushing over the cataract.

pothole: a circular rock basin eroded into bedrock, which was basalt in the case of the Channeled Scabland. Many are the result of circulating, tight eddies or **kolk**-like currents during flooding.

Precambrian: All geologic time prior to 570 million years ago. Comprises 90 percent of all geologic time on Earth.

Purcell Trench Lobe: A lobe of ice that came down the Purcell Trench from Canada, blocking the Clark Fork River along the present-day Idaho-Montana border. Glacial Lake Missoula, responsible for most of the Ice Age floods, formed behind this ice dam (see Plate 1).

quartzite: an extremely hard **metamorphic** rock composed entirely of quartz. Derived from an ancient sandstone, quartzite may display some original horizontal or cross stratification that developed as the sandstone was deposited. Quartzite and associated argillite clasts found in the Columbia Plateau are mostly from **Belt rocks** (1.4 billion to 1.6 billion years old) present in northern Washington, Idaho and Montana. The quartzite from these regions is frequently pale blue, green or brown.

recessional cataract: a tall, steep cliff that forms from the upstream migration of a **cataract** in a flood channel or coulee during the Ice Age floods. A horseshoe-shaped alcove commonly lies at the head of the cataract while a deep **inner canyon** lies below the cataract.

rhythmite: a graded sedimentary bed, several inches to several feet thick, deposited under **slackwater** conditions, especially in backflooded valleys during Ice Age flooding. Some believe that each rhythmite represents a separate outburst flood from Glacial Lake Missoula.

ringed crater: unusual circular features in Columbia River basalt etched out by the Ice Age floods. Concentric rings are basalt dikes that formed as the basalt lava came to rest and cooled.

rip-up clast: large fragments of ripped up, sedimentary material eroded and transported from the Palouse Formation, or older flood deposits during Ice Age flooding. Because rip-up clasts are extremely friable and fall apart in their present state, they were probably frozen before being ripped up and transported by floods.

rock basin: in the Columbia Plateau a depression carved out in weaker basalt bedrock during flooding.

rock bench: a tier of basalt, eroded by the floods, that lies alongside or above a flood channel or coulee. Rock benches usually conform to the tops of basalt lava flows.

rock blade: a narrow and tall ridge or rib of basalt within a flood coulee, often separating adjacent coulees, associated with **cataract recession**.

rock shelter: a cave-like opening that extends a short distance into a hill or cliff side.

sand: small sedimentary particles that are between 0.06 millimeters to 2 millimeters in diameter.

scabland flood: an Ice Age flood that flowed across the Channeled Scabland of southeastern Washington. Most scabland floods were from Glacial Lake Missoula during a time when the Okanogan Lobe obstructed flow and diverted the floodwaters out across the scabland (see Plate 1).

scabland tract: a broad area with multiple interconnected flood channels eroded through Palouse loess down to basalt bedrock.

scarp: a planar, beveled slope. In the Channeled Scabland scarps were eroded in bedrock and in the Palouse Formation during erosion along flood channels. Scarp slopes are steeper than adjacent non-flood-eroded slopes.

scour holes: crescentic depressions behind or in front of large boulders, created as floodwaters moved over and around the stationary boulders.

sediment: solid fragmental material that originates from the weathering and transport, by water, wind or ice, of pre-existing rock or sediment bodies.

sedimentary: pertains to an accumulation of sediment particles, usually under the influence of moving water or wind. One of the three principal rock types, along with **igneous** and **metamorphic**.

seiche: the sudden oscillation of water in a lake, bay or estuary producing fluctuations in water level by earthquakes or wind.

seismic: refers to Earth vibrations and shaking as a result of earthquake activity.

sequence: a succession of geologic events recorded in beds of rock and/or sediment. Lower beds record events that happened earlier than beds higher in the sequence.

silt: tiny sedimentary particles that are 0.004 millimeters to 0.06 millimeters in diameter.

slackwater: refers to areas with slower moving floodwaters associated with Ice Age flooding (such as backflooded valleys and valley margins) where **fine-grained** sediment (mostly sand and silt) was deposited.

soft-sediment deformation: sediment movement that occurs during or soon after sediment deposition and while still saturated with water and easily deformable. Examples of soft-sediment deformation include **convoluted bedding** and **flame structures**.

spillover channel: a **divide crossing** where floodwaters erode enough to carve a somewhat flat-bottomed, trapezoidal-shaped channel across the divide.

steptoe: a hill or ridge of older rock surrounded by engulfing lava flows. The type example of such a feature is Steptoe Butte, located east of the Cheney-Palouse Scabland Tract.

strandline: like a bathtub ring, the level at which a former standing body of water met the land surface. Strandlines may be visible as small terraces etched out by wave activity along former lake shorelines.

striations: Multiple parallel to semi-parallel scratches inscribed into a rock surface by the creep of rock-embedded glacial ice moving over the surface under high pressure

superposition: the sequential order of layers where younger layers rest on top of older, or the process where streams cut down through horizontal layers into a buried ridge or structure below.

talus: large, angular rock fragments derived from and lying at the base of cliffs. Most talus on the Channeled Scabland is composed of basalt fragments shed off steep cliffs since the last Ice Age floods. Also known as scree.

tectonic: pertains to large, regional forces deep within the Earth's crust that cause earthquakes, folds, faults and some fractures observed at or near the surface.

Telford-Crab Creek Scabland Tract: a network of interconnected flood channels and coulees, separated by uplands of Palouse loess, that trends south across the central portion of the Channeled Scabland.

tephra: airfall deposit of all sizes from a volcanic eruption. Tephra deposits in the Columbia Plateau consist of distinctive, light-colored, gritty particles of volcanic ash.

till: an unsorted, heterogeneous mixture of clay, silt, sand and gravel depostited beneath a slowly advancing glacier.

trenched spur: in flood coulees, where the depth, force and momentum of the floodwaters forced the flow to go straight over localized basalt uplands (spurs), cutting new channels across the spurs.

trimline: a distinct boundary along flood channels that separates a lower, eroded area, without soil cover, from a higher area with soil cover preserved. The trimline generally marks the upper height limit for the floods.

unconformity: refers to the contact between beds where one layer is significantly different in age than the overlying bed. Signifies an erosional event or period of non-deposition between beds.

underfit stream: a stream that appears to be too small to have eroded the valley in which it flows.

uniformitarianism: The fundamental geologic principle or doctrine that geologic processes and natural laws now operating to modify the surface of Earth have acted in the same regular manner and with the same intensity throughout geologic time and that past geologic events can be explained by phenomenon and forces observable today. Also referred to as gradualism. Opposite of **catastrophism.**

upland plateau: an elevated, broad basalt plateau or mesa swept clean of Palouse loess and other soil by high-energy Ice Age floods. The plateau surface is usually riddled with erosional longitudinal grooves, potholes and rock basins. Upland plateaus are bordered by deeper erosional flood channels or coulees.

varve: an annual layer of sediment deposited within a glacial lake. Typically, lighter-colored fine sand to silt at the base of a varve transitions upward into darker clay, representing summer versus winter layers, respectively. Normally many varves, each only fractions of an inch thick, occur stacked together within a sequence.

venturi effect: the physical phenomenon that water forced to move through a narrower channel will move faster than the same amount of water moving through a wider channel. As an example, floodwaters moving through the constricted Grand Coulee moved much faster, with significantly more erosive power, than the water at either end the coulee.

vesicle: a cavity of variable shape and size in a lava flow, formed by the entrapment of a gas bubble as the lava cooled and solidified.

Waterville Plateau: a broad, gently rolling upland that lies between Grand Coulee and the Columbia River valley within the western Channeled Scabland. Much of the Waterville Plateau was covered by the Okanogan Lobe and thus not affected by Ice Age floods, except through **Moses Coulee.**

weathering: alteration of sediment or rock at the Earth's surface by long-term exposure to air, water and other agents through various physical, chemical and biological processes.

Wisconsinan: Pertains to the last major glacial cycle during the late **Pleistocene** in North America. The Wisconsinan lasted between about 14,000 years and 80,000 years ago and was preceded by at least 40,000 years of interglacial conditions, similar to what we experience today.

Withrow Moraine: a well-defined ridge of glacial debris (mostly glacial till and Haystack Rocks) deposited at the farthest extent of the **Okanogan Lobe** on the **Waterville Plateau.**

Yakima Folds: Roughly parallel anticlines of folded Columbia River basalt in portions of southern and central Washington. Combined, the Yakima Folds comprise a geologic region called the Yakima Fold Belt.

Selected References

NONTECHNICAL

Allen, J.E., M. Burns and S. Burns. 2009. *Cataclysms on the Columbia:* The Great Missoula Floods, Second Edition. Portland, Oregon: Ooligan Press, 204 p.

Alt, D.D. 2001. *Glacial Lake Missoula and Its Humongous Floods.* Missoula, Montana: Mountain Press, 199 p.

Amara, M.S. and G.E. Neff. 1996. *Geologic Road Trips in Grant County, Washington.* Moses Lake, Washington: Adam East Museum and Art Center, 93 p.

Anglin, R. 1995. *Forgotten Trails: Historical Sources of the Columbia's Big Bend Country,* Pullman, Washington: WSU Press, 287 p.

Bjornstad, B.N. 2006. *On the Trail of the Ice Age Floods: A Geological Field Guide to the Mid-Columbia Basin.* Sandpoint, Idaho: Keokee Books, 308 p.

Carson, R., and S. Babcock. 2009. *Hiking Guide to Washington Geology.* Sandpoint, Idaho: Keokee Books, 272 p.

Ficken, R.E. 1995. *Rufus Woods, the Columbia River, & the Building of Modern Washington.* Pullman, Washington: Washington State University Press, 312 p.

Fritz, J. 2010. *Legendary Lake Pend Oreille: Idaho's Wilderness of Water.* Sandpoint, Idaho: Keokee Books, 406 p.

Jones & Jones. 2001. "Ice Age floods – Study of Alternatives and Environmental Assessment Following the Pathways of the Glacial Lake Missoula Floods," under contract to the U.S. National Park Service, Seattle, Washington, V. 1.

Katz, C., and K.R. Pogue. 2002. *Erratics.* Walla Walla, Washington: Sheehan Art Gallery, Whitman College.

MacInnis, P.E., J. Blake, B. Painter, J.P. Buchanan, B.B. Lackaff and R. Boese. 2000. "The Spokane Valley-Rathdrum Prairie Aquifer Atlas," updated in 2004, Spokane Aquifer Group, Spokane County, Washington, 24 p.

Mason, C.L. 2006. *The Geological History of the Wenatchee Valley and Adjacent Vicinity.* Wenatchee, Washington: The World Publishing Company, 167 p.

Mueller, M. and T. Mueller. 1997. *Fire, Faults and Floods.* Moscow, Idaho: University of Idaho Press, 288 p.

Scheuerman, R.D. and M.O. Finley. 2008. *Finding Chief Kamiakin: The Life and Legacy of a Northwest Patriot.* Pullman Washington: WSU Press, 205 p.

Parfit, M. 1995. "The Floods that Carved the West," Smithsonian, V. 26, No. 1, p. 48-59.

Soennichsen, J.R. 2008. *Bretz's Flood.* Seattle: Sasquatch Books. 289 p.

Symons, T.W. 1882. "Report of an Examination of the Upper Columbia River and the Territory in its Vicinity in September and October, 1881," Ex. Doc. No. 186, 47th Congress, 1st Session, Government Printing Office, Washington D.C.

Weis, P.L. and W.L. Newman. 1989. *The Channeled Scablands of Eastern Washington: The Geologic Story of the Spokane Flood,* Second Edition. Cheney, Washington: Eastern Washington University Press.

Pamphlets

Amara, M.S., and R. Cerna. 2007. *Geologic Trips in the Coulee Corridor National Scenic Byway in Grant and Adams Counties,* Washington. Copyright by authors.

Cunderla, B. and C. Mason. 2005. *Wenatchee Valley Ice Age Floods Geological Trail.* Wenatchee Valley Convention and Visitors Bureau, includes two self-guided driving tours, www.Wenatcheevalley.org.

TECHNICAL Publications

Adema, G.W., R.M. Breckenridge and K.F. Sprenke. 2007. "Gravity, morphology, and bedrock depth of the Rathdrum Prairie." Idaho Geological Survey Technical Report 2007-2, 37 p.

Alho, P., V.R. Baker and L.N. Smith. 2010. "Paleohydraulic reconstruction of the largest glacial Lake Missoula draining(s)." *Quaternary Science Reviews,* doi:10.1016/j.quascirev.2010.07.015.

Anfinson. O., D.R. Gaylord, M.C. Pope and P.R. Cabbage, 2009. "Detrital zircon geochronology applied to late Quaternary megaflood deposits from the Channeled Scabland. Geological Society of America, Abstracts with Programs, V. 41, No. 7, p. 169.

Atwater, B.F. 1984. "Periodic floods from Glacial Lake Missoula into the Sanpoil arm of Glacial Lake Columbia." *Geology,* V. 12, p. 464-467.

Atwater, B.F. 1986. "Pleistocene glacial-lake deposits of the Sanpoil River valley, northeastern Washington." U.S. Geological Survey Bulletin 1661, 39 p.

Atwater, B.F. 1987. "Status of Glacial Lake Columbia during the last floods from Glacial Lake Missoula." Quaternary Research, V. 27, p. 182-201.

Badger, T.C. and R.W. Galster. 2003. "Engineering geology in the central Columbia River valley," in Swanson, T.W., ed., *Western Cordillera and Adjacent Areas.* Boulder, Colorado: Geological Society of America Field Guide 4, p. 159-176.

Baker, V.R. 1973. "Paleohydrology and sedimentology of Lake Missoula flooding in eastern Washington." Boulder, Colorado: GSA Special Paper No. 144, Geological Society of America, 73p.

Baker, V.R. 1978. "The Spokane Flood Controversy and the Martian Outflow Channels." Science, V. 202, No. 4374, p. 1249-1256.

Baker, V.R., ed. 1981 *Catastrophic Flooding: The Origin of the Channeled Scabland,* Benchmark Papers in Geology, V. 55. Stroudsburg, Pennsylvania: Dowden, Hutchinson & Ross, 360p.

Baker, V.R. 1987. "Dry Falls of the Channeled Scabland, Washington," *in* Hill, M.L., *ed. Centennial Field Guide,* Volume 1. Boulder, Colorado: Cordilleran Section of the Geological Society of America, p. 369-372.

Baker, V.R. 1989. "The Grand Coulee and Dry Falls," in Breckenridge, R.M., ed., *Glacial Lake Missoula and the Channeled Scabland.* American Geophysical Union, Field Trip Guidebook T310, Chapter 6, p. 51-57.

Baker, V.R. 1995. "Surprise endings to catastrophism and controversy on the Columbia: Joseph Thomas Pardee and the Spokane Flood Controversy." *GSA Today,* V. 5, p. 169-173.

Baker, V.R. 2001. "Water and the Martian Landscape." Nature, V. 412, p. 228-236.

Baker, V.R. 2002a. "High-energy megafloods: Planetary settings and sedimentary dynamics." Special Publication Number 32 of the International Association of Sedimentologists, in Martini, I.P., V.R. Baker and G. Garzon, eds., *Flood and Megaflood Processes and Deposits: Recent and Ancient Examples,* p. 3-15.

Baker, V.R. 2002a. "The study of superfloods." *Science,* V. 295, p. 2379-2380.

Baker, V.R. 2009. "Channeled Scabland morphology," in Burr, D.M., P.A. Carling and V.R. Baker, eds, *Megaflooding on Earth and Mars*. Cambridge, UK: Cambridge University Press, p. 65-77.

Baker, V.R. 2009. "The Channeled Scabland: A retrospective." *Annual Review of Earth and Planetary Science*, V. 37, p. 393-411.

Baker, V.R. and D. Nummedal, eds. 1978. *The Channeled Scabland*. Washington, D.C.: National Aeronautics and Space Administration, 186 p.

Baker, V.R. and R.C. Bunker. 1985. "Cataclysmic Late Pleistocene flooding from Glacial Lake Missoula: A review," in *Quaternary Science Reviews*, V. 4, p. 1-41.

Baker, V.R., B.N. Bjornstad, A.J. Busacca, K.R. Fecht, E.P. Kiver, U.L. Moody, J.G. Rigby, D.F. Stradling and A.M. Tallman. 1991. "Quaternary Geology of the Columbia Plateau," in Morrison, R.B., ed., *Quaternary Nonglacial Geology; Conterminous U.S., The Geology of North America*, V. K 2. Boulder, Colorado: Geological Society of America, p. 215-250.

Baker, V.R., B.N. Bjornstad, N. Greenbaum, N. Porat, L.N. Smith, M.G. Zreda. 2009. "Possible revised chronology of late Pleistocene megaflooding, northwestern United States." Geological Society of America, Abstracts with Programs, V. 41, No. 7, p. 168.

Behrens, G.W. and P.J. Hansen. 1989. "Geology and related construction problems of the Grand Coulee Dam Project," in Joseph, N.L, and others, eds, Geologic Guidebook for Washington and Adjacent Areas, Information Circular 86. Olympia, Washington: Washington Division of the Geology and Earth Resources, p. 357-369.

Benito, G. and J.E. O'Connor. 2003. "Number and size of last-glacial Missoula floods in the Columbia River valley between Pasco Basin, Washington and Portland, Oregon." Geological Society of America Bulletin, V. 115, p. 624-638.

Berg, A.W. 1990. "Formation of Mima mounds: A seismic hypothesis." *Geology*, V. 18, p. 281-284.

Bjornstad, B.N., K.R. Fecht and C.J. Pluhar. 2001. "Long history of pre-Wisconsin, Ice Age floods: Evidence from southeastern Washington State." *Journal of Geology*, V. 109, p. 695-713.

Bjornstad, B.N., R.S. Babcock, and G.V. Last. 2007. "Flood basalts and Ice Age floods: Repeated cataclysms of southeastern Washington," in Stelling, P. and D.S. Tucker, eds., *Floods, Faults, and Fire: Geological Field Trips in Washington State and Southwest British Columbia*. Geological Society of America Field Guide 9, p. 209-255, Boulder, Colorado, doi: 10.1130/2007/fld009(10).

Booth, D.B., K.G. Troost, J.J. Clague and R.B. Waitt. 2004. "The Cordilleran Ice Sheet," in Gillespie, A.R., et al, eds., *The Quaternary Period in the United States: Developments in Quaternary Science, Volume 1*. Amsterdam: Elsevier, p. 17-44.

Breckenridge, R.M. 1989. "Lower Glacial Lakes Missoula and Clark Fork Ice Dams," in Breckenridge, R.M., ed., *Glacial Lake Missoula and the Channeled Scabland*. American Geophysical Union, Field Trip Guidebook T310, Chapter 3, p. 13-22.

Breckenridge, R.M. 1989. "Evidence for ice dams and floods in the Purcell Trench: Trip A," in Joseph, N.L, and others, eds, *Geologic Guidebook for Washington and Adjacent Areas*. Olympia, Washington: Information Circular 86, Washington Division of the Geology and Earth Resources, p. 309-320.

Breckenridge, R.M. and K.F. Sprenke. 1997. "An overdeepened glaciated basin, Lake Pend Oreille, northern Idaho." *Glacial Geology and Geomorphology*, rp01/1997, http://ggg.qub.ac.uk/papers/full/1997/rp011997/rp01.htm

Bretz, J H. 1923a. "Glacial Drainage on the Columbia Plateau." *Geological Society of America Bulletin*, V. 34, p. 573-608.

Bretz, J H. 1923b. "The Channeled Scabland of the Columbia Plateau." Journal of

Geology, v. 31, p. 617-649.

Bretz, J H. 1927a. "Channeled Scabland and the Spokane Flood." *Journal of Washington Academy of Sciences*, V. 18, p. 200-211.

Bretz, J H. 1927b. "The Spokane Flood: A Reply." *Journal of Geology*, V. 35, p. 461-468.

Bretz, J H. 1928a. "The Channeled Scabland of Eastern Washington." *Geographical Review*, V. 18, p. 446-477.

Bretz, J H. 1928b. "Bars of Channeled Scabland." *Geological Society of America Bulletin*, V. 39, p. 643-702.

Bretz, J H. 1928c. "Alternate Hypotheses for Channeled Scabland." *Journal of Geology*, V.36, p. 193-223, 312-341.

Bretz, J H. 1929. "Valley Deposits Immediately East of the Channeled Scabland of Washington." *Journal of Geology*, v .37, p. 393-427, 505-541.

Bretz, J H. 1930a. "Valley Deposits Immediately West of the Channeled Scabland." *Journal of Geology*, V. 38, p. 385-422.

Bretz, J H. 1930b. "Lake Missoula and the Spokane Flood." *Geological Society of America Bulletin*, V. 41, p. 92-93.

Bretz, J H. 1932. "The Grand Coulee." New York: American Geographical Society, Special Publication No. 15, , 89 p.

Bretz, J H. 1959. "Washington's Channeled Scabland." Olympia, Washington: *Bulletin No. 45*, Washington Division of Mines and Geology.

Bretz, J H. 1969. "The Lake Missoula Floods and the Channeled Scabland." *Journal of Geology*, V. 77, p. 505-543.

Bretz, J H., H.T.U. Smith and G.E. Neff. 1956. "Channeled Scabland of Washington: New Data and Interpretations." *Geological Society of America Bulletin*, V. 67, p. 957-1049.

Brown, K.B, J.C. McIntosh, V.R. Baker and D. Gosch. 2010. "Isotopically depleted late Pleistocene groundwater in Basalt aquifers: Evidence for recharge of glacial Lake Missoula floodwaters?" *Geophysical Research Letters*, V. 37, doi:10.1029/2010GLO44992).

Brunner, C.A., W.R. Normark, G.G. Zuffa and F. Serra. 1999. "Deep-sea sedimentary record of the late Wisconsin cataclysmic floods from the Columbia River." *Geology*, V. 27, p. 463-466.

Busacca, A.J. 1989. "Long Quaternary record in eastern Washington, U.S.A., interpreted from multiple buried paleosols in loess." *Geoderma*, V. 45, p. 105-122.

Busacca, A.J. and E.V. McDonald. 1994. "Regional sedimentation of late Quaternary loess on the Columbia Plateau: Sediment source areas and loess distribution patterns." Bulletin 80, Washington Division of Geology and Earth Resources, p.181-190.

Busacca, A.J., E.V. McDonald and V.R. Baker. 1989. "The record of pre-late Wisconsin floods and late Wisconsin flood features in the Cheney-Palouse Scabland," in Breckenridge, R.M., ed., *Glacial Lake Missoula and the Channeled Scabland*. American Geophysical Union, Field Trip Guidebook T310, Chapter 7, p. 57-62.

Carrara, P.E., E.P. Kiver, and D.F. Stradling. 1996. "The southern limit of Cordilleran ice in the Colville and Pend Oreille valleys of northeastern Washington during the late Wisconsin glaciations." Canadian Journal of Earth Sciences, V. 33, p. 769-778.

Christensen, P.R., N.S. Gorelick, G.L. Mehall, and K.C. Murray. 2009. THEMIS Public Data Releases, Planetary Data System node, Arizona State University, available at http://themis-data.asu.edu.

Clarke, G.K.C., W.H Matthews, R.T. 1984. "Outburst floods from glacial Lake Missoula." Quaternary Research, V. 22, p. 289-299.

Cline, D.R. 1984. "Ground-water levels and pumpage in east-central Washington, including the Odessa-Lind Area, 1967-1981." Olympia, Washington: Water-Supply Bulletin No. 55, Washington State Department of Ecology.

Coleman, N.M. and V.R. Baker. 2009. "Surface morphology and origin of outflow channels in the Valles Marineris region," in Burr, D.M., P.A. Carling and V.R. Baker, eds, Megaflooding on Earth and Mars. Cambridge, UK: Cambridge University Press, p. 172-193.

Craig, R.G. 1987. "Dynamics of a Missoula flood," in Mayer, L. and D. Nash, eds., Catastrophic Flooding. Boston: Allen and Unwin, p. 305-332.

Crosby, C.J. and R.J. Carson. 1999. "Geology of Steamboat Rock, Grand Coulee, Washington." Washington Geology, V. 27, p. 3-8.

Denlinger, R.P. and D.R.H. O'Connell, 2010. "Simulations of cataclysmic outburst floods from Pleistocene Glacial Lake Missoula." Geological Society of America Bulletin, V. 122, p. 678-689, doi: 10.1130/B26454.1.

Easterbrook, D.J. 2003. "Cordilleran Ice Sheet glaciation of the Puget Lowland and Columbia Plateau and alpine glaciation of the North Cascade Range, Washington," in Easterbrook, D.J. ed., Quaternary Geology of the United States. INQUA 2003 Field Guide Volume, Desert Research Institute, Reno, Nevada, p. 265-286.

Easterbrook, D.J. 2003a. "Cordilleran Ice Sheet glaciation of the Puget Lowland and Columbia Plateau and alpine glaciation of the North Cascade Range, Washington," in Swanson, T.W., ed., Western Cordillera and Adjacent Areas. Boulder, Colorado: Geological Society of America Field Guide 4, p. 137-157.

Edgett, K.S., J.W. Rice and V.R. Baker, eds. 1995. "Field trips accompanying the Mars Pathfinder Landing Site Workshop II – Channeled Scabland and Lake Missoula break-out areas in Washington and Idaho," in Golombek, M.P., K.S. Edgett, J.W. Rice, eds., "Mars Pathfinder Landing Site Workshop II – Characteristics of the Ares Vallis region and field trips in the Channeled Scabland, Washington." Lunar and Planetary Institute Technical Report 95-01, Part 1, p. 31-63.

Fecht, K.R., S.P. Reidel and A.M. Tallman. 1987. "Paleodrainage of the Columbia River on the Columbia Plateau of Washington State – A Summary," Bulletin 77. Olympia, Washington: Washington Division of Geology and Earth Resources, Department of Natural Resources, p. 219-248.

Freeman, O.W. 1926. "Scabland mounds of eastern Washington." Science, V. 64, p. 450-451.

Gaylord, D.R., A.J. Busacca and M.R. Sweeney. 2003. "The Palouse loess and the Channeled Scabland: A paired Ice Age geologic system," in Easterbrook, D.J., ed., Quaternary Geology of the United States, INQUA 2003 Field Guide Volume. Reno, Nevada: Desert Research Institute, p.123-134.

Gerstel, W.J. and S.P. Palmer. 1994. "Geologic and geophysical mapping of the Spokane Aquifer – Relevance to growth management." Washington Geology, V. 22, p. 18-24.

Golombek, M.P., K.S. Edgett and J.W. Rice, eds. 1995. "Mars Pathfinder Landing Site Workshop II – Characteristics of the Ares Vallis region and field trips in the Channeled Scabland, Washington." Lunar and Planetary Institute Technical Report 95-01.

Golombek, M.P. and D. Rapp. 1997. "Size-frequency distributions of rocks on Mars and Earth analog sites – Implications for Future Landed Missions." Journal of Geophysical Research, V. 102, No. E2, p. 4417-4129.

Grolier, M.J., and J.W. Bingham. 1978. "Geology of parts of Grant, Adams, and

Franklin Counties, east-central Washington," Bulletin No. 71. Olympia, Washington: Washington Department of Natural Resources, Division of Geology and Earth Resources.

Hendy, I.L. 2009. "A fresh perspective on the Cordilleran Ice Sheet." *Geology*, V. 37, p. 95-96.

Huckleberry, G., B. Lentz, J. Galm and S. Gogh. 2003. "Recent archaeological discoveries in central Washington," *in* Swanson, T.W., ed., *Western Cordillera and Adjacent Areas. Boulder*, Colorado: Geological Society of America Field Guide 4, p. 237-249.

Jaeger, W.L., L.P. Keszthelyi, D.M Burr, A.S. McEwen, V.R. Baker, H. Miyamoto and R.A. Beyer. 2003. "Ring dike structures in the Channeled Scabland as analogs for circular features in Athabasca Valles, Mars." Lunar and Planetary Science Conference XXXIV, Abstract No. 245.

Kahle, S.C., R.R. Caldwell and J.R. Bartolino. 2005. "Compilation of geologic, hydrologic, and ground-water flow modeling information for the Spokane County, Washington, and Bonner and Kootenai Counties, Idaho," Scientific Investigations Report 2005-5227. Denver: U.S. Geological Survey.

Keszthelyi, L.P., V.R. Baker, W.L. Jaeger, D.R. Gaylord, B.N. Bjornstad, N. Greenbaum, S. Self, T. Thordarson, N. Porat and M.G. Zreda. 2009. "Floods of water and lava in the Columbia River Basin: Analogs for Mars," in O'Connor, J.E., Dorsey, R.J. and Madin, I.P., eds., *Volcanoes to Vineyards: Geologic Field Trips Through the Dynamic Landscape of the Pacific Northwest*. Geological Society of America Field Guide 15, p. 845-874, doi: 10.1130/2009.fld015 (34).

Kiver, E.P. and D.F. Stradling. 1989. "The Spokane Valley and Northern Columbia Plateau," in Breckenridge, R.M., ed., *Glacial Lake Missoula and the Channeled Scabland*. American Geophysical Union, Field Trip Guidebook T310, Chapter 4, p. 23-36.

Kiver, E.P., D.F Stradling and U. Moody. 1989. "Glacial and multiple flood history of the northern borderlands: Trip B," *in* Joseph, N.L, and others, eds, *Geologic Guidebook for Washington and Adjacent Areas*, Information Circular 86. Olympia, Washington: Washington Division of the Geology and Earth Resources, p. 321-335.

Komar, P.D. 1983. "Shapes of streamlined islands on Earth and Mars – Experiments and Analysis of the Minimum-Drag Form." *Geology*, V. 11, No. 11, p. 651-655.

Korosec, M.A., J.G. Rigby and K.L. Stoffel. 1980. "The 1980 eruption of Mount St. Helens, Washington, March 20-May 19, 1980," Information Circular 71. Olympia, Washington: Washington Division of Natural Resources, Division of Geology and Earth Resources, 17 p.

Kovanen, D.J. and O. Slaymaker. 2004. "Glacial imprints of the Okanogan Lobe, southern margin of the Cordilleran Ice Sheet." *Journal of Quaternary Science*, V. 19, p. 547-565.

Kukla, G. and J. Gavin. 2005. "Did glacials start with global warming?" *Quaternary Science Reviews*, V. 24, p. 1547-1557.

Landye, J.J. 1973. "Environmental significance of late Quaternary non-marine mollusks from former Lake Bretz, Lower Grand Coulee, Washington," Master of Arts Thesis. Pullman, Washington: Washington State University Department of Anthropology.

Lesemann, J.-E. and T.A. Brennand. 2009. "Jökulhlaups from the southern margin of the Cordilleran Ice Sheet." Geological Society of America annual meeting, Portland, Oregon, Abstracts with Programs, V. 41, No. 7, p. 169.

Lopes, C. and A.C. Mix. 2009. "Pleistocene megafloods in the northeast Pacific." *Geology*, V. 37, p. 79-82.

Lund Snee, J-E. and R.J. Carson. 2009. "Terracettes: Animal, vegetable, or mineral?" Geological Society of America, Abstracts with Programs, 105th Cordilleran Section Meeting.

McCollum, L.B. and M.B. McCollum. 2009. "Late Pleistocene outburst flood formation of lakes located along small drainage divides within the northern Columbia Plateau." Geological Society of America, Abstracts with Programs, V. 41, No. 7, p. 168-169.

McDonald, E.V. and A.J. Busacca. 1988. "Record of pre-late Wisconsin giant floods in the Channeled Scabland interpreted from loess deposits." *Geology*, V. 16, p. 728-731.

McDonald, E.V. and A.J. Busacca. 1989. "Record of pre-Late Wisconsin floods and of Late Wisconsin flood features in the Cheney-Palouse Scabland: Trip C," in Joseph, N.L and others, eds, *Geologic Guidebook for Washington and Adjacent Areas*, Information Circular 86. Olympia, Washington: Washington Division of the Geology and Earth Resources, p. 337-346.

McDonald, E.V. and A.J. Busacca. 1992. "Late quaternary stratigraphy of loess in the Channeled Scabland and Palouse regions of Washington State." *Quaternary Research*, V. 38, p. 141-156.

McKee, B. and D.F. Stradling. 1970. "The sag flowout: a newly described volcanic structure." *Geological Society of America Bulletin*, V. 81, p. 2035-2044.

Meyer, S.E. 1999. "Depositional history of pre-late and late Wisconsin outburst flood deposits in northern Washington and Idaho: Analysis of flood paths and provenance," Master of Science thesis. Pullman, Washington: Washington State University, 57 p.

Miyamoto, H., K. Itoh, G. Komatsu, V.R. Baker, J.M Dohm, H. Tosaka and S. Sasaki. 2006. "Numerical simulations of large-scale cataclysmic floodwater: A simple depth-averaged model and an illustrative application." *Geomorphology*, V. 76, p. 179-192.

Miyamoto, H., G. Komatsu, V.R. Baker, J.M. Dohm, K. Ito and H. Tosaka. 2007. "Cataclysmic Scabland flooding: Insights from a simple depth-averaged numerical model." *Environmental Modeling and Software*, V. 22, p. 1400-1408.

Moody, U.L. 1987. "Late Quaternary Stratigraphy of the Channeled Scabland and Adjacent Area," Doctoral Dissertation. Moscow, Idaho: University of Idaho, 419 p.

Morrison, R. and G. Kukla. 1998. "The Pliocene-Pleistocene (Tertiary-Quaternary) boundary should be placed at about 2.6 Ma, not at 1.8 Ma!" *GSA Today*, No. 8, p. 9.

Mullineaux, D.R., R.E. Wilcox, W.F. Ebaugh, R. Fryxell and M. Rubin. 1978. "Age of the last major scabland flood of the Columbia Plateau in eastern Washington." *Quaternary Research*, V. 10, p. 171-180.

Neff, G.E. 1989. "Columbia Basin Project," in Vol. 1 of *Engineering Geology in Washington*, Bulletin No. 78. Olympia, Washington: Washington Division of Geology and Earth Resources, p. 535-563.

Nickmann, R.J. 1979. "The palynology of Williams Lake fen, Spokane County, Washington," Master of Science thesis. Cheney, Washington: Eastern Washington State University.

Normark, W.R. and J.A. Reid. 2003. "Extensive deposits on the Pacific Plate from Late Pleistocene North American glacial lake outbursts." *Journal of Geology*, V. 111, p. 617-637.

O'Connor, J.E. and V.R. Baker. 1992. "Magnitudes and implications of peak discharges from Glacial Lake Missoula." *Geological Society of America Bulletin*, V. 104, p. 267-279.

O'Connor, J.E. 1993 "Hydrology, hydraulics, and geomorphology of the Bonneville Flood," Geological Society of America Special Paper No. 27. Boulder, Colorado, 83 p.

Olmsted, R.K. 1963. "Silt mounds of Missoula flood surfaces." *Geological Society of America Bulletin*, V. 74, p. 47-54.

Pardee, J.T. 1910. "The Glacial Lake Missoula." *Journal of Geology*, V. 18, p. 376-386.

Pardee, J.T. 1942. "Unusual Currents in Glacial Lake Missoula, Montana." *Geological Society of America Bulletin*, V. 53, p. 1569-1599.

Patton, P.C. and V.R. Baker. 1978. "New evidence for pre-Wisconsin flooding in the Channeled Scabland and eastern Washington." *Geology*, V. 6, p. 567-571.

Reidel, S.P. and P.R. Hooper, eds. 1989. "Volcanism and tectonism in the Columbia River flood-basalt province," Geological Society of America Special Paper No. 239. Boulder, Colorado: Geological Society of America, 386 p.

Rice, J.W. Jr. and K.S. Edgett. 1997. "Catastrophic flood sediments in Chryse Basin, Mars and Quincy Basin, Washington; application of sandar facies model." *Journal of Geophysical Research, E, Planets*, V. 102, No. 2, p. 4185-4200.

Rigby, J.G. 1982. "The sedimentology, mineralogy, and depositional environment of a sequence of Quaternary catastrophic flood-derived lacustrine turbidites near Spokane, Washington," Master of Science thesis. Moscow, Idaho: University of Idaho, 132 p.

Shaw, J., M. Munro-Stasuik, B. Sawyer, C. Beaney, J.-E. Lesemann, A. Musacchio, B. Rains and R.R. Young. 1999. "The Channeled Scabland: Back to Bretz." *Geology*, V. 27, p. 605-608.

Smith, G.A. 1993. "Missoula Flood Dynamics and Magnitudes Inferred from Sedimentology of Slack-Water Deposits on the Columbia Plateau." *Geological Society of America Bulletin*, V. 195, p. 77-100.

Smyers, N.B. and R.M. Breckenridge. 2003. "Glacial Lake Missoula, Clark Fork ice dam, and the floods outburst area: Northern Idaho and western Montana," *in* Swanson, T.W., ed, *Western Cordillera and Adjacent Areas*, Field Guide 4. Boulder, Colorado: Geological Society of America, p. 1-15.

Snyder, D.T. and J.V. Haynes. 2010. "Groundwater conditions during 2009 and changes in groundwater levels from 1984 to 2009, Columbia Plateau Regional Aquifer System, Washington, Oregon, and Idaho," Scientific Investigations Report 2010-5040, U.S. Geological Survey.

Spencer, P.K., M. Mix and R. Burand. 2007. "The Steamboat Rock Silt: Indirect evidence for a moraine-dammed lake in upper Grand Coulee during the last glacial maximum." Geological Society of America, Abstracts with Programs, Cordilleran Section.

Stradling, D.F. and E.P. Kiver. 1989. "The northern Columbia Plateau from the air," in Joseph, N.L. and others, eds, *Geologic Guidebook for Washington and Adjacent Areas*, Information Circular 86. Olympia, Washington: Washington Division of the Geology and Earth Resources., p. 349-353.

Steele, W.K. 1991, "Paleomagnetic evidence for repeated Glacial Lake Missoula floods from sediments of the Sanpoil Valley, northeastern Washington." *Quaternary Research*, V. 35, p. 197-207.

Stuiver, M. and P.J. Reimer. 1993. "CALIB radiocarbon calibration program." Radiocarbon, 35, 215-230.

Swanson, T.W. and M.L Caffee. 2001. "Determination of ^{36}Cl production rates derived from the well-dated deglaciation surfaces of Whidbey and Fidalgo Islands, Washington." *Quaternary Research*, V. 56, p. 366-382.

Sweeney, M.R. 2004. "Sedimentology, paleoclimatology and geomorphology of a late Pleistocene-Holocene paired eolian system, Columbia Plateau," Doctoral dissertation. Pullman, Washington: Washington State University, 204 p.

Sweeney, M.R., A.J. Busacca, C.A. Richardson, M. Blinnikov and E.C. McDonald. 2004. "Glacial anticyclone recorded in Palouse loess of northwestern United States." *Geology*, V. 32, No. 8, p. 705-708.

Symons, Lt. T.W. 1882. "Report of an examination of the upper Columbia River and the territory in its vicinity in September and October 1881 to determine its navigability and adaptability to steamboat transportation." U.S. Army Corps of Engineers, U.S. Government Printing Office, 182 p.

Tolan, T.L., B.S. Martin, S.P. Reidel, J.L. Anderson, K.A. Lindsey, and W. Burt. 2009. "An introduction to the stratigraphy, structural geology, and hydrogeology of the Columbia River Flood-Basalt Province: A primer for the GSA Columbia River Basalt Group field trips," in O'Connor, J.E., R.J. Dorsey and I.P. Madin, eds., *Volcanoes to Vineyards: Geologic Field Trips through the Dynamic Landscape of the Pacific Northwest*, Geological Society of America Field Guide 15, p. 599-643, doi: 10.1130/2009. fld015(28).

Waitt, R.B. Jr. 1980. "About forty last-glacial Lake Missoula jökulhlaups through southern Washington." *Journal of Geology* V. 88, p. 653-679.

Waitt, R.B. 1984. "Periodic Jökulhlaups from Pleistocene Glacial Lake Missoula – New evidence from varved sediment in northern Idaho and Washington." *Quaternary Research*, V. 22, p. 46-58.

Waitt, R.B. Jr. 1985. "Case for periodic, colossal jökulhlaups from Pleistocene Glacial Lake Missoula." *Geological Society of America Bulletin*, V. 96, p. 1271-1286.

Waitt, R.B. Jr. 1987. "Evidence for dozens of stupendous floods from Glacial Lake Missoula in eastern Washington, Idaho and Montana," in M.L. Hill, ed., Centennial Field Guide 1, Trip No. 77. Boulder, Colorado: *Geological Society of America*, p. 345-350.

Waitt, R.B. Jr. and R.M. Thorson. 1983. "The Cordilleran Ice Sheet in Washington, Idaho, and Montana," in H.E. Wright, ed., *Late Quaternary Environments of the United States*, Volume 1, The Late Pleistocene. Minneapolis, Minnesota: University of Minnesota Press, p. 53-70.

Waitt, R.B. and B.F. Atwater. 1989. "Stratigraphic and geomorphic evidence for dozens of last-glacial floods," in Breckenridge, R.M., ed., *Glacial Lake Missoula and the Channeled Scabland*. American Geophysical Union, Field Trip Guidebook T310, Chapter 5, p. 37-50.

Waitt, R.B. Jr. 1994. "Scores of gigantic, successively smaller Lake Missoula floods through Channeled Scabland and Columbia Valley," in D.A. Swanson and R.A. Haugerud, eds., *Geologic Field Trips in the Pacific Northwest*. Boulder, Colorado: Geological Society of America, pp. 1K-1 to 1K-88.

Waitt, R. 2009. "Varied routings of Lake Missoula megafloods down the Channeled Scabland and Columbia Valley." Geological Society of America, Abstracts with Programs, V. 41, No. 7, p. 169.

Waitt, R.B. Jr., R.P. Denlinger and J.E. O'Connor. 2009. "Many monstrous floods down Channeled Scabland and Columbia Valley," in J.E. O'Connor, R.J. Dorsey and I.P. Madin, eds., *Volcanoes and Vineyards: Geologic Field Trips through the Dynamic Landscape of the Pacific Northwest*. Geological Society of America Field Guide 15, p. 775-844, doi:101130/2009.fld015(33).

Walker, E.H. 1967. "Varved lake beds in northern Idaho and northeastern Washington." U.S. Geological Survey Professional Paper 575-B, p. B83-B87.

Washburn, A.L. 1988. "Mima mounds, an evaluation of proposed origins with special reference to the Puget Lowland." Washington Division of Geology and Earth Resources Report of Investigations 29, 53 p.

Index

An *a*, *f*, *pl*, *r* or *t* indicate aerial tours, figures, plates, road tours and trails respectively.

flood heights and, 109f
formation of, 155–156
Great Blade and, 160f
Hudson Coulee and, 153f, 154, 154f
maps, 162f, 397a, pl30,37,40
rates of flow and, 24
trails, road and aerial tours, 301–305t,
353r, 356–357r, 387a, 396–397a
upland plateaus and, 28f, 148f
Dry Coulee (off Moses Coulee), 27, 41f, 310f
Dry Falls
cataracts and plunge pools, 42, 136, 137f,
141–143f, 346f, pl29
depth of floods and, 109f
grooved upland plateau, 32
images, pl29,36
maps, 17f, 27f, 52f, 108f, 131f, pl31
trails, road and aerial tours, 136f, 288–
289t, 289–291t, 346f, 347r, 352r,
387a, 395a
visitor center, 141, 352r, pl31
Wanapum Basalt, 160f, 395a
Dry Falls Dam, 351r
Dry Falls Lake, 22f, 141, 142
Duck Creek Coulee, 341r
dust storms, 13
Dutch Henry Falls, 366f, 367t, 369r

E

Eagle Rock, 276–278t
Earthcaches (geocaches), 195, 274t, 280t,
282t, 283t, 303t, pl40
earthquakes, 46, 130. See also fractures,
tectonic
eddy scars, 187, 188f, 360r
entablatures
Channeled Scabland and, 228
formation of, 5, 6f, 25f
Haystack Rocks and, 172
Lake Lenore Caves and, 157
natural bridges and, 36f, 102f, pl19
plucking and, 34, 35f
Towell Falls, 249t
Turnbull Scabland and, 226t
Yeager Rock and, 173f
Eocene Epoch, 218f, 327r, 337r
Ephrata, 16, 109f, pl30
Ephrata Fan, 52, 109f, 130, 165, 168–169,
pl30
maps, 346r
trails, road and aerial tours, 354–355r,
356r
Ephrata Lake, 356r, pl30
erosion, 5–6f, 8, 24–26, 27f, 59, 126, 128f,
129f, 161. see also preferential
erosion and plucking; specific
features and locations
erratics, 55–58, 201f. see also boulders;
specific locations
escarpments, 44–45f. see also specific
locations

Escure Ranch to Towell Falls Trail, 79f, 83,
247–249t
eskers, 170f, 390a, 391a

F

Fancher Butte, 77f, 217, 234t, 384a, 385a
Farragut State Park, 60f, 203f, 205–207t,
322r, 324f, 325r, pl5,6
Farrier Coulee, 94–96
features (landforms), 3, 4f, 23f. see also
specific features
feeder dikes, 3, pl2
Fish Lake, 77f, 231t, 331r, 378a
Fishtrap Lake, 79f, 230f, 234–235t, 238–
239t, 329r, 337r
flame structures, 50
floods. see entries starting Ice Age floods
folds. see monoclines; ridges, folded
foreset bedded flood gravels, 73
Fort Spokane Trail, 109f, 314t, 315–316t
fosses, 51–52
Foster Coulee, 135, 172, 179–182, 277t. see
also Lake Foster
maps, 108f, 109f, 171f, pl22
trails, road and aerial tours, 283–285t,
387a, 391a
Foster Creek, 15, 111, 119, 120f, 178, 281t
fractures, cooling, 5, 46, 99, 127, 128, 163,
303t, 334r. see also preferential
erosion and plucking
fractures, flood-etched, 81f, 82, 84–86, 242f,
242t, 243t, 378a
fractures, folding, 128, 129
fractures, tectonic, 7–8, 9, 10f, 85f, 163,
242t, 303t. see also Cheney Fracture
Zone; earthquakes
fractures and grooves, curvilinear, 7–8, 9f,
32, 83, 93, 118, 304t, 365r, pl24
Fraser glaciation, 10, 19
Frenchman Springs Member (Wanapum
Basalt), 150f, 261t, 310t

G

geologic faults, 156
Giant Cave Arch, 34, 35f, 109f, 283–285t,
346t
giant current ripples. See ripples, giant
current
Gibralter Rock, 271t, 274–276t
glacial cycles, 10, 12, 19
glacial lakes. See specific lakes
glacial till
formation of, 170–171, 173f
Lake Pend Oreille, 203f, 204t, 206t, 207t,
326r
Purcell Trench Ice Lobe and, 60–62
Steamboat Rock and, 278t, 281–283t
Withrow Moraine and, 173–175, 367–
368r, 369r
glaciers (ice sheets), 57. see also specific lobes

glass, volcanic, 7. *see also* palagonite

gneiss rocks, 370*r*, 372*r*

goat islands, 39, 113, 119, 141, 146, 210–212*t*, 236*t. see also* Steamboat Rock

Goose Creek Coulee, 102–104, 344*r*, 384*a*

gradients of floodwater, 108, 109*f*, 126

Grand Coulee. *see also* Grand Coulee (Lower); Grand Coulee (Upper); *specific features*
    cataracts, 346*r*, 348–349*r*, 391*a*
    elevation, 95*f*
    flood characteristics and, 14, 15, 16, 109*f*
    formation of, 107–109, 111–113, 170*f*, 178, 346*r*
    last floods and, 92
    maps, 171*f*, 176*f*, 346*r*, *pl*10
    moraines and, 171, 175
    Okanogan Lobe and, 108*f*, 110–113, 268*t*, 349*r*, 356*r*
    spillover breach, 72, 76, 94*f*, 109*f*, 114–116*f*, 119, 123*f*, 126*f*, 143, 184, 211, 350, *pl*22
    spillover channels, 31*f*, 94*f*
    trails, road and aerial tours, 321*r*, 330*r*, 345–365*r*, 346*r*, 359*r*, 386–400*a*, 387*a*, 392*a*

Grand Coulee (Lower). *see also* Grand Coulee; *specific features*
    features, 27*f*
    flood depths, 109*f*
    formation of, 41, 107, 136–137*f*, 159
    images, 22*f*
    maps, 27*f*, 108*f*, 162*f*, *pl*30
    topography, 17*f*
    trails, road and aerial tours, 288–308, 352*r*

Grand Coulee (Upper), 9*f*, 52*f*, 126*f. see also* Grand Coulee; *specific features*
    Castle Rock and, 27, 124*f*, 192*pl*
    cataract recession and, 41, 180*f*, 351*r*, 358*r*
    depth of floods, 109*f*
    expansion bars, 131*f*
    formation of, 107, 110–114, 113, 391*a*
    gradient of, 126
    images, *pl*17b,27,28
    maps, 108*f*, 170*f*, *pl*22,45
    potholes, 32*f*
    rates of flow and, 24
    ringed craters and, 47*f*, 101
    sediment, 130
    spillover channels and, 115*f*, 278–283*t*
    trails, 267–308*t*

Grand Coulee Dam, 142, 144, 183. *see also* Columbia Basin Project
    images, 116*f*, *pl*23,25
    maps, 108*f*, 269*t*, *pl*11,22
    trails, road and aerial tours, 193*f*, 268*t*, 270*t*, 392–393*a*

Grande Ronde Basalt (Columbia River Basalt Group)

Bonnie Lake, 86*f*

Castle Lake and, 146

Deep Lake and, 148, 149*f*, 291–293*t*

features and formation, 3, 4*f*, 5

ground water and, 99

hogback islands and, 43, 158*f*

images, *pl*26

Lake Lenore, 43, 157

Lenore Coulee (East), 34*f*, 163*f*, *pl*42

Moses Coulee, 38*f*, 363*f*, *pl*49

Riverfront Park and, 211*f*

Steamboat Rock and, 119

Trail Lake Coulee and, 150*f*

Granite Lake, 218*t*, 223

granitic rocks. *see also* inselbergs
    Candy Point and, 268*t*
    Castle Rock, 122–124
    Columbia Plateau, 232*t*
    Columbia River, 360*r*
    Ephrata Fan and, 168
    erosion and, 208*f*
    Fort Spokane, 315–316*t*
    Grand Coulee (Upper), 110, 116, 393*a*
    Lake Lenore, 304*t*
    Northrup Canyon, 120–122, 121, 271–276*t*
    Olson Hill, 218*f*, 337*r*
    Pend Oreille valley, 198–199*t*
    sand and, 275*t*
    Steamboat Rock and, 119, 278–283*t*, 281*f*, 282*f*

granodiorite, 68, 262*t*, 281*t*, 359*r*

gravel, 48, 87*f. see also* bars, flood; borrow pits; clasts; glacial till

Grays Butte, 234*t*

Great Bar of Moses Coulee, 176*f*, 178, 365*r*, 388*a*, 389*a*, *pl*47

Great Blade, 41, 159–160*f*
    images, 34*f*, 39*f*, 157*f*, 160*f*, 320*f*, 373*f*, *pl*38,39,41
    maps, 109*f*, 162*f*, 346*f*, *pl*40
    trails, road and aerial tours, 109*f*, 301–305*t*, 353*r*, 387*a*, 397–398*a*

Great Cataract Group, 131*f*, 136, 140–141, 395*a*, *pl*31. *see also specific cataracts*

Great Terrace, 370*r*, 371*f*

Green Lake, 141, 142, 144, 291*t*, *pl*35

Green Monarch Ridge, 59, 60–61*f*, 62–63, 65, 195
    maps, 60*f*, *pl*3,4
    trails, road and aerial tours, 196–197*f*, 200*f*, 202*f*, 204*f*, 322*r*

Grimes Lake, 176*f*, 177, 390*a*

grooves, 8, 9*f*, 17*f*, 26, 31–32, 83, 93. *see also* plateaus, grooved upland; *specific locations*

grooves, flood-etched, 45, 81*f*–82, 84, 94, 97*f*, 100, 163, 243*t*. *see also* grooves and fractures, curvilinear; ringed craters; strandlines (wave-cut benches); terracettes

About the Authors

Bruce Bjornstad, left, and Eugene "Gene" Kiver

Bruce Bjornstad was born in Fond du Lac, Wisconsin, in 1951 and moved to New Hampshire a few years later, where he grew up immersed in nature and the out-of-doors. Bjornstad graduated from the University of New Hampshire with a degree in geology before emigrating to Portland, Oregon, where he worked as an outdoor-education instructor for several years. Bruce went on to do graduate work in geology at Eastern Washington University at Cheney, Washington, where he met two inspiring and inseparable professors, Gene Kiver and Dale Stradling. Kiver sat on Bjornstad's thesis committee, which awarded him a graduate degree based on research performed on Ice Age slackwater flood deposits known as Touchet Beds. After a short stint as a mineral-exploration geologist in Nevada, Bjornstad settled down in the Tri-Cities where he's worked on the hydrogeology of the Hanford Site since 1981. During this time Bjornstad maintained his interest in more regional geology, including the Ice Age floods, which resulted in the publication of his first book: *On the Trail of the Ice Age Floods* for the Mid-Columbia Basin in 2006.

Eugene (Gene) Kiver was born in 1937 and raised in Cleveland, Ohio, where he received his undergraduate degree in geology from Case-Western Reserve University. The desire to understand our natural world, the fascination with national parks and the science behind spectacular scenery, and a restless spirit led to his westward migration. Kiver went first to Wyoming for his doctorate in geology at the University of Wyoming and then to Cheney, Washington, for a long career of teaching and research at Eastern Washington University. He drifted westward again after retirement to Anacortes, Washington, on the edge of the Salish Sea. Eastern Washington retains its grip and Kiver returns frequently to his Channeled Scabland residence near Cheney (located on a pendant flood bar!) to further conduct research, lead field trips into the Missoula flood area, and give talks to interested groups. Kiver is professor emeritus at Eastern Washington University and an active member of the Ice Age Floods Institute (IAFI) where he is on the executive board and is a technical adviser for the Cheney-Spokane Chapter of the IAFI.

Bjornstad, in 2007, and Kiver, in 2009, were interviewed on their geology careers for the "Central Rocks" TV program, viewable online at: http://www.geology.cwu. edu/centralrocks.

Own the pair! Order the first volume:

On the Trail of the Ice Age Floods
A geological field guide to the Mid-Columbia Basin

This first volume in the series explores the origins and mysteries of the great floods while providing a hands-on field guide to features, trails and tours in the Mid-Columbia Basin – downstream from the Channeled Scabland covered in *The Northern Reaches*.

During the last great Ice Age that ended some 15,000 years ago, the Pacific Northwest was repeatedly decimated by cataclysmic floods unlike anything of modern times. Giant ancient lakes such as Glacial Lake Missoula were created as lobes of the massive ice sheets blocked river valleys. These "ice dams" broke time and again over the millennia, sending walls of ice-laden water, miles wide and hundreds of feet deep, racing over the land at speeds up to 80 mph – scouring a fantastic landscape and leaving a fascinating geologic record for us to wonder at today.

Geologist Bruce Bjornstad wrote the most comprehensive guidebook yet to the incredible landforms scoured out by the Ice Age floods in the Mid-Columbia Basin. *On the Trail of the Ice Age Floods: A geological field guide to the Mid-Columbia Basin* explores the origins, timing and frequency of the Ice Age floods and describes each of 19 geologic features they left behind. It is also an exciting field guide to features, trails and tours in the Mid-Columbia Basin where we may witness today the awesome power of the ancient floods. The guide includes:

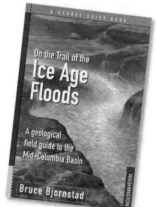

- Explanations of 19 types of landforms
- Guides to 70 flood-formed features
- Thirty off-road hiking and biking trails
- Five driving tours and two aerial tours

"A great way to learn more about the weird landforms you come across while hiking and camping in the Mid-Columbia Basin."
—Bill Bloom, Out There Monthly

"The most comprehensive consumer guidebook to the cataclysmic floods that carved this region's landscape."
—Rich Landers, Outdoors Editor, The Spokesman-Review

Third printing June 2011 • ISBN 978-1-879628-27-4 • $19
308 pages, 262 black-and-white illustrations, maps and photos, 20 color plates, index

www.KeokeeBooks.com

800-880-3573 • 208-263-3573